Environmental Biotechnology

Alan Scragg

Longman

Pearson Education Limited
Edinburgh Gate, Harlow
Essex CM20 2JE
England

and Associated Companies throughout the World

First published 1999

ISBN 0 582 27682 9

British Library Cataloguing in Publication Data
A catalogue record for this title is
available from the British Library.

Library of Congress Cataloging-in-Publication Data
A catalog entry for this title is
available from the Library of Congress.

Set by 35 in 11/12pt Adobe Garamond
Produced by Addison Wesley Longman Singapore (Pte) Ltd.,
Printed in Singapore

Environmental Biotechnology

Contents

Preface

This book covers the influence and application of biotechnology on many aspects of the environment. The influence will be dominated, as is biotechnology in general, by the advances in recombinant DNA technology which have seen application in all areas of biotechnology. Environmental applications of biotechnology have been in four areas: the monitoring of pollution, the treatment of waste, the treatment of already polluted sites and waterways, and the prevention of pollution.

In order to enforce pollution legislation and to determine levels of contamination, the detection and estimation even of very low levels of pollution is required. Biosensors can be used to give real-time on-line measurements. Genetic engineering can be used to generate biomarkers which can provide sophisticated and specific methods for the detection of contaminants. This will have a considerable influence on pollution control, just as recombinant DNA technology has profoundly affected forensic science.

The disposal of organic wastes from domestic, agricultural and industrial sources cannot be eliminated. Many of the advances in the methods of disposal of these organic wastes have been based on a better knowledge of the biological processes involved. The traditional methods of disposal are described, as are the more recent process developments such as fluidised beds and membrane reactors. The book discusses the application of recombinant DNA technology to the better understanding of the aerobic and anaerobic processes involved, and to developments in the removal of nitrates and phosphates.

Industrialisation and the widespread use of chemicals have left a legacy of polluted sites and waterways. These sites need to be cleaned up to comply with current legislation, and biological methods are a viable alternative to chemical methods. The use of biological material, known as bioremediation, may be a slower process than chemical methods, but bioremediation can mineralise even very low levels of contamination and can be cheaper. The underlying metabolic pathways are described along with a number of processes. The use of biological material for the removal of metals and for the extraction of metals from ores is also described.

The prevention of pollution has in the past often been the last option to be considered, but the medical axiom 'prevention is better than cure' is also true of pollution. In this area the use of microorganisms or enzymes to replace chemical synthesis will reduce side-products and energy requirements. Cultivation of genetically engineered plants will reduce the use of agrochemicals, and there is considerable potential in the improvement of plant and animal characteristics. Biotechnology can also be used to produce biofuel which should reduce the production of greenhouse gases, and the development of biodegradable plastics should help to reduce waste. The application of transgenic plants and animals is not without its problems, however, as there is much public concern over the release of such transgenic material into the environment and its use as a food product.

In explaining the influence of biotechnology on environmental sciences, it is inevitable that some areas will see greater application of biotechnology than others. The book does not cover all aspects of environmental science and therefore some areas, such as landfill, will be covered only briefly, as biotechnology has seen greater application in such areas as environmental monitoring and agriculture.

Many thanks to Pat Bonham for the considerable time and effort that he put into editing this text.

Alan Scragg
September 1998

SI units

Prefix	Symbol	Factor
exa	E	10^{18}
peta	P	10^{15}
tera	T	10^{12}
giga	G	10^{9}
mega	M	10^{6}
kilo	k	10^{3}
hecto	h	10^{2}
deka	da	10^{1}
deci	d	10^{-1}
centi	c	10^{-2}
milli	m	10^{-3}
micro	μ	10^{-6}
nano	n	10^{-9}
pico	p	10^{-12}
femto	f	10^{-15}
atto	a	10^{-18}

Chapter 1

Overview

1.1   Introduction

To set environmental biotechnology in context it is perhaps useful to define biotechnology itself. Biotechnology can be described as the application of biological organisms, systems or processes to manufacturing or services. The European Federation of Biotechnology defines biotechnology as 'the integrated use of biochemistry, microbiology, and engineering sciences in order to achieve applications of the capabilities of microorganisms, cultured animal or plant cells or parts thereof in industry, agriculture, health care and in environmental processes' (European Federation of Biotechnology, 1988), which is a somewhat expanded version of their 1982 definition.

The use of the word 'biotechnology' to describe a subject might seem to infer a marked degree of coherence, as in biochemistry, but there is an argument that biotechnology cannot really be regarded as a single subject. Biotechnology, in practice, combines a set of different but interrelated subjects which are applied to a broad spectrum of industries. The choice of subjects which are combined depends on the individual industrial problems. This application to various industries requires a wide range of science and engineering expertise, often concentrated on the development of a single product. Houwink (1989) perhaps best describes biotechnology briefly as 'the controlled use of biological information'. As Houwink pointed out, the study of more than one subject is not itself biotechnology, but when such study is directed towards an application it becomes biotechnology. Thus, biotechnology is in essence multidisciplinary, combining subjects such as microbiology, molecular biology, cell biology and engineering. The relationships between the various disciplines and biotechnology are best illustrated by the hourglass model (Houwink, 1989) where biotechnology acts as an interface between individual scientific disciplines and their various areas of application (Fig. 1.1).

The term 'biotechnology' was first used in 1919 and later in 1938 (Kennedy, 1991). The journal *Biotechnology and Bioengineering* was named in 1962 and the journal *Biotechnology* was launched in 1979. The public in the UK probably first heard of biotechnology in the early 1980s with the publication of the Spinks report, *Biotechnology: Report of a Joint Working Party* (Spinks, 1980), and with the start-up of a number of small biotechnology companies, often specialising in genetic engineering.

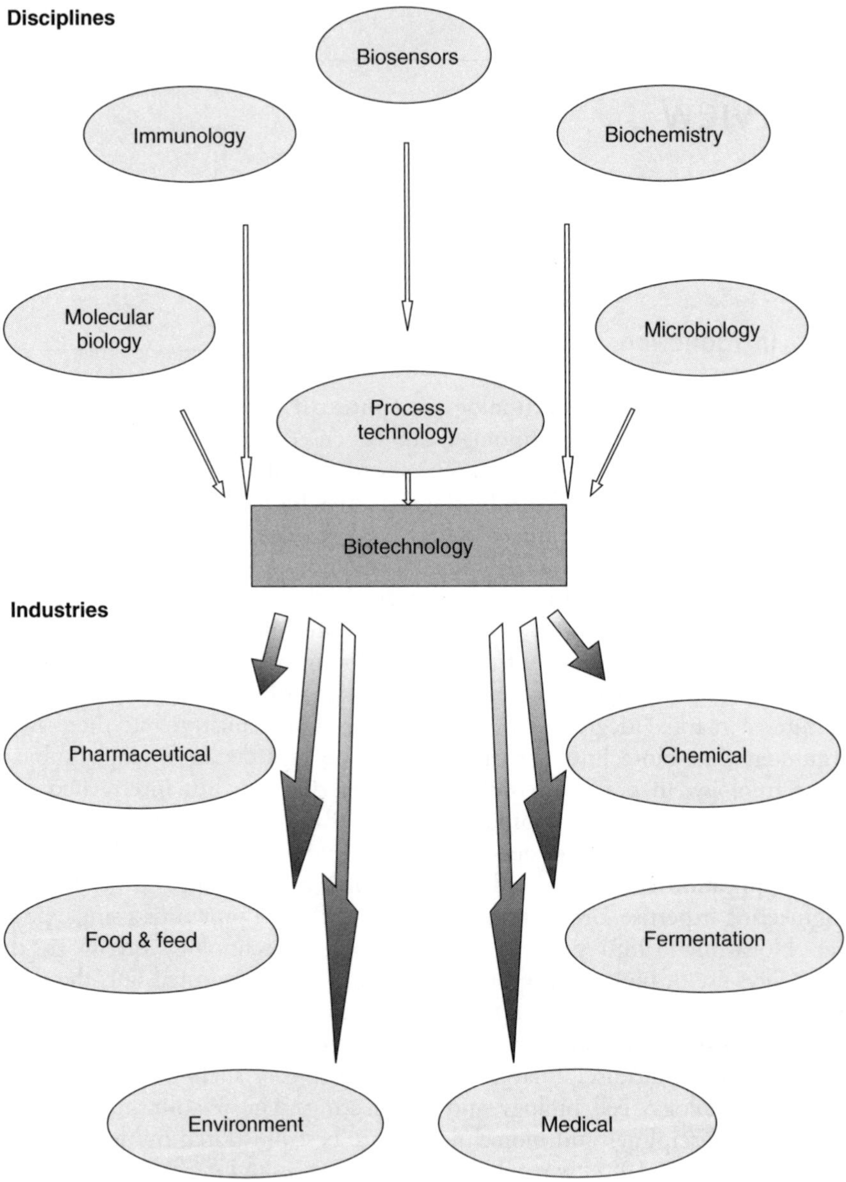

Disciplines

Fig. 1.1   The hourglass model for biotechnology, adapted from Houwink (1989).

1.1.1   Environmental biotechnology

This book attempts to cover the application of biotechnology to the wide range of environmental problems under the title of environmental biotechnology. One definition of environmental biotechnology is 'the specific application of biotechnology to the management of environmental problems, including waste treatment, pollution control, and integration with non-biological technologies'. The application of biotechnology to environmental problems has developed alongside biotechnology in general and in many ways its application has been as an extension of natural processes. Current estimates of the market for environmental biotechnology are in the region of 300 billion dollars worldwide (Golub, 1997) and some 84–94 billion dollars in Europe (Glass et al., 1995). Investment in environmental biotechnology will continue, particularly in the processes of environmental clean-up and remediation and the development of a sustainable technology.

1.1.2 Biotechnology past

Over the centuries microorganisms have been used unwittingly for the preparation of various foods and beverages. This was probably the first example of biotechnology. Such operations for food and drink preparation were carried out in a highly empirical manner without any real knowledge of the microorganisms or processes involved. As our understanding of the science underlying biological processes has increased so the nature of biotechnology has shifted from the empirical to the controlled. To understand this development, the evolution of biotechnology can be divided into a series of eras (Houwink, 1984) as shown in Fig. 1.2. The first biotechnology process was probably the production of alcoholic beverages over 5000 years ago. This was first documented in Egypt from 4000 BC. Recently the Scottish and Newcastle Brewery in the UK produced a beer similar to an ancient Egyptian beer prepared from an emmer wheat strain similar to that found in Egyptian tombs. The beer proved quite palatable. At the same time as brewing was evolving, fermented milk products such as cheese and yogurt were used as a method of preserving milk. As anyone who has attempted alcoholic fermentations will know, it is easy for some microorganisms to convert ethanol to acetic acid, so that vinegar production also developed before 3000 BC (Prave et al., 1987).

The empirical approach changed with the realisation, from the work of Anton van Leeuwenhoek in 1650, that microorganisms existed and that these microbes were the causative agent of such processes as fermentation. The latter advance was based on the work of people such as Pasteur, Koch and Buchner in the nineteenth century. The slow developments in the study of microorganisms led to what is entitled the Pasteur era, where specific products were produced using selected microorganisms. The first was perhaps the microbial production of lactic acid in 1881. Acetone and butanol are important bulk chemicals as solvents, hydraulic fluids and plasticisers, and the production of butanol by bacteria was first discovered by Pasteur. Later Weizmann, working at the University of Manchester in 1914, investigated the use of the anaerobic bacterium *Clostridium acetobutylicum* for the production of butanol to be used in rubber manufacture. However, the bacterium produced acetone, butanol and ethanol. Acetone, apart from being used as a solvent, was also

---

Pre-Pasteur Era: before 1865
  Alcoholic beverages (beer, wine)
  Dairy products (cheese, yogurt)
  Other fermented foods

Pasteur Era: 1865–1940
  Ethanol, butanol, acetone, glycerol
  Organic acids (citric acid)
  Aerobic sewage treatment

Antibiotic Era: 1940–1960
  Penicillin: submerged fermentation
  Large variety of antibiotics
  Animal cell culture technology; virus vaccines
  Microbial steroid transformations

Post-antibiotic Era: 1960–1975
  Amino acids
  Single cell protein (SCP)
  Enzymes (detergents)
  Immobilised enzyme and cell technology
  Anaerobic wastewater treatment (biogas)
  Bacterial polysaccharides (xanthan)
  Gasohol

New Biotechnology Era: 1975–
  Hybridoma technology – monoclonals
  Monoclonal diagnostic tests (1980)
  Genetic engineering (1974)
  Animal diarrhoea vaccines (1982)
  Human insulin (1982)
  Release of genetic engineered plants (1992)
  Genetic engineered food (1996)

Fig. 1.2 Biotechnology calendar of events, adapted from Houwink (1984).

used for the production of the smokeless explosive cordite. Acetone was normally produced by the pyrolysis of wood, which formed calcium acetate which on heating released acetone. About 100 kg of wood was required to produce each kilogram of acetone. With the outbreak of World War I the demand for cordite far outstripped the supply of acetone from wood pyrolysis. Therefore, the microbial process for the production of butanol and acetone using *C. acetobutylicum* went from laboratory scale to production very rapidly in 1915 due to the need for explosives. The biological process was more efficient and cheaper than wood pyrolysis, forming 12 tonnes of acetone per 100 tonnes of molasses used to grow the microorganism. This process continued until the 1950s when it was replaced by the production of acetone from polypropylene produced by the petrochemical industry. The chemical process replaced the biological process as it was cheaper, because the price of molasses had risen, and the biological process produced considerable quantities of waste. The last biological process was operating in South Africa until 1982 because of the embargo on the importation of petrochemical products to that country. This is not the only example of a biological process being rapidly developed due to the pressure of war. This also happened with the antibiotic penicillin. Recent advances in biochemistry, molecular biology and waste treatment have suggested that the biological process for acetone production could be reintroduced as it uses renewable resources and not petrochemicals which have a finite supply (Girbal and Soucaille, 1998). In this period other significant developments were the start of the biological treatment of sewage in 1914, with filter beds and activated sludge plants in Manchester and a number of continental European cities.

Although penicillin was discovered by Alexander Fleming in 1928–29, its large-scale production was not achieved until 1941. Research and development since 1928 by Florey and Chain had made the extraction of penicillin possible, and its ability to treat infection was demonstrated, but its large-scale production was still not possible at the start of World War II. The penicillin-producing organism *Penicillium notatum* was normally grown as a mat on the surface of the medium, which made scale-up very difficult and labour intensive. In 1941 Florey's team moved to the USA where submerged deep fermentation was developed for the cultivation of a related but higher-producing *Penicillium* strain, *P. chrysogenum*. The submerged deep fermentation allowed the large-scale growth of *P. chrysogenum* and required the combined efforts of microbiologists, biochemists and process engineers. However, by 1944 there was sufficient penicillin to treat a great many military casualties. This is another example of the development of a product driven by the needs of a world war.

Although large-scale cultivation of bakers' yeast for baking and of *Aspergillus niger* for citric acid was possible before the development of the penicillin process, the ability to grow microorganisms on a large scale began the 'antibiotic era'. Thus the production of a large variety of antibiotics, such as streptomycin, tetracyclines and cephalosporins, followed.

Other areas of scientific advancement at this time were animal cell culture and microbial steroid transformation. The cultured animal cells were used for virus isolation and vaccine production, for example the first polio vaccine. In the 1950s it was found that microorganisms were able to transform a wide range of compounds, and in most cases these transformations were very specific. Thus microorganisms were able to carry out transformations which would be difficult to carry out chemically. Microbial transformation has been extensively used in the production of steroids.

Knowledge gained in the development of the antibiotic industry was applied to other problems in what is referred to as the post-antibiotic era. Microorganisms were used to produce individual amino acids and vitamins; some 30,000–40,000 tonnes of amino acids such as lysine and glutamic acid (monosodium glutamate) are produced by microbial processes annually. The mass production of enzymes, in particular extracellular enzymes, allowed enzymes to be used in detergents and for the production of glucose from starch.

The production and use of enzymes can be expensive as they have only a limited active life and when added to the substrate they cannot easily be recovered. However, if enzymes are immobilised they can be used in a continuous process and their active life extended. This has meant that some enzyme-based processes can be adopted as immobilisation has reduced the cost of the enzymes to acceptable levels. One example of the use of immobilisation has been the development of a process for the production of high-fructose syrups. Fructose is 1.7 times as sweet as sucrose and therefore can be used in smaller quantities as a sweetener in low-calorie foods and drinks. The production of high-fructose (55%) sweeteners was costly, as the enzyme glucose isomerase which converts glucose to fructose was expensive to prepare. However, if glucose isomerase was immobilised it could be used in a continuous process for the production of high-fructose sugars from glucose syrups, thus reducing the costs. Techniques of immobilisation of both cells and enzymes have also been applied to the development of biosensors.

In the 1960s there was much concern that, with the increase in population in the world, there would be a shortage of food and in particular protein. Alternative sources of protein were sought and these included microorganisms such as algae, bacteria, yeasts and fungi. Algae and yeast had previously been used as both human and animal foods. The main aim was to use microorganisms to produce a high-protein animal feed, and the term 'single cell protein' (SCP) was used to describe this. One feature of SCP production as an animal feed was that its cost had to be low to compete with existing animal food ingredients such as soya bean meal. One of the major costs in the production of microbial biomass (cells) is the substrate, which can account for up to 60% of the cost. Therefore, the substrates used for SCP production should be cheap and available in large quantities. Substrates investigated included either renewable substrates like agricultural wastes, crops containing starch and cellulose, or non-renewable substrates from the petrochemical industry (Sharp, 1989). At that time the petrochemical industry had a surplus of cheap methane, methanol and alkanes and for this reason many of the large petrochemical companies became involved in the production of SCP from these substrates. In order to keep the cost of SCP to a minimum the SCP process needs to be carried out on a large scale, as large-scale processes bring cost reductions.

Perhaps the best known SCP process was developed by ICI for the production of Pruteen, an animal food. ICI had a bacterium, *Methylophilus methylotrophus*, which was capable of growth on methanol. Methanol was produced cheaply from methane coming from the North Sea gas fields. The bacterium passed tests of safety and nutritional value and proved successful as an animal food. ICI built a large plant in the early 1980s for the production of Pruteen with a 1.5 million litre bioreactor which was run in a continuous manner. This was a prodigious technological feat representing a considerable advance in bioprocess technology, and in 1981 6000 tonnes of Pruteen were produced per month. Despite this early technical success the process has now been abandoned for the following reasons:

- Oil/gas and therefore methanol prices increased much more than expected.
- The production of fish and soya bean meal, the main competitor, expanded considerably.

- Food shortages did not develop as expected, due to improvements in the organisation of storage and distribution.
- The 'green revolution', the development of high-yielding crops, has reduced demand for synthetic protein foods.

In an attempt to improve the efficiency of the process, *M. methylotrophus* was genetically engineered to enhance its uptake of ammonia, which was one of the first examples of the application of genetic engineering to a process. However, it is not clear whether a genetically engineered animal food would have been accepted. There remains one successful SCP product, Quorn, which is a human food based on a fungus, *Fusarium graminarium*, which is grown on molasses or hydrolysed starch. Quorn was developed initially by Rank Hovis McDougall and approved for human use in 1982–83. Its sales were initially slow, but changes in eating habits in the late 1980s and early 1990s saw more interest in low-fat, high-fibre vegetarian foods and thus the sales of Quorn increased. The production of Quorn is now carried out by Marlow Foods which is mainly owned by ICI.

The 1970s saw a crisis in oil production due to hostilities in the Middle East which reduced the supply of crude oil to developed countries. Therefore, alternative supplies of fuel were investigated, and one of the products which was examined was ethanol which could be used as a supplement (10–20%) or as a complete replacement for petrol without major changes to car engines. Ethanol can be produced by the fermentation of sugars in the same process as brewing or wine production. Ethanol was introduced as a 100% petrol replacement in Brazil in order to reduce the country's reliance on imported oil, and to develop an ethanol industry. The process used was simple fermentation using yeast and sugar from sugarcane. The fermentation produced 8–10% ethanol which was extracted and purified by distillation. In the 1980s some 75% of the cars in Brazil used ethanol either exclusively or as an additive to petrol. The percentage using ethanol has declined because of the continued low price of crude oil, and at present 50% of the cars in Brazil use alcohol either alone or as a 10% addition to petrol. Another biofuel, methane (biogas), can be formed by anaerobic digestion of sewage or other wastes. Methane has also been developed as a fuel for heating and cooking, particularly in developing countries.

Another microbial product developed at this time was the microbial polysaccharide xanthan which is used in foods to increase their viscosity and in drilling muds due to its viscoelastic properties.

1.1.3 Biotechnology present

The last era recognised by Houwink was named after the 'new biotechnologies' which are principally involved with the application of genetic engineering to all areas of biotechnology, including environmental biotechnology. The other novel development during this era has been that of monoclonal antibodies.

Genetic engineering or recombinant technology developed in the 1970s
and the techniques have revolutionised our ability to isolate, manipulate and
express genes and therefore proteins virtually at will. The ability to isolate a
particular gene, to multiply the gene if required, and to insert the gene into
another organism means that traditional species barriers can be crossed in
ways not possible by traditional breeding, so that for instance human proteins
can be made in plants. The ability to manipulate and transfer genes has had
a dramatic impact on all areas of biotechnology. The transformed organism
can be animal, plant or microorganism and the form of genetic engineering
irrespective of the organism can be of three main types:

- The insertion of a single gene which gives the recipient a new characteristic,
  such as herbicide resistance in cotton plants, or starch degradation (amylase) in
  Saccharomyces cerevisiae.
- The alteration of the operation of existing genes which may change the characteristics of the recipient, for example the change in fruit ripening by reducing the
  activity of polygalacturonase by antisense technology in tomato plants (e.g. Flavr
  Savr^{tm} – see Section 8.2) or changes in oil quality in rapeseed.
- The insertion of a gene so that the recipient produces a specific product, usually a
  protein, which is not aimed at altering the characteristic of the organism but acts as
  a supply of the product. This is often known as biopharming and an example is the
  production of human insulin in the bacterium *E. coli*. The recipient can be bacterial,
  yeast, insect, plant or mammalian cultures depending on the product required and
  the post-translational processing.

Some examples of the development of transgenic technology since 1982 in
three industries – medical, agriculture and food – are given in Table 1.1. The
first medical transgenic product was human insulin (humulin) where the gene
was cloned into the bacterium *E. coli* and the bacterium used to produce
insulin for the treatment of diabetes. This product has the advantage of being
identical to human insulin rather than pig insulin which had previously been
used. There is an alternative supply of human insulin from a process in which
pig insulin is converted enzymatically into human insulin by the alteration of
one amino acid. Human growth hormone has been produced in bacteria and,
although the market for this hormone is limited, the hormone was previously
extracted from human pituitary glands and any extraction from human material carries a risk of viral contamination. Thus many of the transgenic materials
produced for medicine have been developed to provide material which was
either difficult to extract, carried other risks or was very expensive. In contrast
agriculture has seen the genetic engineering of common crops such as maize,
cotton and tomato. In these cases the transgenic plants have been given characteristics such as herbicide and insect resistance or changes to fruit quality.
The food industry has developed a diverse range of transgenic products but
only a few have been adopted. One transgenic product which has been used is
the enzyme chymosin produced by transgenic yeast. Chymosin is the starter
enzyme in cheese production and the transgenic product has been used to
replace calf chymosin (rennet). The cheese is sold as a vegan product as the

Table 1.1 Applications of genetic engineering in the medical, agricultural and food industries

Year Product	Disease/property/action
Medical	
1982 Human insulin (humulin)	Diabetes
1985 Human growth hormone (prototropin)	Growth deficiency
1987 Human growth hormone (humatrope)	Growth deficiency
1991 Intron A	Hepatitis C
1992 Recombinate (factor VIII)	Hemophilia A
1993 Pulmozyme (DNase)	Cystic fibrosis
1994 Albunex	Diagnosis of heart disease
Agriculture	
1992 Flavr Savr^{tm} tomato	Altered ripening
1994 Cotton	Herbicide resistance, glyphosate
1994 Rapeseed/Canola	Altered oil content
1994 Squash	Virus resistance
1995 Potato	Insect resistance
1995 Maize	Insect resistance
1997 Chicory	Male sterile
Food	
1990 Bakers' yeast	Faster carbon dioxide liberation
1991 Bovine chymosin from GM yeast	Cheese production
1994 Brewers' yeast	Starch degradation
1997 Hemicellulase	Xylanase
1997 Riboflavin	Vitamin B$_2$

enzyme was from yeast and it has been labelled as a genetically engineered product.

It is clear that there are tremendous advances to be made with transgenic organisms (genetically manipulated organisms, GMOs) in all areas of biotechnology including environmental biotechnology. However, there is public concern over modern biotechnology as the public perceives that the development of genetically engineered products is motivated mainly by profit, that such crops and animals are unnatural and carry unknown risks, and that transgenic organisms or products should be labelled as such. This feeling of distrust in biotechnology is also involved with the notion of 'playing God', particularly when confronted with animal experiments, with tales of cloned animals and humans. It has been stated that 'genetic engineering is not some minor biotechnology development. It is a radical new technology that violates fundamental laws of nature'. Environmental newsletters have carried articles with titles such as 'Are you ready for frankenfood?' (Kareiva and Stark, 1994). All this unfavourable publicity has seen sales of genetically engineered tomatoes staying at low levels in the USA (Golub, 1997) and there have been calls to label all transgenic products. This resistance may be overcome if the technology seeks to solve what are perceived as problems rather than being introduced just for profit.

Since the EC Novel Foods Regulation of May 1997 there have been several modifications on the labelling of foods, but confusion still exists on which products need labelling. An example has been the importation of soya starch which contains a proportion (10%) of starch from genetic engineered soya plants. The starch itself was not engineered, but there was some concern as the product is used in a wide range of foods and these foods have not been labelled as containing genetically engineered ingredients. However, some supermarkets in the UK have countered this by labelling products not containing genetic engineered products. Companies involved in the use of transgenic plants have run a series of explanations of biotechnology in newspapers in the UK, referring to an information web site (www.monsanto.co.uk) as well as the website for Friends of the Earth (www.foe.co.uk).

1.2   Environmental biotechnology

Environmental biotechnology, therefore, is the application of all components of biotechnology to environmental problems. The subject has perhaps come of age in the last 10 years. Public awareness of environmental issues has been greatly increased by a series of disastrous accidents at Chernobyl, Seveso and Bhopal, and marine spillages from oil tankers such as the *Exxon Valdez* and *Amoco Cadiz*. In a well-publicised accident the tanker *Exxon Valdez* ran aground in Prince William Sound in Alaska, losing 11 million gallons of crude oil. This oil spill polluted a wide area of the shore, killing animals, birds and shore life (see Chapter 5). In 1976 an explosion in a factory producing various chemicals at Seveso near Milan in Italy produced a cloud of trichlorophenol which also contained dioxin. Dioxin, or 2,3,7,8-tetrachlorodibenzo-p-dioxin (TCDD), although it was only a minor component, is very toxic and produced a skin disease (chloracne) in the people affected by the vapour. Some 70,000 animals died or were put down and the long-term effects are unclear. In 1984 another explosion at a chemical plant at Bhopal in India released 30–40 tonnes of methylisocyanate which resulted in 3300 deaths and many injuries. Environmental biotechnology can monitor these kinds of accidents and offer new methods of removing or treating the pollution caused.

Public attention has also been drawn to the increase in greenhouse gases responsible for global warming, which may have a profound effect on the world's climate and sea levels (see Chapter 6). The release of chlorofluorocarbons (CFCs), which are used in refrigeration systems, for example, reduces the ozone layer, allowing more ultraviolet light to reach the earth's surface. As a consequence sunburn and skin cancer are increasing. Thus the protection of the environment has become an important issue in the USA and Europe as the public have become more aware of the problems.

Box 1.1

It has been shown that carbon dioxide makes up a major proportion of what are known as 'greenhouse gases'. Other components of greenhouse gases are ozone, chlorofluorocarbons, methane and nitrous oxide. These gases stop the reflection of solar radiation from the earth and hence cause a slow warming of the earth. Carbon dioxide is responsible for two-thirds of the additional energy trapped. The major source of the increase in carbon dioxide is the burning of fossil fuels.

1.2.1 Legislation

There has been legislation concerning the environment in terms of public health in the UK since 1848. The Public Health Act and many of the subsequent Acts produced were in response to continued industrialisation and were related mainly to sanitation and housing. The response to present concerns about the environment in the UK initiated the Environmental Protection Act 1990 (Table 1.2) which saw the setting up of the Environmental Agency for England and Wales and the Scottish Environmental Protection Agency in the 1995 Environmental Act. These two Acts define the environment as 'consisting of the air, water and land and the medium of air includes the air within buildings and the air within other natural or man-made structures above or below ground' and pollution as 'the release into any environmental medium from any process of substances which are capable of causing harm to man or any other living organisms supported by the environment'. In the USA Acts dealing with clean air, clean water and hazardous waste were passed between 1977 and 1982, and in 1994 the Maritime Pollution Treaty was signed.

However, pollution is not constrained within individual countries and therefore many attempts at cleaning up the environment have had to be carried out on an international scale. One of the most public international meetings was the United Nations Conference on Environment and Development (UNCED) held in Rio de Janeiro in 1992, which resulted in Conventions on Biodiversity and Climate Change, but these have achieved little in real terms to date.

The Rio Declaration also included a number of principles for future action, for example:

- access to environmental information
- the precautionary principle should be widely applied

where national authorities should adopt the policy that the polluter pays.

Conventions are really international treaties under international law which may also contain subsidiary agreements called protocols. The Convention on Climate Change asked developed countries to submit plans to reduce the

Table 1.2   Legislation in environmental biotechnology

UK	USA and international
1848 Public Health Act	
	1957 Treaty of Rome (EU)
	1969 US National Environmental Policy Act (USA); Environmental Protection Agency established in 1970
	1972 Stockholm Declaration established the UN Environment Programme
1974 Control of Pollution Act	
	1977 Federal Water Pollution Act (USA)
	1982 Clean Air Act (USA)
	1986 Single European Act (EU)
	1987 Montreal Protocol (UN), CFCs
1990 Environmental Protection Act	
1991 Water Resources Act	
	1991 Treaty of Maastricht (EU)
1991 Water Industries Act	
	1992 UN Conference on Environment and Development, Rio (UNCED)
	1994 Convention on Biodiversity
	1994 Maritime Pollution Treaty (MARPOL)
1995 Environment Act	

production of greenhouse gases (see Box 1.1). The Montreal Protocol agreed in 1987 covered the production and use of chlorofluorocarbons (CFCs) which were reducing the ozone layer around the world. There have been a number a meetings since Rio, with the latest at Kyoto in 1997, which have ratified the previous agreements, and the polluter pays principle has been adopted in some countries, but otherwise little progress has been made in these meetings on greenhouse gas emissions.

In the 1991 Treaty of Maastricht obligations were added to the original Treaty of Rome (1957) which included to preserve, protect and improve the quality of the environment, to contribute to the protection of the health of individuals, the prudent and rational use of natural resources, and to promote at international level methods to deal with environmental problems. These activities have seen the adoption of a number of Acts in various countries and the setting up of agencies to monitor various parts of the environment, such as clean beaches.

1.2.2   Integrated pollution control

The aims of integrated pollution control are 'to prevent, minimise or render harmless releases of prescribed substances using the best available technology not entailing excessive cost' (BATNEEC). The concept was that pollutants can transfer from air to land and to water, using complex routes (Fig. 1.3). Therefore, any civil and industrial development should consider both public and expert advice as to the effect on the environment as a whole.

1.3   Pollution

Pollution can be very diverse, ranging from organic compounds to metals and gases (Table 1.3). The European Union (EU) recognises a large number of toxic chemicals which it has placed on its 'black list'; less toxic compounds are placed on a 'grey list' (see Table 2.1). The United States Environmental

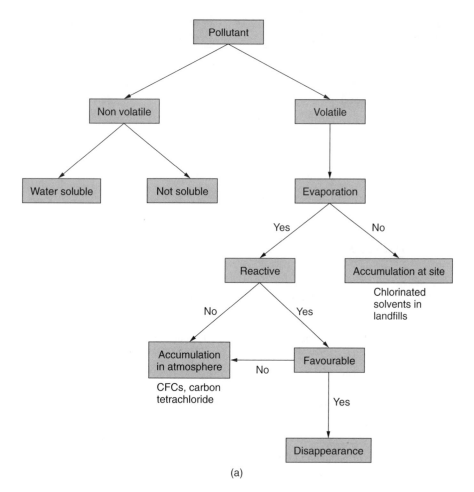

(a)

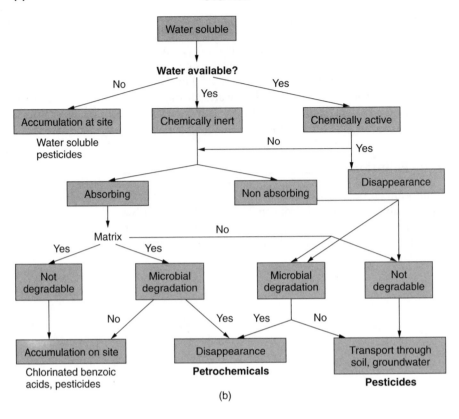

(b)

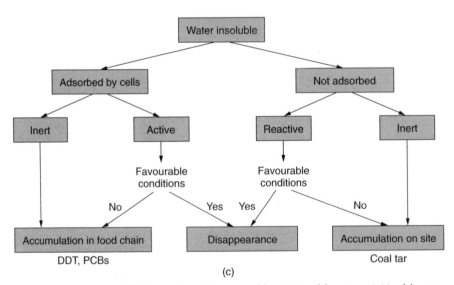

(c)

Fig. 1.3 The fate of pollution in the environment: (a) volatiles; (b) water soluble; (c) water insoluble; DDT, dichlorodiphenyltrichloroethane; PCBs, polychlorobiphenyls.

Table 1.3 Environmental pollutants

Inorganic

Metals: Cd, Hg, Ag, Co, Pb, Cu, Cr, Fe
Radionuclides
Nitrates, nitrites, phosphates
Cyanides
Asbestos

Organic

Biodegradable: sewage, domestic, agricultural and process waste
Petrochemical wastes: oil, diesel, BTEX*
Synthetic: pesticides, organohalogens, PAHs†

Biological

Pathogens: bacteria, viruses

Gaseous

Gases: SO_2, CO_2, NO_x, methane
Volatiles: chlorofluorocarbons, volatile organic compounds (VOCs)
Particulates

* BTEX: benzene, toluene, ethylbenzene, xylenes.
† PAHs: polyaromatic hydrocarbons.

Protection Agency (EPA) also has similar lists (Chapter 2). The reason for placing these compounds on the lists was their toxicity and carcinogenicity, and in many cases these compounds are persistent as they are difficult to degrade. They take a wide range of paths when released into the environment, depending upon their properties and conditions. Figure 1.3 outlines the possible paths which a compound can take leading to the pollution of land, air or water.

Organic wastes from domestic and agricultural sources are generally capable of being broken down by either aerobic or anaerobic microorganisms, and as such do not accumulate in the environment. Inorganic wastes such as phosphate and nitrate can cause problems if the concentrations are high, and their removal is discussed in Chapter 3. Phosphate and nitrate run-off from agricultural land can cause eutrophication of waterways. Eutrophication is 'the nutrient enrichment of waters which results in the stimulation of an array of changes, among which is increased production of algae which are found to be undesirable and interfere with the water uses'.

1.3.1 Industrial pollution

Pollution can be derived from a multitude of industries and can come in many forms, as can be seen in Table 1.3. It can be found on contaminated sites left over from defunct industries, and there are high levels of contaminants in many estuaries, rivers and lakes due to current waste releases. Metals from a number of industrial processes can pollute air, water and land. Metals are clearly not degraded by biological systems but organisms can accumulate metals. This process of retaining metals is known as bioaccumulation (Box 1.2). The ability of biological material to accumulate metals is being put to use in the removal of heavy metals from water and contaminated sites.

Box 1.2

Biomagnification can be defined as the increase in a pollutant in tissues of successive organisms of the food chain. In a similar manner metals cannot be degraded but are capable of being taken up by organisms and stored in a process known as bioaccumulation.

Bioaccumulation describes the increase in a compound in an organism compared with the level in the environment.

Bioconcentration refers to the concentration of a pollutant directly from the water. Often the pollutants which bioaccumulate are lipophilic and as a consequence are stored or accumulate in the fats and oils. Bioconcentration can be given a numerical value, the bioconcentration factor (BCF), which is often quoted:

$$\text{Bioconcentration factor} = \frac{\text{concentration of a compound in an organism}}{\text{concentration in surrounding environment}}$$

Organic industrial wastes such as food process waste can be biologically degraded and treated in a similar way to domestic sewage. However, many of the synthetic chemicals produced by industry are found on the EPA list of toxic chemicals, and because they are not found in nature they are known as xenobiotic, from the Greek *xenos*, meaning new. The degradation of these synthetic chemicals is dependent on their structure which can influence important parameters like solubility and toxicity. Often the lower the solubility of a compound in water the greater its solubility in lipids and the greater the accumulation in the fatty tissues of the organism. Therefore, these types of compounds have a greater toxic potential. In general organic compounds containing halogen atoms are slow to degrade, and the rate of degradation is influenced by the type of halogen atom, its position in the molecule and the number of atoms present. In some cases it takes up to 15 years or more for a compound to be reduced by 50%. Therefore, in essence they are permanent and accumulate in the environment. Some examples of the structure of slowly degrading compounds are shown in Fig. 1.4. The aqueous solubility of organic compounds compared with their ability to bioaccumulate is given in Fig. 1.5. Some fungi and bacteria have been isolated that can degrade these types of compounds but the degradation is slow, and work is in progress to harness these organisms to treat waste streams and contaminated sites (see Chapter 5).

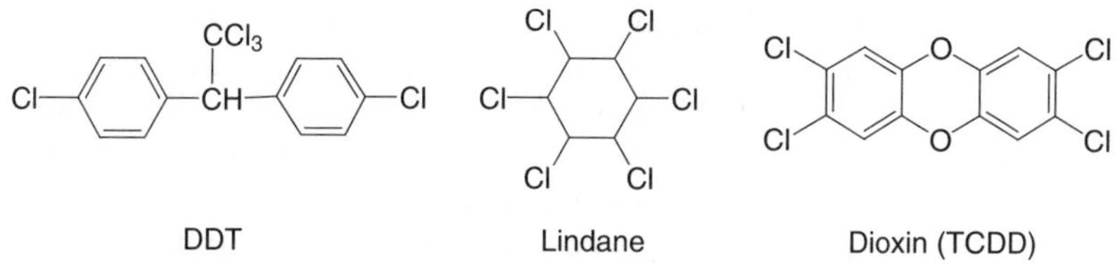

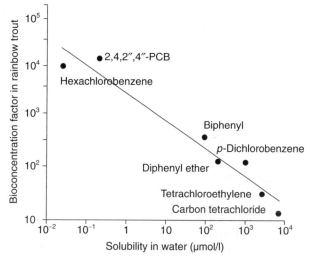

Fig. 1.4 The structure of some slowly degrading organochlorines: polychlorobiphenyls (PCBs); 2,3,7,8-tetrachlorodibenzo-*p*-dioxin (TCDD); dichlorodiphenyltrichloroethane (DDT).

Fig. 1.5 The aqueous solubility of various organic compounds against the bioconcentration factor in rainbow trout (Reeve, 1994).

Another group of industrial wastes are the petrochemicals – oil, petrol and diesel. Pollution of the environment with petrochemical wastes results from tank leakage or the more spectacular major marine spills. There are natural microorganisms that occur widely in the environment which are capable of degrading petrochemicals. Biotechnology is developing methods of enhancing their activity either *in situ* or off site (*ex situ*).

1.3.2 Gaseous pollution

Gaseous pollution consists of particulates, volatiles and gases like carbon dioxide, sulphur dioxide and nitrous oxide produced by industrial processes. There are physical methods for trapping particulates and removing sulphur dioxide and nitrous oxide. Also under development and trial are biofiltration units which are capable of removing volatile organic compounds (VOCs), such as dichloromethane (Chapter 5).

Chlorofluorocarbons (CFCs) are used in air conditioning, foam production and aerosols. CFCs have been implicated in the destruction of the ozone layer, allowing more ultraviolet light to reach the earth's surface. The Montreal Protocol which was signed in 1987 required the phasing out of the use of CFCs by 1997 for developed nations and by 2007 for developing nations. However, as CFCs have a long half-life (50–400 years) the short-term effects of the ban may be slight.

Burning of fossil fuels also produces sulphur dioxide and nitric oxide and the main sources of these pollutants are power stations. Sulphur dioxide and nitric oxide in the atmosphere reduce the pH, producing acid rain, which has the effect of reducing the pH of waters and soils, killing plants and corroding buildings. Legislation now seeks to reduce the levels of sulphur and nitrous oxide emissions from power stations. A number of approaches have been made:

- Burning less fossil fuel, switching to gas or other energy sources.
- Using low-sulphur coal or reducing the sulphur content by some process of desulphurisation (biological, Chapter 5).
- Improving combustion.
- Flue gas desulphurisation using an alkali such as limestone.

1.3.3 Greenhouse gases

Many of the gaseous pollutants are formed by the burning of fossil fuels – oil, coal and gas. Oil is composed of a complex mixture of straight and branched paraffins which is refined before use. The fraction with a boiling point above 350°C is used in power stations. Natural gas consists mainly of simple paraffins, methane, propane and butane. Coal, in contrast, is a very complex mixture of high molecular weight compounds as it is derived from plants exposed to high pressure and temperature. All these fuels are burnt in power stations and the main constituents of the exhaust gases are water, carbon dioxide, sulphur dioxide and nitric oxide.

The land and the seas and oceans exchange carbon dioxide in a balanced manner. Plants fix carbon dioxide during photosynthesis and respiration, and upon decomposition release carbon dioxide back to the atmosphere. The oceans act as a sink by dissolving carbon dioxide and algae in the ocean, also fix carbon dioxide photosynthetically. The burning of fossil fuel releases large amounts of carbon dioxide which was fixed millions of years ago when the plants which formed coal were alive. It is the release of this carbon dioxide that is causing a significant increase in the amount of this gas in the atmosphere. The carbon dioxide in the atmosphere traps heat radiated from the earth, so that an increase will cause global warming. An alternative to fossil fuels, other than fission or fusion, would be the use of biologically derived fuels which would result in no net gain in carbon dioxide as the carbon dioxide released was removed from the environment during photosynthesis (carbon dioxide neutral).

1.4   Biotechnological treatment of pollution

Biotechnology will probably not be a complete solution to environmental pollution but can act as part of an integrated approach to its control and removal. Biotechnology is involved in the following areas:

- Environmental monitoring
- Remediation of polluted sites
- Reduction or removal of current wastes
- Prevention of pollution.

1.4.1   Environmental monitoring

Central to the implementation of any environmental act is the ability to determine what chemicals are present or being released, their concentration and their potential environmental risk. It is estimated that some 60,000 chemicals are in common use and many hundreds are newly introduced each year. Assays which give accurate, sensitive results which can be used in an on-line situation would be of great benefit (Chapter 2).

1.4.2   Bioremediation

Bioremediation is the biological treatment and removal of pollution from the environment. A long history of industrialisation in developed countries has left a legacy of industrial pollution of land, water and air. Industries such as petrochemical, smelting, mineral extraction, gasworks and other sources such as landfill have left a long list of polluted sites. Legislation will now require local authorities to list contaminated sites and perhaps oversee their clean-up. It has been estimated that in the UK there are some 100,000 sites which will cost between £10,000 and £20,000 million to clean up. In the USA it has been estimated that the bioremediation component of environmental biotechnology will be some $500 million by the year 2000.

The use of microorganisms for the removal of pollution is not new, as biological sewage treatment has been practised for decades. The principal organisms are bacteria and fungi which have the ability to degrade hydrocarbons such as oil, coal tar, and chlorinated compounds such as pesticides. Although metals cannot be degraded, they can be accumulated by microorganisms and therefore removed from the environment. Various types of bioremediation strategies have been developed (Chapter 5) to treat polluted land and water, although there is only a limited knowledge of the processes involved, as mixed populations of microorganisms are used and the dynamics of such populations are complex. In addition, the bioremediation process depends greatly on the quality and quantity of the pollution and is affected by other factors such as toxic agents, temperature, nutrient bioavailability and oxygen limitation.

1.4.3   Removal or reduction of pollution from current processes

Bioremediation can be applied to the wastes from various processes in an 'end of pipe' system. Biotechnology offers some of the most environmentally friendly solutions. Examples are the removal of metals and radionuclides from waste streams, and reed beds for the degradation of organic pollutants and the bioaccumulation of metals. Another example is the reduction of volatile organic compounds (VOCs) from waste gases by passage through a biofilter (Chapter 5).

1.4.4   Prevention of pollution (clean technology)

Biotechnology can help towards the cleaner production of existing products. The drive towards greener processes which are environmentally sustainable is a preferred option to the clean-up of the pollution once formed, but until recently it has not received much attention. The use of enzymes or bacteria instead of chemical processes has the potential to reduce the use of feedstock and the energy required for the processes as lower temperatures are used. In addition, the enzymes and bacteria themselves are also biodegradable. One example is the microbial removal of sulphur compounds from coal prior to combustion (Chapter 5). Another is the use of fungi to pretreat logs before pulp and paper production which reduces the use of energy and bleaching materials. The development of biodegradable plastics would be of considerable use in the reduction of solid waste, as much (about 20% on average) of the material deposited in landfill sites consists of plastics. (These plastics are derived from non-renewable petrochemicals and are resistant to degradation.) Microorganisms are capable of producing biopolymers which can be used as plastics and are biodegradable, but the high cost of biopolymers has restricted their application to date (Chapter 5.)

The demand for energy shows no evidence of declining, and electricity generation uses coal, oil and gas, in addition to nuclear and hydropower. Coal, oil and gas supplies are limited, and all produce greenhouse gases on combustion; therefore alternatives are required to replace these fossil fuels and to reduce greenhouse gases. Biological alternatives are the combustion of rapidly growing plants (willow, *Miscanthus*) and plant oil (rapeseed oil), and ethanol production. Ethanol can be used in petrol engines with little modification to the engine and can be produced from sugar and starch, so that it represents a very suitable petroleum replacement.

Thus, in conclusion, environmental biotechnology will be applied in the following areas:

- Transgenic organisms will continue to be developed, in particular plants for herbicide/insecticide resistance. This will help to reduce the use of biocides but the commercialisation of transgenic organisms will depend on the public's view of the products.
- Bioremediation for the clean-up of wastes will continue to expand.
- The monitoring of environmental contamination is essential.
- The long-term developments will perhaps be in the areas of biofuels and clean technology.

1.5 References

European Federation of Biotechnology (1988) Definition of biotechnology. *EFB Newsletter*, September, no. 5, p. 2.

Girbal, L. and Soucaille, P. (1998) Regulation of solvent production in *Clostridium acetobutylicum. Tibtech*, **16**, 11–16.

Glass, D. J., Raphael, T., Valo, R. and Van Eyk, J. (1995) Growing international markets and opportunities in bioremediation. *Genet. Eng. News*, **15**, 6–9.

Golub, E. S. (1997) Genetically enhanced food for thought. *Nature Biotechnol.*, **15**, 112.

Houwink, E. H. (1984) *A Realistic View of Biotechnology*. European Federation of Biotechnology, DECHEMA, Frankfurt-am-Main, Germany.

Houwink, E. H. (1989) *Biotechnology: Controlled Use of Biological Information*. Kluwer Academic Publishers, Dordrecht, The Netherlands.

Kareiva, P. and Stark, J. (1994) Environmental risks in agricultural biotechnology. *Chemistry & Industry*, January, 52–55.

Kennedy, M. J. (1991) The evolution of the word 'biotechnology'. *Trends in Biotechnol.*, **9**, 218–220.

Prave, P., Faust, U., Sittig, W. and Sukatsch, D. A. (1987) *Fundamentals of Biotechnology*. VCH, Weinheim, Germany.

Reeve, R. N. (1994) *Environmental Analysis*. John Wiley & Sons, Chichester, UK.

Sharp, D. H. (1989) *Bioprotein Manufacture*. Ellis Horwood, Chichester, UK.

Spinks, A. (1980) *Biotechnology: Report of a Joint Working Party*. HMSO, London.

1.5.1 Recommended reading

Creuger, W. and Creuger, A. (1991) *Biotechnology – A Textbook of Industrial Microbiology*. Freeman, New York.

Glazer, A. N. and Nikaido, H. (1994) *Microbial Biotechnology*. Freeman, New York.

Hurst, C. J. (1996) *Manual of Environmental Microbiology*. ASM Press, Herndon, VA.

McEldowney, J. F. and McEldowney, S. (1996) *Environment and the Law*. Addison Wesley Longman, Harlow, UK.

McEldowney, S., Hardman, D. J. and Waite, S. (1993) *Pollution: Ecology and Biotreatment*. Longman Scientific and Technical, Harlow, UK.

Moses, V. and Cape, R. A. (1991) *Biotechnology, the Science and Business*. Harwood Academic, London.

Moses, V. and Moses, S. (1995) *Exploiting Biotechnology*. Harwood Academic, Chur, Switzerland.

Chapter 2

Environmental monitoring

2.1 Introduction

Pollution has been defined by Holdgate (1979) as 'the introduction into the environment of substances or energy liable to cause hazards to human health, harm to living resources and ecological damage, or interference with legitimate uses of the environment'. Thus pollutants can be derived from many sources and can take many forms. Some of the main groups of environmental pollutants which can contaminate land, water and air are inorganics such as metals and nitrates, organics such as sewage, petrochemicals and synthetic compounds, biological agents such as pathogens, and gaseous substances including volatiles, gases and particulates (Table 1.2, Chapter 1).

This chapter describes the methods for determining a number of environmental parameters and the influence that recombinant DNA technology will have on these. Techniques such as polymerase chain reaction (PCR) will be applied to the determination of microbial populations in many habitats not accessible by conventional techniques. The development of biosensors will also be described.

The fate of pollutants in the environment depends on the nature of the compound, and the environmental conditions and possible fates are given in Fig. 1.3 (Chapter 1). The pollution can originate from contaminated sites of defunct industries such as gasworks, from existing domestic and industrial sources as in the case of sewage pollution and metals from industries such as electroplating, and from accidents and spillages as at Seveso and from the oil tanker *Amoco Cadiz* (Chapter 1). These pollutants can be single compounds or complex mixtures in which some of the components can be at very low concentrations. In addition, many of these contaminants are not restricted to their initial sites but, depending on conditions, can migrate and contaminate other parts of the environment such as lakes, rivers, reservoirs, estuaries and the sea.

In order to administer the numerous Acts concerning the pollution of the environment, and the permitted levels of contamination, detection and monitoring of the level of pollution are essential. Of the possible pollutants indicated in Table 1.2 (Chapter 1), the European Union places the most dangerous compounds on its 'black' list and those less dangerous on a 'grey' list (Table 2.1). In the USA the Environmental Protection Agency (EPA) has a list of 129

Table 2.1   European Union lists of toxic compounds

Black List

1. Organohalogen compounds and substances which may form such compounds in the aquatic environment.
2. Organophosphorus compounds.
3. Organotin compounds.
4. Substances, the carcinogenic activity of which is exhibited in or by the aquatic environment.
5. Mercury and its compounds.
6. Cadmium and its compounds.
7. Persistent mineral oils and hydrocarbons of petroleum.
8. Persistent synthetic substances.

Grey List

1. The following metals and their compounds: Zn, Cu, Ni, Cr, Pb, Se, As, Mo, Ti, Sn, Ba, Be, B, U, Va, Co, Th, Te, Au.
2. Biocides and their derivatives not in the 'Black' list.
3. Substances which have a deleterious effect on the taste and/or smell of products for human consumption derived from aquatic environments; compounds liable to give rise to such in water.
4. Toxic or persistent organic compounds of silicon and substances which give rise to such compounds in water, excluding those which are biologically harmless or are rapidly converted in water to harmless substances.
5. Inorganic compounds of phosphorus and elemental phosphorus.
6. Non-persistent mineral oils and hydrocarbons of petroleum origin.
7. Cyanides, fluorides.
8. Certain substances which may have an adverse effect on the oxygen balance, particularly ammonia and nitrites.

Source: Mason, 1996.

priority pollutants. These are shown in Table 2.2 and indicate the diversity of the problem of monitoring and evaluation. Many of these compounds have strict legal upper limits on land and water. Thus any monitoring must take into consideration the type or types of contaminants present, their availability and the possibility that biomagnification and bioaccumulation may occur. Thus environmental monitoring must be able, in many cases, to detect with accuracy and consistency contaminants at very low levels. Environmental bio-technology may offer a number of accurate and reliable monitoring techniques as alternatives to the usual chemical analysis.

2.2 Sampling

The collection of a representative sample from a homogeneous source is no problem, but with soil, air and water samples this is rarely the case. Often soil contamination may be very localised and waste stream contamination may be intermittent and poorly mixed.

Table 2.2   US Environmental Protection Agency (EPA) Priority List

Volatile organic compounds (31)

Acrolein
Acrylonitrile
Benzene
Toluene
Ethylbenzene
Carbon tetrachloride
Chlorobenzene
1,2-Dichloroethane
1,1,1-Trichloroethane
1,1-Dichloroethane
1,1-Dichloroethylene
1,1,2-Trichloroethane
1,1,2,2-Tetrachloroethane
Chloroethane
2-Chloroethyl vinyl ether
Chloroform

1,2-Dichloropropane
1,3-Dichloropropane
Methylene chloride
Methyl chloride
Methyl bromide
Bromoform
Dichlorobromomethane
Trichlorofluoromethane
Dichlorodifluoromethane
Chlorodibromomethane
Tetrachloroethylene
Trichloroethylene
Vinyl chloride
1,2-*trans*-Dichloroethylene
bis(Chloromethyl) ether

Extractable into solvent under neutral or alkaline conditions (46)

1,2-Dichlorobenzene
1,3-Dichlorobenzene
1,4-Dichlorobenzene
Hexachloroethane
Hexachlorobutadiene
Hexachlorobenzene
1,2,4-Trichlorobenzene
bis(2-Chloroethoxy)methane
Naphthalene
2-Chloronaphthalene
Isophorone
Nitrobenzene
2,4-Dinitrotoluene
2,6-Dinitrotoluene
4-Bromophenyl phenyl ether
bis(2-Ethylhexyl) phthalate
Di-*n*-octyl phthalate
Dimethyl phthalate
Diethyl phthalate
Di-*n*-butyl phthalate
Acenaphthylene
Acenaphthene
Butyl benzyl phthalate

Fluorene
Fluoranthene
Chrysene
Pyrene
Phenanthrene
Anthracene
Benzo(a)anthracene
Benzo(b)fluoranthene
Benzo(k)fluoranthene
Benzo(a)pyrene
Indeno(1,2,3-c,d)pyrene
Dibenzo(a,h)anthracene
Benzo(g,h,f)perylene
4-Chlorophenyl phenyl ether
3,3'-Dichlorobenzidine
Benzidine
bis(2-Chloroethyl) ether
1,2-Diphenylhydrazine
Hexachlorocyclopentadiene
N-Nitrosodiphenylamine
N-Nitrosodimethylamine
N-Nitrosodi-*n*-propylamine
bis(2-Chloroisopropyl) ether

Extractable into solvent under acid conditions (11)

Phenol
2-Nitrophenol
4-Nitrophenol
2,4-Dinitrophenol
4,6-Dinitro-*o*-cresol
Pentachlorophenol

p-Chloro-*m*-cresol
2-Chlorophenol
2,4-Dichlorophenol
2,4,6-Trichlorophenol
2,4-Dimethylphenol

Table 2.2 *(Cont'd)*

Pesticides, polychlorobiphenyl (PCB) and related compounds (24)

α-Endosulfan	Heptachlor
Endosulfan sulfate	Heptachlor epoxide
α-BHC	Chlordane
β-BHC	Toxaphene
γ-BHC	Aroclor 1016†
Aldrin	Aroclor 1221
Dieldrin	Aroclor 1232
4,4'-DDE	Aroclor 1242
4,4'-DDD*	Aroclor 1248
4,4'-DDT	Aroclor 1254
Endrin	Aroclor 1260
Endrin aldehyde	2,3,7,8-Tetrachlorodibenzo-*p*-dioxin (TCDD)

Metals (13)

Antimony	Mercury
Arsenic	Nickel
Beryllium	Selenium
Cadmium	Silver
Chromium	Thallium
Copper	Zinc
Lead	

Miscellaneous

Cyanides	Asbestos

* DDD = dichlorodiphenyldichloroethane (related to DDT).
† PCBs (polychlorinated biphenyls) consist of 209 distinct compounds with 1–10 chlorine atoms attached to the biphenyl molecule. PCBs were prepared as complex mixtures under the name Aroclor, where the number 1248 indicates 12 carbon atoms and 48 chlorine atoms.
Source: Keith and Telliard, 1979.

2.2.1   Land (site) sampling

(Contaminated sites often require some form of survey, since it is rare for the site history and management to be sufficiently well documented to give full information on the pollution present. Some directives (BSI, 1988) suggest that 17 samples should be taken for a 5-hectare site, at three different depths, which should be increased to 30 samples for sites below 0.5 hectares. However, contamination is frequently patchy so that the number of samples taken will depend on how small an area the contamination covers. Table 2.3 gives the probability of locating contamination using random sampling grids. These grids can be rectangular, square, diamond-shaped or herringbone. The drawback of

Table 2.3   Probability of locating contamination using random sampling grids

Contamination as % of total area	Percentage probability		
	Number of samples taken		
	10	30	50
1	10	26	39
5	40	79	92
10	65	96	99
25	94	100	100

Source: Cairney, 1987.

these types of grid is that they can generate a large number of samples which can be expensive to analyse. Therefore, a site history can be of great use in directing the sampling process, and reducing costs.

2.2.2   Water sampling

Sampling of most wastewaters and contaminated water is difficult due to their highly variable nature (Keith, 1988). To obtain an accurate assessment, samples will have to be taken over a time period, over different sections of the waterway, and at different depths. There are various automatic methods of taking samples which can be used. Some industrial discharges into waterways are intermittent, which will extend the time over which sampling must be carried out. Where to sample in the waterway depends on any inflow and outflow of water and on stratification, and the whole waterway may need to be assessed. If groundwater is to be monitored, wells will have to be drilled and the very process of drilling can alter or contaminate samples. Contamination can come from the drilling method, the casing material and the sample method. These types of consideration have to be evaluated when choosing the sampling method and analysing the results.

When a specific organism is to be surveyed in the environment in order to assess contamination, the samples have to be as representative as possible. One example is the sampling of the edible mussel *Mytilus edulis* which accumulates metals and can therefore be used as an indicator of metal pollution. The following points have to be taken into consideration in sampling the mussels:

- Time of year: late winter favoured as metal concentrations stable at that time
- Size or age: dominant size taken
- Position on shore: from rocks to avoid contamination by silt
- Sample size: a minimum of 25 samples
- Treatment after sampling: washed in fresh water, soft tissue sampled, this being the site of accumulation.

2.2.3 Air sampling

Air sampling is beset by much the same problems as water sampling but is also influenced by wind direction and strength. The purpose of sampling is to obtain a representative sample, and in general there are three sampling systems used for air: pumped systems, pre-concentration and grab samples. In the pumped system the sample is pumped directly from the air into the analyser. In cases where the pollutant is present at very low concentrations, pre-concentration is required before analysis. An example of the type of system is the adsorption of the contaminant onto activated charcoal for removal and analysis at a later date. Grab samples involve the capture of samples of air in bottles, syringes, bellows and bags for analysis later. Under normal conditions the air is well mixed and samples are normally taken at a height of 2 metres, but if a boundary layer forms, stratification of the air may occur, and towers will be required to take samples above 2 metres.

Whatever sample has been taken, whether soil, water or air, if it cannot be analysed immediately, careful storage is required as pollutants can be lost or changed during storage.

The very large number of methods available for the analysis of environmental pollutants can be divided into physical, chemical and biological. Clearly it is in the biological methods that biotechnology will have the greatest influence.

2.3 Physical analysis

The physical methods which can be used to determine the levels of pollutants and other compounds in water and on land are in general as follows.

- Gravimetric: used to determine suspended solids (SS), total or volatile solids and sulphate levels.
- pH: very acid or alkaline conditions will be corrosive and restrict biological activity. Easily measured with a pH electrode.
- Colorimetric: colour and turbidity are important in water quality. These can be determined using comparison tubes, colour discs, colorimeters and spectrophotometers.
- Dissolved oxygen: this can be measured using an oxygen electrode. Oxygen levels are very important in water quality in order to maintain aerobic biological organisms.
- Ion specific electrodes: these electrodes can be used to determine the levels of ammonia, nitrate, nitrite, calcium, sodium and other ions. The determination of nitrate and nitrite is important as minimum levels have been set for water quality.

The oxygen and ion electrode technology allows the possibility of automated analysis, remote sensing and monitoring. However, many of the newer electrodes suffer from instability and all are prey to fouling and damage.

2.4 Chemical analysis

There are a number of texts (Tebbutt, 1998; Mason, 1996; Gray, 1989) which outline standard chemical methods for the determination of environmental components such as chloride, nitrate, nitrite and phosphate. Metals can be determined by chemical methods or by atomic adsorption. The detection of the wide range of organic compounds requires techniques such as HPLC (High Performance Liquid Chromatography) and GC (Gas Chromatography), which can be linked to mass spectrometers in order to identify the compounds separated.

The oxygen demand in a waterway can be estimated by measuring the chemical oxygen demand (COD). COD is determined by refluxing the sample with potassium dichromate in concentrated sulphuric acid with silver sulphate as a catalyst (mercuric sulphate is also added to complex any chlorides present). The sample is refluxed for 2 hours and the potassium dichromate remaining is determined by titration against ferrous ammonium sulphide. This will give a measure of the oxygen required for the oxidation of the contents in the sample. A different measurement is the total organic carbon (TOC) which measures the organic carbon present and not the oxygen requirement. TOC is measured by the electrical combustion of the sample and the carbon dioxide formed determined by infrared analysis. Both measurements are useful in defining the waste in terms of its total carbon content and how much of the carbon could impose a chemical oxygen demand.

2.5 Biological analysis

2.5.1 Microbiological methods

Traditional microbiological methods of microscopical analysis, and a variety of methods for viable counts using selective media, have been used in the assessment of the contamination of the environment by pathogens and in the study of microbial communities. The viable count method relies on the premise that each colony formed has been derived from a single cell and, by using selective media, the number of bacteria such as *Salmonella* and coliforms can be estimated. These selective techniques tend to favour assessment of the faster-growing species and some of the important slower-growing species can be missed. In addition, unless the conditions from where the sample was removed can be reproduced, some bacterial species may fail to grow and can be missed. Therefore, the growth characteristics of the organisms of interest need to be known before their numbers can be estimated accurately.

An example of the difficulties of estimating microbial populations which use specific substrates or cultural requirements is the estimation of petroleum-degrading organisms (Mesarch and Nies, 1997). Petroleum-degrading bacteria are abundant in soil and numerous plating techniques have been used for their estimation, including plates containing petroleum, polyaromatic hydrocarbons and crude oil. However, these have been shown to be difficult to use as some of the substrates are volatile and the results variable. It has been shown that a medium containing benzoate was better at discriminating petroleum-degrading organisms and could show difference in the microbial populations between clean and petroleum-contaminated soil (Mesarch and Nies, 1997).

Normal microbial methods are suitable for suspended microbial cultures consisting of single cells, but in most environmental situations the microorganisms exist as aggregates or as biofilms (Costerton *et al.*, 1995). Anaerobic and aerobic wastewater treatment uses mixed microbial populations most of which occur in aggregates, whereas trickle filters, rotating biological contactors and fluidised bed reactors (Chapter 3) use biofilms containing a mixed population. Direct microscopical analysis of biofilms can only really determine cell morphology. Recently biofilms have been investigated using techniques such as scanning and transmission electron microscopes and confocal scanning laser microscopes (CSLM) which can give much higher resolution (Stams and Oude Elferink, 1997). Biofilms appear to be much more complex than was at first thought, with the microorganisms forming separate microcolonies. Thus biofilms vary considerably in terms of depth, density, porosity and diffusivity, which affects the supply of nutrients and removal of wastes. Sampling of aggregates and biofilms cannot be carried out unless some form of disruption can be used. Unless the disruption is complete, microbial numbers can be underestimated. In addition, the conditions in an aggregate or biofilm may be difficult to reproduce on a selective medium and, although slow-growing species may be dominant in nature, they may be underestimated in a plate assay.

Other direct methods exist for the estimation of microbial numbers, including immunology and flow cytometry. Microbial populations can be detected and specific bacteria localised by the use of antibodies. Bacterial envelopes are strong antigens and both monoclonal and polyclonal antibodies have been prepared against specific bacterial antigens. The antibodies can be linked to fluorescent dyes or enzymes and these labels used to estimate the numbers and position of specific bacteria. Enzyme linked immunoadsorbent assay (ELISA) has also been used to study biofilms. These techniques are very specific, inexpensive and easy to use, provided the antibodies are available. One example of the use of immunological techniques has been the detection of methanogens in anaerobic bioreactors. The ELISA technique is a widely used format which can handle a large number of samples. Polyclonal antibodies against eight methanogens (Sorensen and Ahring, 1997) have been used in the ELISA technique to study their levels during anaerobic digestion of cow and pig manure. A combination of antibodies and fluorescent dyes has been used with flow cytometry to sort cells from mixed environmental populations (Davey and Kell, 1996). The disadvantage of the flow cytometry technique is that the cells have to be extracted from the samples before they can be sorted.

Bacteria can also be detected and identified by the analysis of their patterns of phospholipid ester-linked fatty acids (PLFAME) or phospholipid fatty acids (PLFA). This method has been used to study methanogens and sulphate-reducing bacteria but the technique is not as sensitive as nucleic acid-based techniques and the patterns can be altered by changes in environmental conditions (Bottger, 1996).

BOX 2.1

The flow cytometer was developed for animal cells in order to separate and count cells with different DNA contents (haploid N, diploid 2N). A stream of liquid containing the cells is broken up into a series of droplets at a concentration that gives about one cell per droplet. These droplets are passed between a light source and a fluorescent detector. If the cells are stained with a fluorochrome such as fluorescein, rhodamine or the DNA with DAPI (diamidino-2-phenylindole) they will fluoresce at a specific wavelength which can be detected. If required the detector will electrostatically deflect the droplet and in this way cells can be sorted as well as counted.

2.5.2 Physiological monitoring

Biological Oxygen Demand was established in 1912 by the Royal Commission on sewage disposal as an important parameter of water quality. Since then it has been a key parameter in the monitoring of water quality and treatment. The Biological Oxygen Demand (BOD) is a measure of the oxygen demand in a sample as a result of its organic content.

BOX 2.2

BOD is normally measured by incubating a sample of the waste, diluted if necessary with a volume of activated sludge. Activated sludge is a mixture of aerobic organisms produced by the treatment of waste. The dissolved oxygen is measured before and after incubation for 5 days. The precise test procedure is given in a number of handbooks on water analysis. The test, although slow, does give reasonable results with normal sewage, but the test is biological and will be affected by the time of incubation, the temperature and the microorganisms present. For a typical waste this is not a problem, but wastes that contain high levels of nitrogenous material will require longer than 5 days for complete oxidation. If the waste is too strong the oxygen will be depleted before oxidation is complete, and certain compounds require the presence of certain microorganisms for oxidation as they are toxic to many microorganisms.

Variations in the BOD assay are to extend the incubation to 7 days, to oxidise ammonia by addition of allylthiourea, and the dilution of the sample. Although widely used, the BOD assay has a number of deficiencies:

- It is slow, taking 5 days before results are obtained.
- It is time-consuming and expensive for a large number of samples.
- It does not fully represent the natural conditions.
- Oxidation may not be complete in 5 days.

- It can be difficult to interpret with wastes containing high levels of non-degradable organic material.
- It is imprecise, particularly with low levels of organic material.

Due to these concerns, alternative methods have been investigated, including absorbence and fluorescence (Comber et al., 1996). It was shown that there was a correlation between BOD and absorbence but this was not true for fluorescence. As yet BOD still remains the main indicator of the level of organic material in wastes. BOD is clearly related to the chemical oxygen demand (COD), where COD measures all the oxidisable material in the waste and BOD measures only the biodegradable organic material. Thus the two values will not be the same as some wastes contain organic materials such as lignins which are degraded so slowly as to be regarded as non-biodegradable. The ratio of COD to BOD provides a useful guide to the type of organic materials in the waste, but because of the rapidity of obtaining the results TOC is often used to define highly contaminated wastes.

Microbial activity can also be followed by a number of indirect methods such as gas production (Beaubien et al., 1995), levels of ATP and the ability of active cells to reduce tetrazolium compounds from colourless to a blue colour.

2.5.3 Recombinant DNA technology

Recombinant DNA technology has reached a level where it can now be used to follow genes or specific DNA sequences, and therefore microorganisms, within the environment. Thus it can be used to study:

- the microbial ecology of soils and water, in particular those extreme habitats such as hydrothermal vents
- anaerobic and aerobic digesters
- contaminated groundwater
- evaluation of diversity
- bioleaching processes
- release of GEMs (genetic manipulated microorganisms)
- bioremediation processes.

The first step in the technology is the extraction and isolation of DNA from the samples. A number of methods are available for the extraction of nucleic acids from samples of soil, water and sediment and these can be divided into two categories (Fig. 2.1). The first methods used were the direct extraction of DNA using chemicals such as alkalis (Ogram et al., 1987), detergents such as SDS (sodium dodecyl sulphate) and the enzyme lysozyme to disrupt the bacteria in situ (Saano et al., 1995). The DNA can then be extracted with SDS, phenol or chloroform or a mixture of phenol and chloroform. The second method involves the extraction of the microorganisms before lysis (Bakken and Lindahl, 1995), the cells being broken using conventional methods and the DNA extracted (Torsvik et al., 1995). More recently bead mills (Smalla et al., 1993) and lysozyme combined with freeze-thawing (Tsai

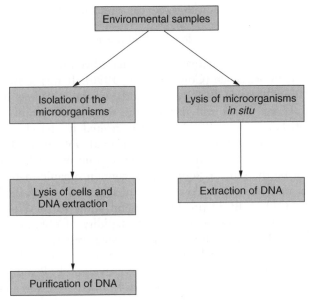

Fig. 2.1   The various methods for the extraction of DNA from environmental samples.

and Olson, 1991) have been used to extract DNA directly, with yields of up to 90%. Both extraction techniques are lengthy, require large samples and can have low yields due to the complex nature of the samples and the need for highly pure DNA. DNA purification techniques currently used include treatment with cetyl-trimethylammonium bromide (CTAB), spin columns, spin cartridges, agarose gels, CsCl precipitation and ion-exchange chromatography. However, the development of the technique of polymerase chain reaction (PCR) means that only small amounts of DNA need to be extracted from environmental samples. Polymerase chain reaction (PCR) can amplify genes or DNA sequences present in only small numbers, and thus improves the detection many fold (Graham, 1994). The PCR technique can be used with very specific primers to detect minor genes or with less specific primers to detect groups of genes.

Once extracted and purified the DNA is probed for a specific gene or DNA sequence which can act as a marker for a microorganism or group of microorganisms under investigation. The probe can be constructed as an oligonucleotide (a short chain of DNA or RNA) if the sequence of the specific gene is known, and these can be designed to bind to very specific targets or to a wide range of species. Probes can also be prepared from cloned genes, or from cDNA synthesised from extracted mRNA. One of the most promising series of probes are those based on the gene coding for the ribosomal RNA, in particular the 16S subunit (ssrRNA) (Hugenholtz and Pace, 1996). The 16S subunit ribosomal RNA has highly conserved regions and variable regions, so that if the probes are made to the conserved region the probe will detect a group of

Box 2.3

PCR (polymerase chain reaction) is a technique which was first reported in 1985 for the amplification of specific genes. Once pure DNA has been extracted, the double-stranded DNA is separated into two strands by heating to 95°C for around 2 minutes. Short single-stranded oligonucleotides (primers) and the *Taq* polymerase (temperature tolerant DNA polymerase) are added and the mixture cooled to 60°C. This lowering of the temperature allows the primers to anneal to specific sections of the single-stranded DNA complementary to their base sequence. As the mixture contains nucleotide triphosphates the *Taq* now synthesises new strands of DNA complementary to the DNA template and extending from the primer for up to 10 kb in length (Fig. 2.2). The lower temperature is normally held for about 2 minutes and then the reaction mixture raised to 95°C. This separates the original and new strands. Another set of binding sites are now available for the primers and when cooled to 60°C after 2 minutes the *Taq* polymerase starts another round of synthesis. This process is repeated for a number of cycles until the primers or nucleotide run out or the cycling is stopped.

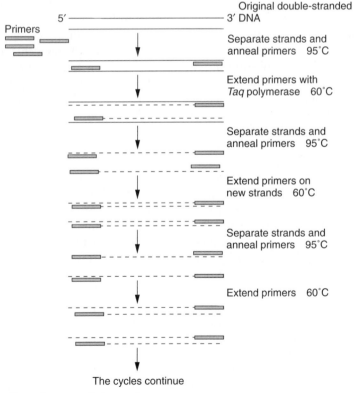

Fig. 2.2 The polymerase chain reaction.

related organisms, whereas if the variable region is used the probe will be much more specific (Woese, 1987). At present there are some 3000–5000 full or partial sequences for the ssrRNA and this number is constantly increasing; these are available in databanks such as GenBank and EMBL, so that a considerable number of probes can be designed.

For these probes to be able to indicate a gene or sequence they all need some form of label. The incorporation of radioactive labels into the probes can be carried out by nick translation, primer extension or end labelling. The radioactive labels can be replaced by non-radioactive labels based on biotin which, when incorporated into nucleotides, can react with streptavidin which itself can be linked to antibodies or enzymes. The antibody or enzyme reaction can be used to indicate the presence of the probe. The probes once labelled can be used to detect those specific sequences in the extracted DNA or in some cases in a bacterial colony. The most commonly used methods of using probes are dot blot and Southern blot techniques.

Other nucleic acid-based techniques which can be used to follow changes in the population in the environment are restriction fragment length polymorphism (RFLP) and denaturing gradient gel electrophoresis (DGGE). In RFLP analysis restriction enzyme degradation of extracted DNA or PCR-amplified DNA yields a specific number of bands of DNA fragments after gel electrophoresis. At this stage the bands can be probed using the Southern blot technique. Changes in the distribution of the bands indicate changes in the DNA structure or sequence. In DGGE analysis two DNA fragments differing in only a single base substitution, deletion or insertion can be separated. The method depends on the pattern of DNA melting as the temperature or denaturant concentration (formamide, urea) increases. The melting of part of the DNA affects the rate of migration through the polyacrylamide gel and the melting of the DNA is affected by its base composition (Box 2.5), changes in its base composition altering the melting temperature. These processes are summarised in Fig. 2.4.

The use of recombinant DNA techniques for the study of bacterial communities, particularly those in environments difficult to reproduce, allows the assessment of bacterial diversity without cultivation. An example is the use of whole cell hybridisation with domain- and kingdom-specific fluorescent-oligonucleotide 16S derived probes to study the diversity of the thermophilic microorganisms in deep-sea hydrothermal vents (Harmsen et al., 1997). The variation in microbial populations has been investigated by extracting the nucleic acids, amplifying the 16S rRNA gene by PCR, cloning the fragments and comparing the gene sequences. The resulting sequences have shown that the majority of microorganisms in the explored habitats have previously been unknown and only a small fraction of the microbial diversity has been detected by cultural methods (Polz and Cavanaugh, 1997). Quantitative hybridisation can also provide an estimate of the dominance of individual populations. Microbial diversity in the natural environment has also been investigated by using variation in the 16S RNA and a taxonomy based on this data has been presented (Woese et al., 1990).

Box 2.4

Southern blot is a technique used to detect specific sequences in DNA fragments. The DNA under investigation is cut into fragments of various sizes by *restriction enzymes*. These enzymes cut the DNA at specific base sequences which are unique for each enzyme. The fragments of DNA can then be separated by size by agarose gel electrophoresis. Once separated the DNA fragments can be transferred to nitrocellulose or nylon membranes by overlaying the gel with the membrane for up to 24 hours under moderate pressure. This will transfer the DNA from the gel to the membrane, forming a precise replica of the DNA fragments as they have been separated on the gel (Fig. 2.3). Once transferred the DNA fragments can be fixed in place by drying at 80 °C for 2 hours and the DNA denatured. Denaturation of the DNA allows the probe to anneal with the complementary sequences in the DNA strands which can then be detected by autoradiography or enzyme activity.

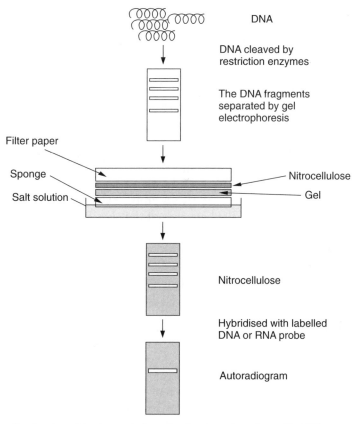

Fig. 2.3 The Southern blotting technique for the detection of specific DNA sequences. The Southern blotting DNA fragments are transferred to the nitrocellulose, whereas in so-called Northern blotting RNA fragments are transferred.

Box 2.5

If the temperature or the concentration of denaturant, formamide or urea is increased, blocks of DNA called domains melt at discrete temperatures (T_m). These domains can be from 25 to several hundred base pairs in length and thus DNA fragments of 100–1000 base pairs can have two to five melting domains. The melting temperatures are between 60 and 80°C and can be affected by the base sequence of the DNA region. In practice the DNA is electrophoresised at a high temperature, typically 60°C, in a polyacrylamide gel containing a gradient of denaturant equivalent to a temperature gradient of about 10°C. A DNA fragment which reaches its T_m value will have a domain melt and the DNA mobility will be slowed, and the mobility will be further slowed as other domains melt when their T_m is reached. Thus DNA fragments with small differences in base composition will have different T_m values and can therefore be separated. The system has been improved by attaching a high melting domain (GC clamp) to the test DNA so that the whole DNA can be melted before the clamp, and therefore all the DNA can be analysed. A second improvement has been to use the system to analyse heteroduplexes between control and test DNA samples as any mismatch between the two DNA fragments will cause the DNA to melt at a lower temperature. In addition the control DNA can be radioactively labelled so that the gel can be autoradiographed directly, avoiding gel blotting.

DNA technology has been used to follow the bacterial population in activated sludge and the population dynamics in a trickle-bed bioreactor. It has been clear that culture techniques are not capable of providing full details of the population in activated sludge; 16S rRNA probes have shown that the dominant organisms were those of the beta class of the class Proteobacteria, whereas the culture methods had shown that the gamma subclass of Proteobacteria was dominant (Snaidr *et al.*, 1997). The trickle-bed study used *in situ* fluorescent hybridisation with 16S and 23S rRNA probes and showed different results from those obtained by culture methods; the population proved to be very diverse.

Recombinant technology can be used to estimate the degree of genetic variation in the determination of biodiversity (Karp *et al.*, 1997) and to detect bioleaching bacteria (De Wulf-Durand *et al.*, 1997). In the case of bioleaching, PCR was used to amplify the 16S rRNA obtained from the bacterial population associated with an acidic mining environment. The monitoring of the release of genetically engineered microorganisms (GEMs) is essential if the risk factors associated with such releases are to be evaluated. GEMs can be followed on the basis of their unique DNA sequences (Jansson, 1995).

Many of the molecular probes are based on the small subunit ribosomal RNA (ssrRNA). The ribosomal RNA genes can then be detected by fractionating the DNA, cloning fragments into the bacteriophage lambda and screening

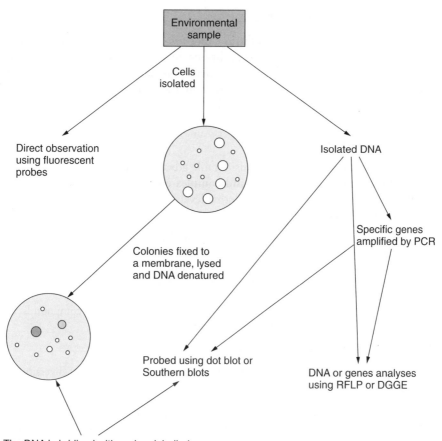

Fig. 2.4 The use of molecular biology techniques to detect specific microorganisms or groups of microorganisms.

the clones for rRNA genes. This method is slow but can be improved by the use of the polymerase chain reaction (PCR). The rRNA genes can be amplified directly from the isolated DNA by using rRNA primers. The techniques allow the amplification of DNA and thus the identification of rare genes and DNA at very low levels. Clones can then be dot or colony blotted with specific probes, or subjected to restriction fragment polymorphisms (RFLP). Phylotypes can be visualised *in situ* using fluorescent-linked oligonucleotide probes and microscopes fitted with fluorescence detectors. Fluorescence can also be linked to flow cytometry to count cell numbers and to confocal scanning laser microscopy to follow the arrangements of the cells. However, oligonucleotide probes require sequence data for their design and at present there are not many sequences available.

2.6 Monitoring pollution

The biological monitoring of pollution uses two main groups of techniques: firstly, those which describe the conditions *in situ* by the measurement of changes in species within the environment (*biomarkers*) upon exposure to pollution (Huggett *et al.*, 1992), and secondly those that use biological material to estimate the toxicity of a particular chemical in isolation.

2.6.1 Biomarkers

The use of 'biomarkers' has the considerable advantage in that it measures the action of the pollutants in the real and complex environment where there may be many complex interactions at sublethal levels. The advantages of biomarkers can be outlined as follows:

- The determination can be taken over a period of time and not the single sample often used in chemical analysis.
- They can indicate the risks of exposure to a particular chemical.
- By determining the effects in different habitats the different routes to exposure can be established.
- Biomarkers can provide information on the toxicity of single compounds or mixtures in the real and complex environment at sublethal levels.

Biomarkers can be of the following types:

- Ecological: here changes in population density, key species and species diversity are determined after exposure.
- Behavioural changes: feeding activities, net spinning, bacterial mobility.
- Physiological indicators, heavy metal accumulation, CO_2 production, change in sludge process rates, changes in microbial activity, and biological oxygen demand (BOD).
- Biochemical indicators: cytochrome p450, metallothioneins, specific enzymes.
- Immunochemistry, ELISA, RIA (radioactive immune assay) detection of pathogen population changes, enzymes or pollutant.
- Genetic indicators, DNA probes for species, bacterial luciferase *(lux)* gene constructs, ssrRNA probes.

An example of biochemical indicators is the enzyme cytochrome 450 which is induced by exposure to organic contaminants and metallothioneins which are proteins induced upon exposure to metals. Both of the proteins can be measured either as protein or as mRNA.

Toxicity bioassay (see later) relies on lethality measurements which are generally lengthy and expensive, whereas microorganisms can themselves be used as specific and sensitive systems for the detection of pollutants. This is based on the ability of the pollutant to generate a response at the gene level, due to the induction of enzymes. The extent of this expression serves as a measure of the available concentration of the pollutant. A rapid and sensitive method of screening for gene expression is to fuse the relevant promoter sequences to those for a product which is easily detected. The *gus*A gene product will cleave the substrate X-gal (5-bromo-4-chloro-3-indolyl β-D-galactoside) to give a blue colour and this gene can be fused to the relevant promoter.

An example is the insertion into an *E. coli* strain of a plasmid containing the *lacZ* which codes for the enzyme β-galactosidase; this enzyme has been linked to the *ars*R which codes for the regulatory protein for the ars operon (Scott *et al.*, 1997). The ars operon is involved in the removal of antimonite and arsenic from the cell. Thus, when the cells containing the plasmid are exposed to antimony or arsenite, the enzyme β-galactosidase is induced and this can be assayed by the addition of π-aminophenyl β-D-galactopyranoside. The product of the reaction π-aminophenol can be determined electrochemically. Thus a bacterial sensing system has been developed that responds to antimonite and arsenite.

These techniques require the addition of a substrate which upon cleavage forms a product which can easily be determined, but there is another group of genes where the product does not require substrate addition. These genes are those encoding for light production, the luciferase enzyme *lux*AB from prokaryotes and the *luc* gene from eukaryotes, and more recently a green fluorescent protein coded by the *gfp* gene from a jellyfish *Aequorea victoria* (Kendall and Badminton, 1998; Misteli and Spector, 1997). These types of marker gene have been placed under the control of the promoter of genes associated with a response to toxic compounds. Thus, if the engineered bacteria are exposed to a toxic compound, it will trigger light production which can be easily detected (Fig. 2.5). An example is the construction of an *E. coli* strain which contained the promoter (*alk*B) from *Pseudomonas oleovorans* and the *lux*AB genes of *Vibrio harveyi* (Sticher *et al.*, 1997). The cells responded to alkanes by the production of light and were used to detect soil contamination by heating oil. Bioluminescence was used to track genetically engineered *Xanthomonas campestris* after release into the environment (Shaw *et al.*, 1992). *X. campestris* was engineered to contain the *lux* gene which under the conditions used was constantly bioluminescent. The emission of light was detected using a special camera which provided real-time measurement of the organisms after release into the field.

2.6.2 Toxicity testing using biological material

Toxicity bioassay often relies on the measurement of the lethal effects of the compound on a specific biological system and this is usually carried out with a single pollutant. Some examples of the use of biological material to detect the effect of the compound on a specific organism are as follows:

- *Daphnia*
- Microtox[tm], Biotox[tm]
- Algal test, *Selenastrum* spp.
- Ames test
- Seed germination tests.

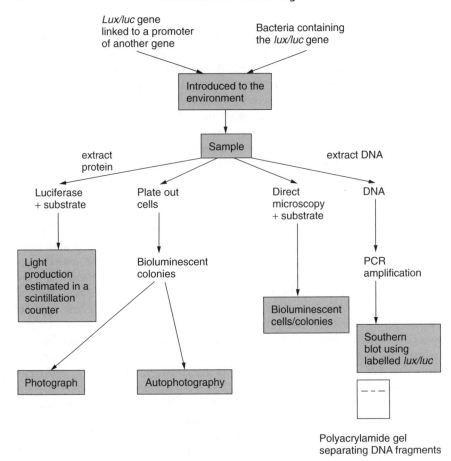

Fig. 2.5 The use of genes which code for protein which can emit light in the detection of the effects of pollution in the environment.

The *Daphnia* test uses the loss of mobility of the water flea *Daphnia pulex* after 48 hours' exposure to measure toxicity. The Microtox™ and Biotox™ systems use the reduction in the light emission by luminous bacteria such as *Photobacterium fisceri* and *P. phosphoreum* as a measurement of the toxicity of a compound over 15 minutes' exposure. The use of algae for toxicity testing was introduced in 1964 when the alga *Selenastrum capriconutum* was applied to limnology (Skulberg, 1964) and algae are now used for the assessment and evaluation of water quality (USEPA, 1971).

The Ames test was developed to test substances for their ability to produce mutations in bacteria. The test consists of the treatment of a *Salmonella typhimurium* mutant which requires the amino acid histidine (his^-) for growth with the test compound along with an extract of rat liver. The rat liver is added as many non-toxic compounds can be converted to mutagens by the enzymes present in the mammalian liver which are not found in bacteria. If the compound is a mutagen then reverse mutations will occur and colonies will form on *his⁻* medium. The number of colonies will give a measure of the mutagenic potential.

Another development involving the use of genetic manipulation for the use of biological material for the estimation of toxicity has been the generation of a transgenic strain of the nematode *Caenorhabditis elegans* (Candido and Jones, 1996). The strain contains the *lacZ* gene from *E. coli* fused to the *hsp* 16. The *lacZ* gene codes for the enzyme β-galactosidase and the *hsp* 16 are inducible genes which are induced when the nematode undergoes a heat stress response. Thus when the nematode is stressed the enzyme is induced in the nucleus of the worm. The enzyme can be detected by the addition of a substrate such as *o*-nitrophenyl-β-galactopyranoside (ONPG) which will produce a blue colour when cleaved by the enzyme.

2.7 Biosensors

Biosensors can be defined as devices which incorporate a 'biological sensing element' in close proximity or integrated with a signal transducer. The components are shown in Fig. 2.6 where the sensing element uses the unique specificity of biological molecules which can give the sensitivity and specificity needed to detect single compounds in complex mixtures (Hall, 1990). The types of biological material which can be used in a biosensor are proteins, antibodies, enzymes, hormone receptors, whole cells, organelles, lectins and DNA (gene-specific probes). These biological components need to be immobilised in order to keep them in contact with the transducer. There are a large number of techniques for the immobilisation of the biological material which

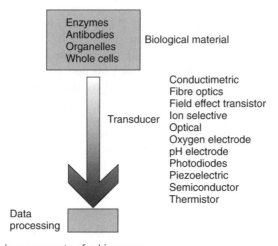

Fig. 2.6 The basic components of a biosensor.

are based on entrapment in polymers or behind membranes, and the attachment by adsorption, covalent binding or ionic attachment to some form of matrix. The response of the biological material can be either catalysis or affinity binding. The main transducers can be electrochemical, photometric, thermometric and acoustic.

The advantages of biosensors for environmental monitoring are:

- on-line sensing, real-time monitoring
- fast response
- portable in many cases
- operate in complex mixtures
- less expensive and time consuming than conventional methods
- very specific in response
- high sensitivity.

The most commonly used biological materials in biosensors are enzymes and the main applications have been in the lucrative medical field. However, biosensors are beginning to be used for environmental monitoring (Denizen and Turner, 1995).

The traditional BOD analysis takes up to 5 days for the assay to be carried out, but a biosensor constructed with microorganisms trapped behind a semipermeable membrane will respond rapidly to the organic molecules in the sample by consuming oxygen. The oxygen levels are followed by an oxygen electrode (Clark) which can be correlated to the level of organic material.

Biosensors which are sensitive to pesticides have been developed using the enzyme acetylcholinesterase and choline oxidase. Acetylcholinesterase converts acetocholine to choline, and choline oxidase converts the choline to betain and hydrogen peroxide. Hydrogen peroxide formation can be monitored amperometrically. Pesticides inhibit the action of acetylcholinesterase and therefore produce a reduction in peroxide formation which can be used to estimate toxicity.

There have been a number of reports of biosensors for phenols based on the oxidation of phenols to catechols and quinones by the enzyme tyrosinase where the reaction requires oxygen. If the enzyme tyrosinase is linked to an oxygen electrode, levels down to about 50 ppb could be detected. Metals such as lead and cadmium can be detected by their inactivation of oxidases and dehydrogenases linked again to an oxygen electrode. The detection of gases has been an area of considerable interest, but to date the only gas to be detected using a biosensor is carbon dioxide using bacteria linked to an oxygen electrode. Thus biosensors can provide cheap, reliable and accurate monitoring of the environment which will also give real-time analysis.

2.8 Conclusions

Biotechnology in the form of recombinant DNA technology will influence the monitoring of the environment in the following areas:

- Techniques like PCR will be used to determine the microbial populations in environmental areas such as hot springs and hydrothermal vents, which is not possible with conventional techniques. These techniques will also be used to estimate biodiversity in these types of habitat.
- Biomarkers using microorganisms with the green fluorescent protein gene inserted can be used to monitor pollution *in situ*.
- Recombinant DNA technology can be used to follow the introduction of GEMs into the environment.
- Biosensors will be able to determine the levels of contaminants in the environment and perhaps provide real-time on-line monitoring.

2.9 References

Bakken, L. R. and Lindahl, V. (1995) Recovery of bacterial cells from soil, in J. T. Trevors and J. D. van Elsas (eds), *Nucleic Acids in the Environment: Methods and Applications*. Springer Verlag, Heidelberg, pp. 9–27.

Beaubien, A., Hu, Y., Bellahcen, D., Urbain, V. and Chang, J. (1995) Monitoring metabolic activity of denitrification processes using gas production measurements. *Water Research*, **29**, 2269–2274.

Bottger, E. C. (1996) Approaches for identification of microorganisms. *ASM News*, **62**, 247–250.

British Standards Institution (1988) *Code of Practice for the Identification of Contaminated Land and its Investigation*. DD175, HMSO, London.

Cairney, T. (1987) *Reclaiming Contaminated Land*. Blackie, London.

Candido, E. P. M. and Jones, D. (1996) Transgenic *Caenorhabditis elegans* strains as biosensors. *Tibtech*, **14**, 125–129.

Comber, S. D. W., Gardner, M. J. and Gunn, A. M. (1996) Measurement of absorbance and fluorescence as potential alternatives to BOD. *Environ. Technol.*, **17**, 771–776.

Costerton, J. W., Lewandowski, Z., Caldwell, D. E., Korber, D. R. and Lappin-Scott, H. M. (1995) Microbial biofilms. *Annu. Rev. Microbiol.*, **49**, 711–745.

Davey, H. M. and Kell, D. B. (1996) Flow cytometry and cell sorting of heterogeneous microbial populations: the importance of single cell analyses. *Microbiol. Rev.*, **60**, 641–696.

Denizen, M. J. and Turner, A. P. F. (1995) Biosensors for environmental monitoring. *Biotechnol. Adv.*, **13**, 1–12.

De Wulf-Durand, P., Bryant, L. J. and Sly, L. I. (1997) PCR-mediated detection of acidophilic, bioleaching-associated bacteria. *Appl. Environ. Microbiol.*, **63**, 2944–2948.

Graham, A. (1994) A haystack of needles: applying the polymerase chain reaction. *Chemistry & Industry*, September, 718–721.

Gray, N. F. (1989) *Biology of Waste Water Treatment*. Oxford University Press, Oxford.

Hall, E. A. H. (1990) *Biosensors*. Open University Press, Milton Keynes, UK.

Harmsen, H. J. M., Prieur, D. and Jeanthon, C. (1997) Distribution of microorganisms in deep-sea hydrothermal vent chimneys investigated by whole-cell hybridization and enrichment culture of thermophilic subpopulations. *Appl. Environ. Microbiol.*, **63**, 2876–2883.

Holdgate, M. W. (1979) *A Perspective of Environmental Pollution*. Cambridge University Press, Cambridge.

Hugenholtz, P. and Pace, N. R. (1996) Identifying microbial diversity in the natural environment: a molecular phylogenetic approach. *Tibtech*, 14, 190–197.

Huggett, R. J., Kimerle, R. A., Mehrle, P. M. and Bergman, H. J. (eds) (1992) *Biomarkers*. SETAC Special Publications Series, Lewis Publishers, Ann Arbor, MI.

Jansson, J. K. (1995) Tracking genetically engineered microorganisms in nature. *Current Opinion in Biotechnol.* 6, 275–283.

Karp, A., Edwards, K. J., Bruford, M., Funk, S., Vosman, B., Morgante, M., Seberg, O., Kremer, A., Boursot, P., Arctander, P., Tautz, D. and Hewitt, G. M. (1997) Molecular technologies for biodiversity evaluation: opportunities and challenges. *Nature Biotechnol.*, 15, 625–628.

Keith, L. H. (ed.) (1988) *Principles of Environmental Sampling*. American Chemical Society, Washington, DC.

Keith, L. H. and Telliard, W. A. (1979) ES & T special report: priority pollutants I – a perspective view. *Environ. Sci. Technol.*, 13, 416–423.

Kendall, J. M. and Badminton, M. N. (1998) *Aequorea victoria* bioluminescence moves into an exciting new era. *Tibtech*, 16, 216–224.

Mason, C. F. (1996) *Biology of Freshwater Pollution*, 3rd edition. Longman Scientific and Technical, Harlow, UK.

Mesarch, M. B. and Nies, L. (1997) Modification of heterotrophic plate counts for assessing the bioremediation potential of petroleum-contaminated soils. *Environ. Technol.*, 18, 639–646.

Misteli, T. and Spector, D. L. (1997) Applications of green fluorescent protein in cell biology and biotechnology. *Nature Biotechnol.*, 15, 961–964.

Ogram, A., Sayler, G. S. and Barkay, T. (1987) The extraction and purification of microbial DNA from sediments. *J. Microb. Methods*, 7, 57–66.

Polz, M. F. and Cavanaugh, C. M. (1997) A simple method for quantification of uncultured microorganisms in the environment based on *in vitro* transcription of the 16S rRNA. *Appl. Environ. Microbiol.*, 63, 1028–1033.

Saano, A., Piipola, S., Linstrom, K. and Van Elsas, J. D. (1995) Extraction and analysis of microbial DNA from soil, in J. T. Trevors and J. D. van Elsas (eds), *Nucleic Acids in the Environment: Methods and Applications*. Springer Verlag, Heidelberg, pp. 49–67.

Scott, D. L., Ramanathan, S., Shi, W., Rosen, B. P. and Daunert, S. (1997) Genetically engineered bacteria: electrochemical sensing systems of antimonite and arsenite. *Anal. Chem.*, 69, 16–20.

Shaw, J. J., Dane, F., Geiger, D. and Kloepper, J. W. (1992) Use of bioluminescence for detection of genetically engineered microorganisms released into the environment. *Appl. Environ. Microbiol.*, 58, 267–273.

Skulberg, O. M. (1964) Algal problems related to the eutrophication of European water supplies, and a bioassay method to assess fertilizing influences of pollution of inland water, in Skulberg, K. (ed.), *Algae and Man*. Plenum Press, New York.

Smalla, K., Cresswell, N., Mendonca-Hagler, L. C., Wolters, A. C. and Van Elsas, J. D. (1993) Rapid DNA extraction protocol from soil for polymerase chain reaction-mediated amplification. *J. Appl. Bacteriol.*, 74, 78–85.

Snaidr, J., Amann, R., Huber, I., Ludwig, W. and Schleifer, K.-H. (1997) Phylogenetic analysis and *in situ* identification of bacteria in activated sludge. *Appl. Environ. Microbiol.*, 63, 2884–2896.

Sorensen, A. H. and Ahring, B. K. (1997) An improved enzyme-linked immunosorbent assay for whole-cell determination of methanogens in samples from anaerobic reactors. *Appl. Environ. Microbiol.*, **63**, 2001–2006.

Stams, A. J. M. and Oude Elferink, S. J. W. H. (1997) Understanding and advancing wastewater treatment. *Current Opinion in Biotechnol.*, **8**, 328–334.

Sticher, P., Jaspers, M. C. M., Stemmler, K., Harms, H., Zehnder, A. J. B. and van de Meer, J. R. (1997) Development and characterization of a whole-cell bioluminescent sensor for bioavailable middle-chain alkanes in contaminated groundwater samples. *Appl. Environ. Microbiol.*, **63**, 4053–4060.

Tebbutt, T. H. Y. (1998) *Principles of Water Quality Control*, 5th edition. Pergamon Press, Oxford.

Torsvik, V., Daae, F. L. and Goksoyr, J. (1995) Extraction, purification and analysis of DNA from soil bacteria, in J. T. Trevors and J. D. van Elsas (eds), *Nucleic Acids in the Environment: Methods and Applications,* Springer Verlag, Heidelberg, pp. 29–48.

Tsai, Y. L. and Olson, B. H. (1991) Rapid method for direct extraction of DNA from soil and sediments. *Appl. Environ. Microbiol.*, **57**, 1070–1074.

US Environmental Protection Agency (EPA) (1971) Algal assay procedure bottle test. *National Eutrophication Research Program*, Corvallis, OR.

Woese, C. R. (1987) Bacterial evolution. *Microbiol. Rev.*, **51**, 221–271.

Woese, C. R., Kandler, O. and Wheelis, S. (1990) Towards a natural system of organisms. *Proc. Natl. Acad. Sci.*, **87**, 4576–4579.

2.9.1   Recommended reading

Atlas, R. M. and Bartha, R. (1993) *Microbial Ecology.* Longman, Harlow, UK.

Hall, E. A. H. (1990) *Biosensors.* Open University Press, Milton Keynes, UK.

Huggett, R. J., Kimerle, R. A., Mehrle, P. M. and Bergman, H. J. (eds) (1992) *Biomarkers.* SETAC Special Publications Series, Lewis Publishers, Ann Arbor, MI.

Reeve, R. N. (1994) *Environmental Analysis.* John Wiley & Sons, Chichester, UK.

Trevors, J. T. and Van Elsas, J. D. (1995) *Nucleic Acids in the Environment: Methods and Applications.* Springer Verlag, Heidelberg.

Chapter 3

Sewage treatment

3.1 Introduction

The use of microorganisms in the disposal of sewage was developed around 1910–1914 in Manchester and a number of continental European cities. In earlier days, sewage was buried or run into rivers and waterways. In the nineteenth century the population of most cities expanded greatly due to industrialisation, so that the volume of sewage produced was too much for this type of disposal and rivers and canals became very polluted. In the UK rivers such as the Thames became anaerobic and devoid of aquatic life, producing unpleasant smells, and they were largely responsible for the spread of diseases such as typhoid and cholera. Sewage pollution was so acute in London that it was the practice for those who could afford it to move to the country in the summer. The treatment of sewage is linked to the provision of clean water, as polluted water is the cause of many diseases. The elimination or reduction of waterborne diseases by the introduction of sewers and sewage disposal probably did more for the health of the population than the introduction of antibiotics later in the century.

This chapter covers the methods of treating domestic liquid waste and sewage and the engineering and biological modifications to the processes that have been developed over the years.

3.1.1 Pollution

The disposal of sewage by running it into the sea or a waterway allows the indigenous microbial population to degrade the waste. The dilution of the waste meant that the organic content of the waterway did not reach too high a value. Natural waterways contain a population of microorganisms that utilise dissolved organic compounds, that in turn are part of the food chain for protozoa, insects, worms and fish. Under normal conditions in a waterway, this population of organisms forms a balanced ecosystem. The balanced system can be destabilised by the addition of excess metabolisable organic material, such as high levels of sewage. The addition of metabolisable organic compounds causes a considerable increase in the growth and metabolism of the aerobic microbial population of the waterway which will use up all the available oxygen dissolved in the water.

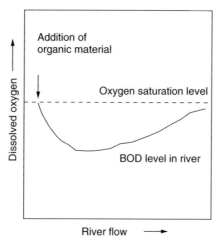

Fig. 3.1 Reduction in dissolved oxygen as an organic waste is applied to a river ('BOD sag').

Figure 3.1 illustrates the effect of the addition of biodegradable organic material to a river. The dissolved oxygen level drops rapidly at the point of addition (often known as BOD sag), but provided the amount of organic material added is not too high, the oxygen level will rise slowly as the material moves downstream from the addition site. The subsequent rise in dissolved oxygen is due in part to mixing and dilution with unaffected flowing water in the waterway and the metabolism of the organic material. However, if the organic addition is too great, the increased microbial metabolism keeps the conditions in the waterway anaerobic. The anaerobic condition, if it persists, causes the aerobic microorganisms to decline or die and allows the anaerobes to increase. Anaerobic metabolism is slower than aerobic metabolism, so that the rate of degradation of the organic material decreases, which can lead to build-up of excess organic material. The continued lack of oxygen leads to the death of other aquatic organisms such as fish and crustacea. In addition, the anaerobic metabolism produces gases such as hydrogen sulphide and methane which can be an indication of the anaerobic condition in the waterway. Stagnant waters such as lakes and ponds become anaerobic more rapidly on the addition of excess organic material as they have no flow to mix the system and to add clean water.

Domestic waste comes in two forms – liquid or solid. This chapter concentrates on the treatment of the liquid domestic waste, sewage. Domestic wastewater is derived from private homes, commercial buildings and institutions such as schools and hospitals. In some cases it may have additions of industrial wastewater from processes such as brewing, baking, paper mills and metal processing. In general, however, treatment plants normally accept only domestic wastewater, and industrial plants have to treat their own waste prior to returning it to waterways or to the domestic wastewater system. If an industrial waste is discharged to the sewers, the water company normally makes a charge for its treatment.

Table 3.1   Typical analysis of sewage

Component	Concentration (mg/l)
Total solids	300–1200
Suspended solids	100–350
Total organic carbon (TOC)	80–290
BOD_5*	110–400
COD†	250–1000
Total nitrogen	20–85
Ammonia	12–50
Nitrites	0
Nitrates	0
Total phosphorus	4–15

* See Box 2.2, Chapter 2.
† See Chapter 2.

Waterways are affected not only by the addition of biodegradable wastes (nutritional pollution) but also frequently by chemical and physical pollution. Chemical pollution is mainly industrial with the release of acids, alkalis and toxic compounds which can poison the living organisms in the waterway. Physical pollution is the release into the waterway of materials which can change the physical conditions in the waterway. This type of pollution mainly consists of the release of large quantities of warm water from power stations which use large volumes of water for cooling. The change in temperature of the water can encourage excess growth of native organisms or growth of a new organism, thus changing the balance of the normal population.

3.1.2   Sewage

Sewage consists of some 99.9% by weight of water containing dissolved organic material, suspended solids, microorganisms (pathogens) and a number of other components. The suspended solids can range from >100 μm to colloidal in nature. The composition, concentration and condition of the waste may differ widely depending on the origin, time or weather conditions. An example of the composition of domestic sewage is given in Table 3.1. The strength can vary daily and with season and can be diluted by rainwater.

In typical sewage, 75% of the suspended solids and 40% of the dissolved material are organic. The dissolved organic materials are a mixture of proteins, carbohydrates, fats and detergents. There are substantial inorganic components in sewage, including sodium, calcium, magnesium, chlorine, sulphates, phosphates, bicarbonates, nitrates and ammonia with traces of heavy metals. The oxygen demand created by the organic material in sewage is usually expressed as BOD_5 (Biological Oxygen Demand) in g/m^3 or mg/l (see Box 2.2, Chapter 2). The oxygen demand of the sewage can also be estimated by means of a chemical technique using an oxidising agent and this is known as the chemical oxygen demand (COD). Sewage normally has a BOD_5 value of 200–600 mg/l (Table 3.1), whereas wastes from some industrial and agricultural processes such as tannery waste and animal slurry can have much higher BOD_5 values of up to 50,000 mg/l.

3.2   Function of waste treatment systems

The main function of domestic waste treatment systems is to reduce the organic content as far as possible in order to be able to return the water to rivers and coastal waters without causing nutritional pollution, especially to those rivers used as a source of drinking water. In addition, the system should remove suspended matter, reduce pathogen content, and increasingly remove nitrates, heavy metals and man-made chemicals.

The quality of the treated waste released from the treatment system depends on the volume and condition of the receiving water and its ability to dilute the waste, and on whether there is to be water abstraction further downstream. In general a 20:30 standard is adopted, which is an effluent level of 20 mg BOD_5/l and 30 mg/l suspended solids (SS) when the effluent is to be diluted 8:1. Some idea of the values needed is given in Table 3.2 which gives the secondary drinking water standards for water supplies.

The volume of domestic wastewater from toilets, baths, washing machines, etc., in the UK is about 9 million m^3/day; industry uses about 7 million m^3/day and with average run-off due to rainfall this gives a total of about 18 million m^3/day, all of which needs treating before it can be returned to the rivers or canals. It has been calculated that each person in the UK contributes on average some 230 litres of sewage per day. Thus, although the scale of sewage treatment is enormous, it is a very dilute growth medium and its value per tonne is very low compared with other biotechnological processes (Wheatly, 1985).

Table 3.2   Secondary drinking water standards

Component	Concentration
BOD_5	30 average monthly/inland 20 mg/l
Suspended solids	30 average monthly/inland 30 mg/l
Chloride	250 mg/l
Colour	15 units
Copper	1 mg/l
Iron	0.3 mg/l
Manganese	0.1 mg/l
Sulphate	400 mg/l
Zinc	5 mg/l
Total dissolved solids	1000 mg/l
Odour	nil
pH	7.5 ± 1

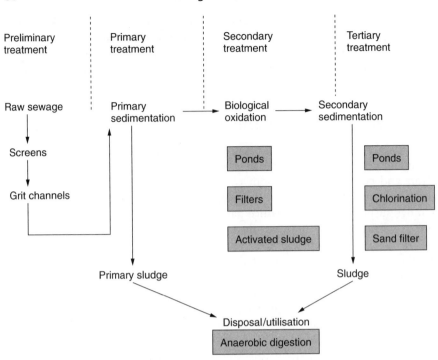

Fig. 3.2 The various stages of the sewage treatment system. The raw sewage is collected and the large debris and grit removed. Suspended solids are settled out in the primary sedimentation tank and it is the effluent from the tank that is treated by biological processes in ponds, trickling filters and activated sludge processes. After treatment the microbial flocs are removed by secondary sedimentation and the resulting sludge is either recycled in the activated sludge system or combined with the primary sludge for disposal. The effluent from the secondary sedimentation may require tertiary treatment such as maturation ponds, sand filters and chlorination.

3.3 Treatment

The first attempts at using microorganisms to treat sewage used single cultures, but as sewage is a complex mixture processes developed which used the naturally occurring mixed microbial population. In the treatment process potentially polluting materials are brought into contact with the microbial population under conditions where they are broken down and metabolised. As the nature and composition of wastewater can vary so much, there is no single waste treatment process, but four stages of treatment are generally incorporated: preliminary, primary, secondary and tertiary stages (Fig. 3.2).

- Preliminary treatment: this is the removal of large debris and grit. The large debris is normally collected on screens and often macerated or broken up with various grinders and added back to the system. Other solids such as grit, derived from the run-off from roads, are removed in a grit channel and can be recycled after washing.

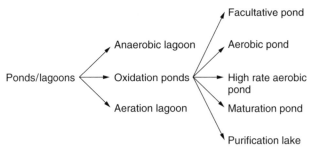

Fig. 3.3 The types of ponds and lagoons which can be used for waste treatment.

- Primary treatment: the sewage is allowed to settle for 1.5–2.5 hours which removes the suspended solids which flocculate easily and reduces the BOD_5 load by about 40–60%.
- Secondary treatment: the effluent from the primary treatment still contains the dissolved organic materials and 40–50% of the suspended solids. It is at this stage that biological action is used to remove the organic material. The biological reactions can be either aerobic or anaerobic, although the aerobic treatment is the most widely used as it is more rapid. A number of processes can be used in the aerobic or anaerobic treatment, including lagoons/ponds, trickling filters, activated sludge, rotating biological contactors and anaerobic digesters.
- Tertiary treatment: this may be required to remove phosphates, nitrates and pathogenic microorganisms to produce potable water and to prevent eutrophication. The processes can involve chemical precipitation, disinfection with chlorine, filtration through sand filters and the use of maturation ponds.

3.3.1 Lagoons or ponds

Ponds or lagoons were used for sewage treatment long before the controlled use of microorganisms was developed at the beginning of the twentieth century, and ponds are popular alternatives to aerobic sewage treatments in countries where land is freely available and sunshine plentiful. Ponds or lagoons can be operated aerobically, anaerobically or using a mixture of the two processes, and Fig. 3.3 shows the various types of pond and lagoon.

Facultative ponds are generally shallow (1–2.5 m) and the biological processes which occur are represented in Fig. 3.4. The pond combines both aerobic and anaerobic conditions. The organic matter in solution or the fine suspended material is broken down by the aerobic organisms which are supplied by oxygen both by diffusion and mixing from the surface and by the algae growing on or near the surface. The algae use sunlight, carbon dioxide and the inorganic compounds present in the sewage for their growth. Much of the suspended solids settle to the bottom of the pond where the conditions are anaerobic. The anaerobic organisms break down these solids to yield methane, nitrogen and carbon dioxide and this can represent some 30% of the BOD load. Some of the operating parameters of facultative ponds are given in Table 3.3; 70–95% of the BOD load can be removed in 7–50 days.

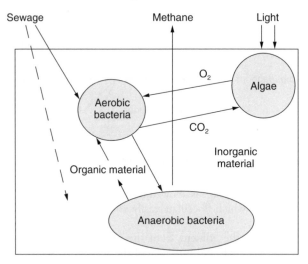

Fig. 3.4 Facultative pond where anaerobic organisms are found in the lower regions and aerobic organisms in the surface regions, and additional oxygen is supplied by the algal population at the surface.

Table 3.3 Parameters for facultative ponds

Depth (m)	1–3
Retention time (days)	7–50
BOD_5 loading kg/acre/day	9–22
BOD_5 removal (%)	70–95
Algal concentration (mg/l)	10–100
Effluent suspended solid concentration (mg/l)	100–350

Aerobic ponds are much shallower than facultative ponds, being up to 1 m in depth so that light can reach the bottom. Their shallowness means that more oxygen is supplied by algal photosynthesis in addition to diffusion from the surface.

High-rate aerobic ponds are aerobic ponds that are operated to ensure maximum algal metabolism and growth. Light is generally the limiting nutrient for algal growth in ponds so that the ponds are much shallower, 0.2–0.5 m deep, to avoid shading, and oxygen production by the algae is often enhanced by some form of mixing. The algae produced in such high-rate ponds are often harvested and used for both animal and fish food.

Maturation ponds are generally of similar construction to facultative ponds but are used as a tertiary treatment with longer retention times of 7–15 days which allow suspended solids to settle before the water is discharged into a waterway.

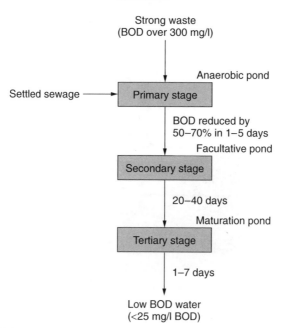

Fig. 3.5 A possible sequence of ponds for the treatment of waste. Strong wastes with a BOD over 300 mg/l are usually treated in an anaerobic pond followed by treatment in a facultative pond with a final polishing in a maturation pond. Settled sewage can be run directly into the secondary stage (the facultative pond).

Anaerobic lagoons or ponds are mainly used for the pretreatment of wastes before they are passed on to facultative ponds. The lagoons and ponds are suitable for high-strength wastes with BOD values above 300 mg/l. Anaerobic conditions are maintained by increasing the depth of the pond to 1–7 m and increasing the BOD load. The retention times can vary from 2 to 160 days with the removal of 70–80% of the BOD added. Purification lakes are large lakes used to remove the pollution from a river and, as such, function as large maturation ponds. Aeration lagoons, unlike the other ponds, are used in the primary treatment of sewage or industrial waste. They are generally deeper than high-rate ponds at 3–4 m and oxygen supply is provided by mechanical means using diffusion aeration units or surface aerators which also mix the waste.

All these various ponds can be used in isolation but frequently they are combined. High BOD wastes over 300 mg/l are normally treated first in an anaerobic lagoon or pond for 1–5 days which will remove 50–70% of the BOD load. The effluent is then passed to the second stage, a facultative pond with a retention time of 20–40 days (Fig. 3.5). The facultative pond can take low-strength wastes directly without their passing through the anaerobic pond. The final stage is one or more maturation ponds where the suspended solids will settle out over a period of up to 7 days. This type of sequence can give clean final effluents of <25 mg/l BOD and <75 mg/l COD.

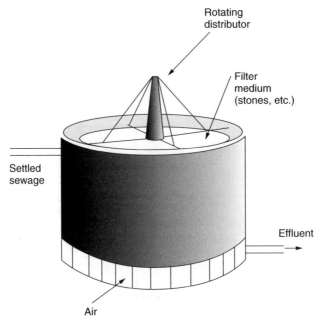

Fig. 3.6 Trickling filter design. The circular vessel 1–3 m in depth is filled with stones, clinker or slag and settled sewage is run from the rotating arms onto the bed. The organic material in the sewage is metabolised by the microbial biofilm which develops on the stones. The clean effluent is collected at the bottom of the filter.

3.3.2 Trickling filter

Most microorganisms in nature are associated with or attached to solid surfaces and these are known as biofilms. The trickling filter is based on a randomly packed solid medium which will act as a surface on which a mixed culture of microorganisms will attach and grow. If sewage is run through such a filter the attached biomass will metabolise the organic content. The biofilm which develops on the filter packing will give the filter a high biomass content, as the solid packing has a high surface area and the high biomass content should be able to metabolise the sewage rapidly.

In its early form the trickling filter consisted of a bed 1–3 m deep packed with stones, clinker or slag 40–60 mm in diameter (Fig. 3.6). The gaps between the stones allow air to penetrate the bed and this is improved by having ventilation at the base. The wastewater is applied by a rotating distribution system, and the treated water is collected by a drain at the base. Such a filter does not require inoculation but develops its own population which is a complex mixture of bacteria, fungi, protozoa, algae, and larger organisms such as insects and worms (Wheatly, 1985). A biofilm develops on the packing, made up principally of bacteria and fungi. The biofilm is in a dynamic equilibrium which can alter as the content of the waste stream changes and

Table 3.4 Properties of material used for filter beds

Material	Size (mm)	Specific surface area (m²/m³)
Slag	50	125
Clinker	62	120
Rounded gravel	25	150
	62	65
PVC	—	85–220
Polypropylene	—	120–190

Source: derived from Gray, 1989.

can also be affected by seasonal changes. Once the biofilm reaches a certain thickness, layers will be detached and these suspended solids are collected in a settling tank.

Filter systems are widely used for secondary treatment as they have the advantage that once constructed they require little or no maintenance, are economical, and are tolerant to changes in wastewater composition.

As the efficiency of the filter depends upon the biomass contained in the biofilm, any increase in the solid phase area will increase the load potential of the filter. Filter design has been improved by the incorporation of a plastic solid phase, either random or modular in design, which has increased the biofilm area significantly, and thus allows the filter to handle a higher BOD load (Table 3.4). Trickling filters have been used in a single-pass process, producing an effluent of a high standard. However, if the load on these filters increases over time, due to an increase in population or the addition of stronger industrial effluents, the system will need more than one filter unit. The most common modification to deal with these types of changes is to have a degree of recirculation which will even out fluctuations, using a two-stage system where the first filter is used at a high rate and the partially treated waste is passed on to the second filter for final treatment. In some cases the two filters can be alternated to allow the primary one to recover from the effects of a high loading. In this way filter units can treat more waste without the need to construct more filter units.

3.3.3 Activated sludge process

In this process the waste is brought into contact with a high concentration of microorganisms present as aggregates under aerobic conditions. The waste from the primary stage is run continuously into an aerated tank to produce plug flow where the biomass present metabolises the organic content, forming more cells or biomass (Fig. 3.7). The effluent from this continuous stream is run into a settling tank where the biomass and non-degraded solids settle out. The clarified effluent is virtually free of solids and, apart from a final polishing or tertiary treatment, can be run into a river. In order to keep the biomass

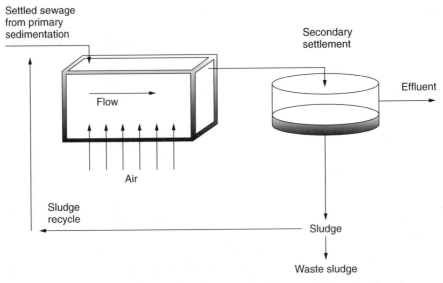

Fig. 3.7 The activated sludge process. The settled sewage is run into a long tank at the same time as recycled sludge (20%) is added. The mixture is passed down the tank where it is aerated. At the end of the tank the mixture is passed into a settlement tank where the microbial aggregates and any remaining solids settle out; some of this sludge is recycled and the remainder collected for disposal.

level as high as possible to give a high conversion rate of the dilute substrate, some of the settled biomass (20%) or activated sludge is recycled by adding it to the start of the tank. The normal operation is a plug flow system in a rectangular tank, typically 6–10 m wide, 30–100 m long and 4–5 m deep.

3.3.4 Mixed liquor suspended solids and sludge residence time

The population of the activated sludge is much the same as that which develops on the trickling filter except that it is less heterogeneous and therefore less adaptable to changes in waste composition. Most of the biomass occurs as flocs or aggregates and the concentration of biomass in the tank is referred to as the mixed suspended solids concentration (MLSS). Normal MLSS levels range between 1500 and 3500 mg/l and can be controlled by the amount of activated sludge recycled.

Systems used for waste treatment can best be compared by their ability to treat waste per unit volume. For trickling filters the waste treated per unit volume can be expressed as hydraulic and organic loads. The hydraulic load is expressed as cubic metres of wastewater treated per day per cubic metre of filter. In general a high load for a filter will be above 3 m³/m³/d and the upper limit is set by the filter becoming flooded and anaerobic. The organic load is expressed as BOD removed per cubic metre per day (kg BOD/m³d). A BOD load of below 0.6 kg/m³/d is regarded as a low rate. To achieve an exit BOD value of 20 mg/l, organic loads of up to 1.0 kg/m³/d are normally used in a single pass. However, if nitrification, the removal of ammonia, is required, the flow and organic load have to be reduced as the organisms responsible for nitrification grow only slowly.

The retention time of the waste within the aeration tank of an activated sludge system is referred to as the hydraulic retention time (HRT) which in a conventional sludge system will be at least 5 hours. The organic loading is expressed as kg BOD/m³/d, as for the trickling filter, and is normally around 0.4–1.2 kg BOD/m³/d. Sludge loading is the ratio of biodegradable organic material to the active biomass:

$$\text{sludge loading} = \frac{\text{flow rate} \times \text{BOD}}{\text{volume} \times \text{biomass}}$$

A normal sludge loading rate will be in the region of 0.15. Conventional activated sludge systems produce an effluent up to the 20:30 standard with a BOD load which is generally 0.5–1.5 kg/m³/d, a sludge age of 2–3 days and an HRT of 5–14 hours. The sludge concentration is 2–3 kg/m³. The sludge production is 0.5 kg biomass per kg BOD treated, a yield of approximately 50%.

3.3.5   Aeration

As the activated sludge is an aerobic process considerable effort is made to maximise the supply of oxygen and avoid oxygen limitation of growth. One of the most common methods of providing oxygen is to introduce air at the base of the tanks through spargers or porous 'diffusers'. The porous diffusers provide a stream of small bubbles; the smaller the bubbles the better the aeration due to the increase in bubble volume to area ratio. Bubbling with air is generally sufficient to provide all the oxygen needed as sewage is a fairly dilute substrate (200–250 g/m³ or mg/l) and therefore the oxygen demand is fortunately low. Air flow rates of 7–10 m³/m³ of sewage are normally used. If increased aeration is required mechanical surface aeration can also be used and there are a number of designs which include a partly submerged paddle (the Kessener brush) or turbines rotating at the surface (Simcar) (Fig. 3.8). Air can also be entrained in the activated sludge by withdrawing some of the sludge and pumping it back into the tank using a venturi or a high speed jet. The activated sludge tank is operated as a plug flow reactor and as such the oxygen requirement will drop as the BOD is reduced as the material passes down the reactor. In order to even out the altering oxygen requirement a number of operational modes have been developed.

Where constant aeration is provided along the tank this will not match oxygen requirements due to the reduction in substrate along the tank. To avoid this, tapered aeration has been developed where a diminishing supply of air is introduced along the tank (Fig. 3.9). This can be achieved in a series of tanks as well as in a long plug flow tank.

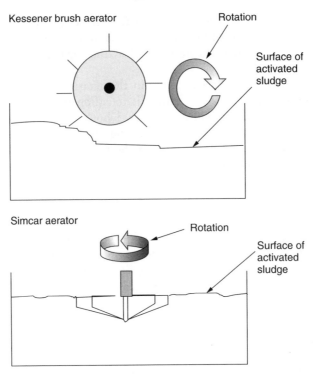

Fig. 3.8 The two forms of surface aerators for the activated sludge process, the Kessener brush and the Simcar aerator. Both aerators agitate the surface, increasing diffusion of oxygen into the liquid.

In the conventional activated sludge process the biomass is essentially in the form of flocs due in part to the production of extracellular bacterial polymers. The exact nature of this material is not known but it is responsible for forming aggregates 20–1000 µm in diameter. There is rapid attachment of suspended and colloidal material to these flocs as soon as the activated sludge is mixed with the sewage. Once attached the breakdown of the material takes much longer in a process known as stabilisation. In the contact stabilisation process the adsorption and stabilisation take place in separate tanks (Fig. 3.9). The contact period is usually 0.5–1.0 hours, the sludge is settled and the returned sludge aerated for up to 5 hours to complete oxidation (stabilisation). The process can be achieved in a single tank if the waste enters the tank towards the end and is then recycled after a short contact time.

With step aeration there is an incremental waste and sludge feed along the length of the tank which should go some way to balance the oxygen supply (Fig. 3.9). Step aeration can be carried out in a series of tanks as well as in a single tank.

Incremental sludge feeding has a similar effect as step aeration except that the recycled sludge is fed into the tank along its length, and the waste run in at a single point.

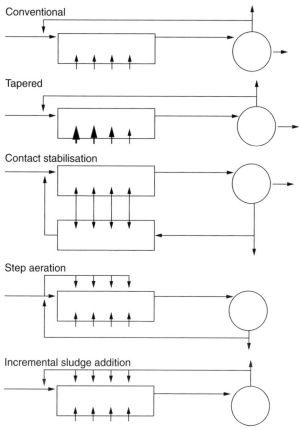

Fig. 3.9 Alternative operating systems for the activated sludge process: tapered aeration where more air is supplied at the start when the organic load is greatest; contact stabilisation where the sludge is mixed with the sewage and aerated before returning to the process; step aeration where sludge and sewage are added along the length of the tank; and incremental sludge addition where recycled sludge is added to the tank along its length.

All the previous systems used a continuous plug flow, but completely mixed systems have been developed similar to those found in fermentation bioreactors where the object is to produce a homogeneous suspension within the reactor. This requires both aeration and mixing to be provided. A settling area can be provided to separate the sludge before the effluent is released. The advantages of such a system are the increased aeration, which allows an increased BOD loading, and the ability to withstand BOD shocks. The disadvantages are that the sludge produced is more difficult to settle out due to its smaller floc size.

3.3.6   Mode of operation

Irrespective of the type of system used, the rate of supply of sewage has to be regulated in order to achieve an effluent level of 20 mg/l BOD. However, by

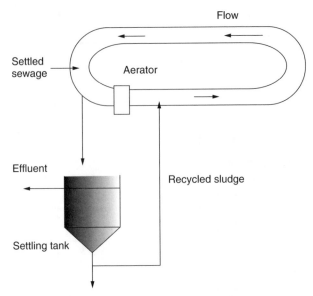

Fig. 3.10 The Pasverr ditch. Settled sewage and recycled sludge are mixed and passed around an oval ditch by an aerator which both mixes and aerates the system. After one cycle the sludge is separated from the liquid and some sludge returned to the system.

altering the operating conditions different loading and conversion rates are possible. The conventional activated sludge system tries to keep the biomass as high as possible by sludge recycling. In the extended aeration variation the biomass and substrate remain in contact much longer and under these conditions growth is very much substrate limited, which means that less aeration is required and sludge production is reduced as the cellular metabolism is directed towards energy formation rather than cell growth. The best example of such a process is the Pasverr or oxidation ditch (Fig. 3.10). This is an oval ditch, 1–3.5 m in depth, fitted with gates or paddles which aerate and give it a directional flow. The waste is run into the ditch just before the aerator and travels around the whole ditch at 0.3–0.6 m/s before it is run off into a settling tank. Some of the settled sludge is added back to the system just after the aerator.

High-rate operations involve only the partial treatment of the waste and are often used as the first part of the treatment of industrial waste and sometimes for domestic waste. The conditions which favour a high growth rate and sludge formation are linked to increased aeration.

3.4   Modifications to existing processes

3.4.1   Biotower

The development of plastic media as the packing for trickling filters has been followed by the development of tall tower filters without the need for support.

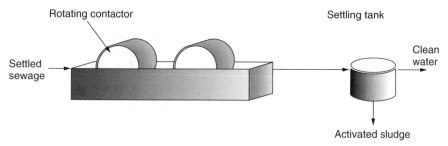

Fig. 3.11 The rotating biological contactor consists of one or more rotating drums of porous material which supports the biofilm. About one-third of the drum is immersed in the sewage so that as the drum rotates aeration is provided when the cells are out of the liquid. The rate of rotation is 1–2 rpm.

These tower bioreactors, because of their high surface area, can handle a high BOD loading, and in some cases forced air has been supplied to the base of the tower to increase the rate of degradation. The towers are used mainly to reduce BOD in high-strength wastes and are often added to a conventional system ahead of the aeration tanks to smooth out variations in BOD and to increase plant capacity.

3.4.2 Rotating biological contactor

The availability of plastic media has also seen another development – the rotating biological contactor. Here a drum of honeycomb plastic or closely spaced discs is slowly rotated (1–2 rpm) with the base (40%) of the drum in the settled sewage or waste water (Fig. 3.11). A typical unit may be 5–8 m in length and 2–3 m in diameter and separated into a series of chambers. The chambers help to maintain a form of plug flow. Aeration occurs as the drum rotates free of the liquid. The large area and good aeration means that the rotating contactor can handle a wide range of flows, needs only short contact times and has 4–5 times the capacity of a conventional filter, and no recycle is required. The disadvantages of the rotating biological contactor are the fact that in cold climates the system needs covering, as well as the costs of running the motor and of maintenance.

3.4.3 Fluidised bed

One method of increasing the area of the support in a biofilm reactor is to use smaller and robust biofilm supports such as sand. However, sand coated with a biofilm in a reactor would soon clog and trap particles and become anaerobic. To overcome this problem the bed of sand can be fluidised by the upward flow of liquid. The area for biomass support is 3300 m^2/m^3 compared with 150 m^2/m^3 for rounded gravel which supports an MLSS of 40,000 mg/l compared with 1500–3500 mg/l for activated sludge. The high biomass clearly

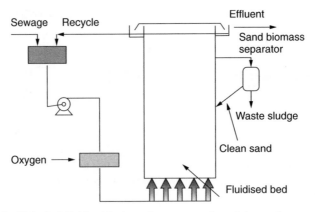

Fig. 3.12 The biological fluidised bed reactor uses small particles such as sand to support the biofilm. The settled sewage is aerated by bubbling air or oxygen prior to pumping the sewage into the base of the vessel to fluidise the sand. Excess biomass can be removed by extracting some of the sand, sonnication and returning the clean sand to the vessel.

has a considerable oxygen demand which is supplied by injection into the settled sewage of pure oxygen prior to entering the fluidised bed (Fig. 3.12). The biomass build-up on the sand particles can be controlled as coated sand can be extracted, the biomass removed from the sand in a cyclone and the cleaned sand returned to the vessel. This type of system has proved particularly useful for treating high-strength wastes, especially those from industrial sources. The fluidised beds operate with short retention times of around 20 minutes but the system is expensive to operate due to the use of oxygen and the costs of pumping.

An alternative to the use of fluidised beds is the airlift bioreactor where the biomass forms as a biofilm on small particles about 0.3 mm in diameter. The bed is fluidised by the introduction of air at the base of the vessel which also supplies oxygen. The advantage of such a system is that a higher biomass coats the particles due to the better oxygen supply, which means that with the same concentration of organic waste there is a lower growth rate and therefore less sludge generated.

3.4.4 Deep shaft process

The deep shaft process was a development from ICI's single cell protein work and was based on the airlift design of bioreactor. The airlift design operates by introducing air at the bottom of the vessel. The introduced air will reduce the overall density of the liquid and the air bubbles will rise; these factors combine to cause a flow of water upwards. If this upward flow is separated from the rest of the vessel by a partition (draft tube), a circulating flow will be generated so that both mixing and aeration can be achieved by sparging air (Fig. 3.13(a)). The airlift bioreactor is normally a very tall narrow vessel so that with a height

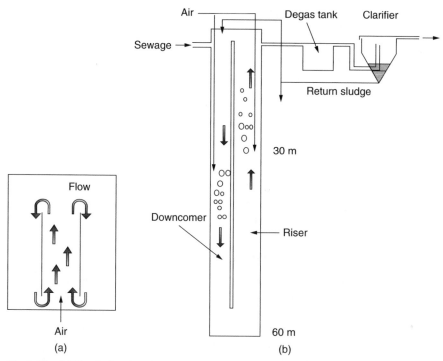

Fig. 3.13   (a) The design for an airlift bioreactor where air causes a flow of liquid around the vessel and also mixes the contents. (b) A 60 m deep shaft process for the treatment of settled sewage. The depth of the shaft ensures that oxygen is forced into solution. Once a flow has been established air is added to the downcomer.

of 100 m or more a pressure of about 10 atmospheres will be found at the base. The high pressure will force more oxygen into solution, improving aeration considerably. In practice the deep shaft bioreactor is sunk in the ground either as concentric pipes or divided vertically (Fig. 3.13(b)) and, because of its increased aeration, often has to be installed to treat high BOD industrial wastes. Once a flow has been started, air can also be injected into the downcomer to be carried downwards to the base of the vessel. A deep shaft process has been installed at Marlow Foods' single cell protein plant (Quorn) to treat the waste from the cultivation process, and others have been installed worldwide. The system has the advantage that it requires only a small space compared with conventional systems and due to the high aeration rate will deal with high BOD wastes containing 3–6 kg BOD/m³d with a 90% treatment rate. This rate is intermediate between the high rate and that of conventional sewage treatment, but the process produces less sludge. Figure 3.13(b) shows the details of a full-scale installation for the treatment of sewage which is capable of treating 30,000 m³/d waste at 600 mg/l BOD where the sewage is retained in the vessel for one hour.

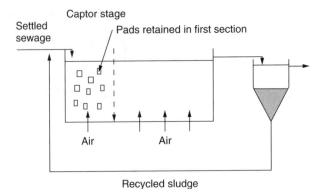

Fig. 3.14 The Captor process. A high biomass is retained at the start of the process by immobilising the biomass in plastic pads.

3.4.5 Addition of pure oxygen

The aeration of the activated sludge can be improved by the addition of pure oxygen to a closed system or to open tanks. The closed system has the advantage that the oxygen is not lost to the atmosphere, but the presence of a high oxygen concentration does constitute an explosive hazard requiring strict safety precautions. The high aeration also causes an accumulation of carbon dioxide which can reduce the pH and thus reduce nitrification. A system like this was marketed in the UK as the Unox system. The tanks are divided into a series of compartments each of which is mixed by a surface aerator. This type of system can be used to sustain a higher biomass (increased MLSS), with lower sludge production and double the loading rate.

3.4.6 Captor process

In order to maintain a high biomass at the start of the plug flow process of waste treatment by activated sludge, a modification has been used. Here the activated sludge biomass was immobilised in reticulated plastic pads measuring 25 mm × 25 mm × 12 mm, of a similar nature to washing-up pads. The activated sludge microorganisms which form aggregates readily colonise these pads. The pads are retained in the early part of the aeration tank by screens and have been shown to give higher biomass levels of 6–8 g/l (Fig. 3.14). To maintain an active biomass some of the pads are stripped of excess biomass by a system which removes the pads, squeezes out the sludge and returns the empty pads to the tank.

3.4.7 Membrane bioreactors

The development of ultrafiltration and microfiltration membranes for biological separations has allowed this technology to be applied to wastewater treatment. The membrane allows the passage of small molecules while retaining the microorganisms making up activated sludge (Brindle and Stephenson, 1996). A membrane bioreactor was first used to treat landfill leachates, but since that time three types of membrane systems have been developed: solid/liquid separation, the gas permeable system and the extractive process.

Membrane bioreactors have been used in both aerobic and anaerobic modes where the high biomass retained gives a rapid breakdown of the organic compounds, enables high loads to be handled and, as the solids are retained, renders the hydraulic retention time independent of the solids. Because of the high biomass in the system, membrane bioreactors require a good supply of oxygen, but a low substrate to biomass ratio reduces the amounts of sludge formed. Apart from many experimental systems, over 20 full-scale membrane bioreactor units have been installed in the Netherlands and Germany.

As the membrane will allow gases to pass through while retaining the biomass, these bioreactors can provide bubble-free aeration with a high surface area for oxygen transfer. The membrane also provides a support for biofilm formation. In the extractive process the membrane allows chemical pollutants to pass through into the biomass where they can be degraded. The membrane system can also separate the biomass from a biologically hostile waste stream and this type of system has been tested with pollutants such as nitrobenzene, benzene and dichloroaniline with over 99% removal. Membrane bioreactors are more expensive than conventional activated sludge and trickling filter processes but have the advantage that less sludge is generated, they have a high COD removal and good oxygen supply and appear to be suitable for small plants and where high-quality effluent is required.

3.5 Removal of nitrogen compounds

Waste streams contain not only biologically metabolisable organic materials but also nitrogen- and phosphorus-containing compounds. The nitrogen-containing compounds in sewage are ammonia, proteins and amino acids (Table 3.1). Increasingly nitrates are being found in wastewater as a result of run-off from agricultural land. Ammonia is formed from urea, a major constituent of urine, and can also be formed during the natural breakdown of proteins and can be found in some industrial wastes. Ammonia has an offensive smell, is poisonous to aquatic life at concentrations as low as 0.5 mg/l, and increases the chlorine dosage needed for the treatment of drinking water. The European Inland Fisheries Advisory Commission (EIFAC) has recommended that the maximum unionised ammonia concentration should be 0.025 kg/m^3 (20 g/m^3 total ammonia).

Nitrogen-containing compounds are required for the synthesis of proteins by all types of microorganisms during their growth. The microorganisms normally utilise ammonia first but nitrates and urea can also be used. In waste treatment systems a third of the total nitrogen content is removed by assimilation during growth, and the rate of removal depends on the biomass level and rate of growth in the waste treatment system.

3.5.1   Nitrification

The level of ammonia in wastewater (domestic) is about 25 mg/l (g/m³) but industrial wastes can contain up to 5 g/l ammonia with the recommended level at 20 mg/l (25 g/m³). Ammonia is oxidised rapidly to nitrate in the environment and in wastewater treatment systems in a process known as nitrification. The conversion is carried out by two groups of chemoautotrophic bacteria which use the oxidation of ammonia as a source of energy. The first stage of ammonia oxidation is carried out mainly by the genera *Nitrosomonas* and *Nitrosococcus, Nitrosospira, Nitrocystis* and *Nitrosogloea*. The reaction is as follows, although the oxidation of ammonia is more complex than is given in the equation:

$$2NH_4^+ + 3O_2 \rightarrow 2NO_2 + 4H^+ + 2H_2O + \text{(energy 480–700 kJ)}$$

The energy released is used by the organisms to synthesise cell components from inorganic sources. The release of hydrogen ions can cause a drop in pH and it is clear that a good supply of oxygen is required. The growth of nitrifying bacteria is very slow (μ_{max} 0.46–2.2/d) compared with that of heterotrophic bacteria (μ_{max} 0.1–1/d).

The nitrite formed is converted to nitrate by the genera *Nitrobacter, Nitrocystis, Nitrosococcus* and *Nitrosocystis*, but *Nitrobacter* has been the most studied. The reactions are as follows:

$$2NO_2^- + O_2 \rightarrow 2NO_3^- + \text{(energy 130–180 kJ)}$$

As the oxidation of nitrite to nitrate yields less energy than the oxidation of ammonia, the cell yield of *Nitrobacter* is less than that of *Nitrosomonas* and the growth rates are also slow with a μ_{max} of 0.28–1.44/d. The characteristics of the organisms involved in nitrification affect the wastewater treatment as follows:

- The growth rate is slower than that of heterotrophic organisms so that the organic load has to be balanced to their slower growth rate, otherwise the organisms will be washed out.
- There is a low cell yield per unit of ammonium oxidised.
- The organisms require a significant amount of oxygen, 4.2 g per g NH_4 converted.
- The system may need some form of buffering due to the acid conditions produced by the hydrogen ions.

If nitrification is not required in the sewage process then a higher rate of flow can be used.

3.5.2   Denitrification

Nitrification in treatment plants and soils combined with the nitrates from agricultural run-off can give rise to high nitrate levels (above 50 mg/l) in waterways which are used to supply drinking water. High nitrate levels are associated with one disease, methaemoglobinaemia, which affects children below the age of 6 months. The children have an incomplete digestive system and the intake of nitrate leads to the accumulation of nitrite ions which enter the blood system and block haemoglobin oxygen transport. Thus the EC have set an absolute limit of 50 mg/l for nitrate, and a recommended limit of 25 mg/l, although a number of UK water treatment systems are working at 80 mg/l. Nitrate can be converted to nitrite in the human stomach and nitrite has been shown to be converted to carcinogenic nitrosamines, leading to concern over the development of stomach cancer on consumption of high-nitrate water.

Nitrate removal or denitrification can be carried out by ion exchange or biological processes. The ion exchange process depends on the resin's affinity which on a conventional anion exchange resin is:

$$SO_4^{2-} \gg NO_3^- > Cl^- \geq HCO_3$$

Any sulphate in the waste will bind in preference to nitrate, but once this has occurred nitrate will exchange with chloride. Once the resin is exhausted it will require regeneration with excess sodium chloride which yields a solution containing high concentrations of sodium sulphate, sodium nitrate and sodium chloride, which will need disposal. Adding this high-salt solution to waterways is unacceptable and in practice it is passed onto the sewage works for treatment.

The biological conversion of nitrate to nitrite and eventually nitrogen occurs under conditions where oxygen is very low or absent. The process of oxidation involves the loss of electrons and in normal conditions oxygen acts as an electron acceptor, but when oxygen levels are low inorganic ions such as nitrate, phosphate and sulphate can act as electron acceptors. In wastewater where nitrification has occurred, combined with nitrate from agricultural run-off, the concentration of nitrate will be higher than that of sulphate or phosphate. A number of facultative heterotrophic microorganisms occur in sewage treatment systems which are capable of converting nitrate to nitrogen provided an electron donor is present. The electron donor is usually an organic compound and in some cases methanol has been used to supplement the normal organic source. The reactions with methanol are as follows:

$$3NO_3^- + CH_3OH \rightarrow 3NO_2^- + CO_2 + 2H_2O$$

$$2NO_2^- + CH_3OH \rightarrow N_2 + CO_2 + H_2O + 2OH^-$$

The process of denitrification requires low oxygen levels (anaerobic), an organic carbon energy source, a level of nitrate of 2 mg/l or above, and a pH of 6.5–7.5.

3.5.3 Nitrification and denitrification processes

Within the sewage system the processes of biological nitrification and denitrification can be organised in a number of ways. In general, the first step, the removal of ammonia by nitrification, can be carried out in parallel with

Table 3.5 Parameters for biological nitrification/denitrification processes

Process	Hydraulic retention time (days)	t (h)*	MLVSS (mg/l)[†]	pH
Carbon removal	2–5	1–3	1–2	6.5–8.0
Nitrification	10–20	0.5–3	1–2	7.4–8.6
Denitrification	1–5	0.2–2	1–2	6.5–7.0

* t (h) retention time.
† MLVSS, mixed liquor volatile suspended solids.

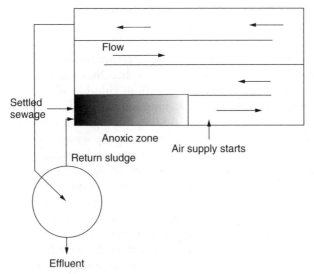

Fig. 3.15 An activated sludge process with the provision of an anoxic zone at the start in order to achieve denitrification. The anoxic zone is formed by stopping aeration at the first stage where the organic material is highest.

the removal of organic material, provided that the hydraulic retention time is not too short (Table 3.5). Denitrification, in contrast, requires a change in growth conditions from aerobic to anaerobic and an organic carbon source. Both nitrification and denitrification can be achieved by partitioning the sewage treatment system (Fig. 3.15) (Lee et al., 1997) or by providing separate reactors which can be used with both suspended and fixed film cultures (Fig. 3.16) (Tchobanoglous and Burton, 1991). In the single vessel the anoxic zone is situated at the start of the aeration tank where anoxic conditions are achieved by stopping aeration and the carbon level is high. The process using separate vessels is much easier to use and control.

Another system for combined nitrification and denitrification is the sequencing batch reactor (SBR) where a single vessel is used but a programmed

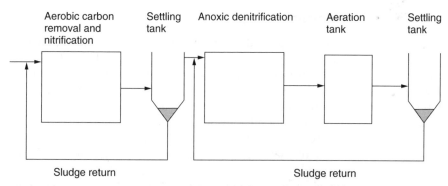

Fig. 3.16 An outline of a two-stage process for both nitrification and denitrification. In the first stage the normal activated sludge process occurs with the removal of organic materials and nitrification. In the second stage anoxic conditions cause denitrification which is followed by an aeration tank to strip out the nitrogen formed to ensure precipitation in the settling tank.

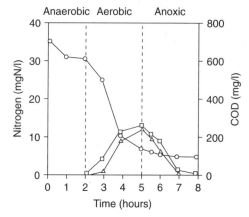

Fig. 3.17 The levels of ammonia ($\circ$), nitrate ($\square$), and nitrite ($\triangle$) in a sequencing batch reactor. The three sequences of anaerobic, aerobic and anoxic are followed by a 1.5-hour settlement phase and a 0.5-hour decantation phase (Rhee *et al.*, 1997).

sequence of operations are applied which can be feeding, anaerobic conditions, aerobic conditions, sludge settling, and effluent removal. This type of operation has been used for the treatment of a number of wastes such as agricultural run-off and landfill leachates, but it has the potential for combining nitrification and denitrification. An example of nitrate, nitrite and ammonia levels in a sequencing batch reactor is given in Fig. 3.17. The ammonia levels drop during the initial anaerobic phase and the subsequent aerobic phase. Nitrate concentration in contrast is low at the start but rises due to nitrification in the aerobic phase. Both nitrate and nitrite were denitrified during the anoxic phase. The sequencing mode can also be applied to anaerobic reactors (Ndon and Dague, 1997) and in two-stage processes (Ra *et al.*, 1998) where the second stage is the anoxic phase.

3.6   Sludge treatment

Conventional activated sludge and filter processes produce large volumes of primary sludge in addition to the excess settled secondary sludge (activated sludge). Almost 1 million tonnes (dry weight) are produced each year in the UK. In the activated sludge process this secondary sludge is mainly the microbial biomass produced by the metabolism of the organic material. The microbial yield on settled sewage is about 50%. A proportion of this biomass is recycled (20%) and the remainder is combined with the primary sludge for disposal. In the trickling filters the same problem applies except that with a lower loading less sludge is produced but there is no recycle. Therefore, large volumes of sludge are formed which have a solids content of about 1–4% and represent one of the main problems of disposal in wastewater treatment. The waste sludge is a mixture of organic material and microbial cells which can be degraded by other microorganisms. There are a number of methods employed to dispose of excess sludge. These are:

- dumping at sea
- landfill
- incineration
- spray irrigation (agricultural disposal)
- drying
- composting
- anaerobic digestion.

In the UK until recently 67% of the sludge was disposed of on land, 29% dumped at sea, and 4% removed by incineration. It was agreed at the 1990 North Sea Conference to phase out disposal of sewage sludge at sea by 1998 to comply with EC Urban Wastewater Treatment Directive 91/271/EEC. The banning of sludge dumping at sea was a measure to improve coastal water quality, although there was no substantial evidence of environmental damage other than chromium accumulation. Thus there will be a need to find a replacement for dumping at sea.

Of the 67% sludge disposed on land some 16% goes into landfill sites, either solely or co-disposed with domestic wastes in the UK. A much higher proportion is landfilled in the UK than in other European countries where incineration and composting are used more widely. In the USA in 1993 62% of domestic waste was landfilled, 16% combusted and 4% composted. Despite recent reductions in landfill use in the USA it is clear that most of the waste is placed in landfill. However, of the 6000 landfill sites used in the USA in 1991, 3000 will be closed by the year 2000. This will mean that new sites will be needed but there is considerable public resistance to the formation of new sites.

The large-scale incineration of sewage sludge is expensive, with high capital costs, and is only a partial disposal option as the ash formed needs disposal. However, the development of autothermic incineration has made incineration more attractive. In the process primary and secondary sludges are mixed

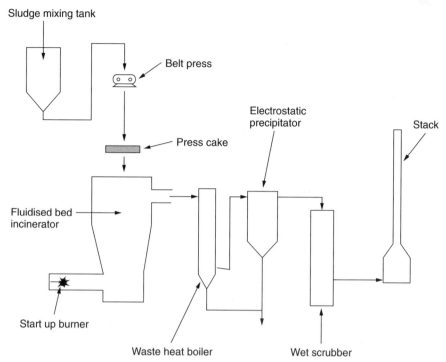

Fig. 3.18 An outline of the process of autocalorific sewage sludge incineration, including an electrostatic precipitator and wet scrubber to clean the flue gases (Ottewell, 1990).

together and water removed by pressing so that a cake of 30% solids is produced which can support autothermic combustion. Advanced combustion systems such as fluidised beds working at temperatures of 750–850°C create more heat than is required to heat the inlet air and remove the water from the sludge. This means that once the process has started, no fuel needs to be added as the sludge itself generates sufficient heat (Fig. 3.18). The ash formed can be removed by an electrostatic precipitator and a wet scrubber will remove sulphur dioxide, hydrogen fluoride and hydrogen chloride. The ash contains the heavy metals which are present in the sludge and represents 30% of the original dry mass and 1–2% of the volume and is normally disposed of in landfill sites.

Some sludge is disposed of by some form of agricultural use (Wheatly, 1985). Any sludge which is applied to agricultural land is required to have some form of biological or chemical treatment to reduce the levels of pathogens unless it is injected below the surface. These treatments are:

- pasteurisation, heating at 70°C for 30 min or more
- anaerobic digestion at 35°C for 12 days
- thermophilic aerobic digestion, 7 days at 55°C
- composting (see Chapter 4)

Table 3.6 The limits of metals in activated sludge and soil treated with sludge

Metal	Concentration in sludge (mg/kg)	Concentration in soil (mg/kg)
Cadmium	20–40	1–3
Copper	1000–1750	50–140
Nickel	300–400	30–75
Lead	750–1200	50–300
Zinc	2500–4000	150–300
Mercury	16–25	1–1.5

Source: Attewell, 1993.

- alkali stabilisation, pH >12 for 2 hours
- liquid storage, 3 months
- drying and storage, 3 months.

All these methods reduce the pathogen content of the sludge before it is applied to the land, but there are restrictions on what crops are grown and how soon the land can be used for certain crops. Treated sludge can be applied to land to be used for growing turf or potatoes, but the land cannot be used for growing fruit or vegetable crops until 10 months after application. Prior to drying, the sludge is normally conditioned so that its ability to settle before dewatering is improved. Often polyvalent ions such as Fe^{iii} or Al^{iii}, polyelectrolytes or soil is added to improve precipitation. Dewatering is often carried out in drying beds, but filtration and centrifugation have also been used to produce a compact cake.

Almost all sludge contains heavy metals, as microorganisms have the ability to sequester metals, so that the application of sludge to soils carries with it the risk of producing high levels of heavy metals in the soil. There are limits for metals in sewage sludge (Table 3.6) and in soil.

3.7 Anaerobic digestion

Liquid wastes had been treated anaerobically in simple anaerobic ponds for thousands of years before the development of anaerobic digestion in closed vessels. One of the best methods of disposing of excess sludge is to subject it to anaerobic digestion, a process that has been used in large sewage works for some time. However, more recently anaerobic processes have been used to treat industrial wastes containing a high content of insoluble or organic compounds.

The advantages of anaerobic digestion are that the process produces much less biomass or sludge, forms methane (biogas) and requires no aeration, and the associated smell is less as the process is enclosed. The methane can be used as a fuel to run boilers or to generate electricity with about 1.16×10^7 kJ

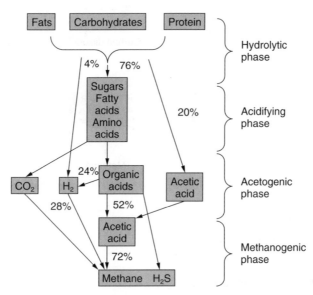

Fig. 3.19 The stages of the anaerobic breakdown of sewage to biomass and biogas.

produced per 1000 tonnes of COD removed (Speece, 1983). The disadvantages of anaerobic digestion are that the process requires good mixing, a temperature in the region of 37°C, a substrate with a high BOD (1.2–2 g/l) and long retention times of 30–60 days. The requirement for a high BOD waste means that anaerobic digestion is suitable for some agricultural and industrial wastes but is not suitable for normal sewage.

Anaerobic digestion is a complex process involving a considerable number of reactions and three main groups of organisms, and can be divided into four main stages. The first stage is the hydrolysis of the fats, proteins and carbohydrates which make up the main components of sewage (Fig. 3.19) to form fatty acids, alcohols and ketones by hydrolytic microorganisms such as *Clostridium*, *Eubacterium* and *Bacterioides*. In the second stage, the acidifying phase, fatty acids are then converted to acetate, carbon dioxide and hydrogen. Other amino acids and sugars are converted to acetate, hydrogen and carbon dioxide. The reactions are carried out by bacteria such as *Peptococcus* and *Propionibacterium*. Acetate and hydrogen can also be formed directly from the primary components of the sludge. In the third phase, the acetogenic phase, organic acids are converted to acetate and carbon dioxide by bacteria such as *Syntrophobacter*, *Desulfovibrio* and *Syntrophomonas*. The fourth phase is the formation of methane by the methanogenic bacteria *Methanobacterium*, *Methanobacillus*, *Methanococcus* and *Methanosarcina* which are some of the most oxygen-sensitive bacteria known. About 20 species of methanogenic bacteria are known and these are found in intimate contact with the acetogenic bacteria. The methanogenic bacteria convert hydrogen, carbon dioxide and acetate to methane as follows (Fig. 3.20):

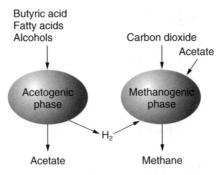

Fig. 3.20 The intimate relationship between the acetogenic and methanogenic bacteria.

$$4H_2 + HCO_3 + H^+ \rightarrow CH_4 + 3H_2O$$

$$CH_3COO + H_2O \rightarrow CH_4 + HCO_3$$

3.7.1 The anaerobic process

The first anaerobic digesters were simple sealed vessels in which the contents were not mixed or heated, but since then a number of different designs have been developed including upflow sludge blanket, fixed film, fluidised bed and two-stage processes. The simplest design is the contact process where the waste is mixed with recycled anaerobic sludge and retained in a sealed vessel at 30–37°C. After 30–60 days digestion is complete, the mixture is separated, and the liquid discharged for further treatment, much of the biomass being returned to the vessel (Fig. 3.21). The problem with this type of system is that it subjects the methanogens, which are strict anaerobes, to an aerobic environment when the vessel is discharged, and even if this exposure is only for a short time it will affect their activity. To avoid this disturbance the other designs have been developed which are based on continuous flow systems.

In the upflow sludge blanket the waste is introduced at the bottom of the vessel into the area where the sludge settles (Fig. 3.22). Therefore the waste immediately contacts the sludge, ensuring a more rapid rate of reaction. Mixing is achieved by the incoming flow of waste and by the gas generated, and at the top of the vessel the biomass, liquid and gas are separated in a settling section. These types of vessel have been applied successfully to a number of wastes at high loading rates.

In order to maintain a high biomass level and good contact with waste, fixed-film or immobilisation biomass has been used. Porous material such as plastics, and solids such as gravel, sand and glass granules have been used to immobilise the anaerobic microorganisms (Fig. 3.22). This type of system can be operated in a number of modes and in either an upflow or a downflow mode. In the fixed-bed reactor the waste passes upwards through the particles coated with biomass. This system does suffer from channelling and clogging. An alternative is the fluidised bed reactor where the cells are immobilised on

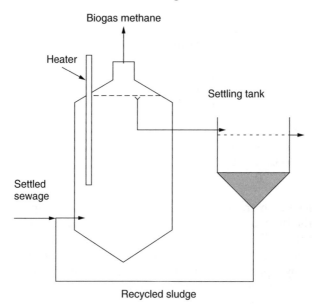

Fig. 3.21 Conventional anaerobic sludge process.

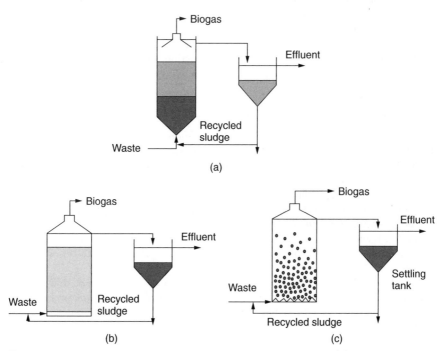

Fig. 3.22 Different systems for the anaerobic treatment of waste: (a) upflow anaerobic sludge blanket, (b) fixed bed anaerobic reactor, (c) anaerobic fluidised bed reactor.

Table 3.7 A comparison of some anaerobic processes

Reactor type	COD loading rate (kg/m³d)	COD removal (%)
Contact	1–6	80–95
Upflow filter	1–10	80–95
Fluidised bed	1–20	80–87
Downflow filter	5–15	75–88
Upflow sludge blanket	5–30	85–95

Source: Speece, 1983.

sand particles which are fluidised by the upflow of waste (Fig. 3.22). A comparison of the function of these various types is shown in Table 3.7 where it is clear that the upflow sludge blanket has the highest loading rate and COD removal. Attempts have been made to separate anaerobic digestion into a two-stage process by separating the acidifying stage from methanogenesis by using two separate vessels run under different conditions and flow rates.

3.8 Conclusions

- The aerobic treatment of sewage will continue with any new systems based on improvements in the engineering to provide better mixing and aeration.
- Recombinant DNA technology will be increasingly used to follow the population dynamics in both aerobic and anaerobic digestion systems.
- Better management of landfill for gas production and leachate recycling should increase the rate of degradation and allow the reuse of landfill sites.

3.9 References

Attewell, P. (1993) *Ground Pollution*. E & FN Spon, London.
Brindle, K. and Stephenson, T. (1996) The application of membrane biological reactors for the treatment of wastewaters. *Biotechnol. Bioeng.*, **49**, 601–610.
Gray, N. F. (1989) *Biology of Waste Water Treatment*. Oxford University Press, Oxford.
Lee, Y. D., Shin, E. B., Choi, Y. S., Yoon, H. S., Lee, H.S., Chung, L. J. and Na, J. S. (1997) Biological removal of nitrogen and phosphorus from wastewater by a single sludge reactor. *Environ. Technol.*, **18**, 975–986.
Ndon, U. J. and Dague, R. R. (1997) Ambient temperature treatment of low strength wastewater using anaerobic sequencing batch reactor. *Biotechnol. Letters*, **19**, 319–323.
Ottewell, S. (1990) Sewage sludge incineration. *The Chemical Engineer*, 477, 14.
Ra, C. S., Lo, K. V. and Mavinic, D. S. (1998) Real-time control of two-stage sequencing batch reactor system for the treatment of animal wastewater. *Environ. Technol.*, **19**, 343–356.
Rhee, S. K., Lee, J. J. and Lee, S. T. (1997) Nitrite accumulation in a sequencing batch reactor during the aerobic phase of biological nitrogen removal. *Biotechnol. Letters*, **19**, 195–198.

Speece, R. E. (1983) Anaerobic biotechnology for industrial wastewater treatment. *Environ. Sci. Technol.*, **17**, 416–427.

Tchobanoglous, G. and Burton, H. (1991) *Wastewater Engineering*, 3rd edition. McGraw-Hill, New York.

Wheatly, A. D. (1985) Wastewater treatment and by-product recovery. *Critical Reports in Applied Chemistry*, **11**, 68–106.

3.9.1 Recommended reading

Attewell, P. (1993) *Ground Pollution*. E & FN Spon, London.

Clark, R. B. (1997) *Marine Pollution*, 4th edition. Oxford University Press, Oxford.

Droste, R. L. (1998) *Theory and Practice of Waste and Wastewater Treatment*. John Wiley & Sons, Chichester, UK.

Gray, N. F. (1989) *Biology of Waste Water Treatment*. Oxford University Press, Oxford.

Horan, N. (1997) *Biological Wastewater Treatment Systems*, 2nd edition. John Wiley & Sons, Chichester, UK.

Tebbutt, T. H. Y. (1998) *Principles of Water Quality Control*, 5th edition. Pergamon Press, Oxford.

Williams, P. T. (1997) *Waste Treatment and Disposal*. John Wiley & Sons, Chichester, UK.

Chapter 4

Clean technology, domestic, industrial and agricultural wastes

4.1 Introduction

In Chapter 1 potential environmental pollutants were outlined in Table 1.3 which classified them as inorganic, organic, biological and gaseous. The organic wastes can be divided into three groups: those originating from biological sources which are naturally biodegradable, those produced from the petrochemical industry, and a wide range of synthetic chemicals. In Chapter 3 the treatment of liquid domestic waste (sewage), a biodegradable product, has been described, including processes for the reduction of ammonia, nitrate and nitrite. In the present chapter the treatment and disposal of biological organic wastes from domestic, agricultural and industrial sources are covered. In addition, the reduction or elimination of waste production involving *clean technology* is also covered.

4.2 Clean technology

Much of the thinking about the application of biotechnology to waste treatment involves the treatment of the waste once it has been produced in some form of 'end-of-pipe' process. This approach is not always a satisfactory solution, as many treatments just transfer the pollution to another area. Thus, the best solution is to eliminate or reduce pollution at source and therefore waste minimisation or pollution prevention has been placed at the top of the waste management hierarchy. The second option in the hierarchy is recycling, followed by treatment and finally disposal. This is almost the reverse of previous practice where wastes of all description have been treated after production rather than prevented. The reduction in pollution at source, sometimes known as clean technology, can take a number of forms which can involve procedural changes, technology changes, and changes in material input. The procedural changes include loss prevention, materials handling, and improvements in the running of plants and factories, and are unlikely to be affected by biotechnology. The technology changes can include alterations in process engineering including process changes, operational settings and automation. Changes in input material can reduce waste, substitution of one chemical by a less toxic one will reduce hazards, and the recycling of material can reduce raw material use (Fig. 4.1). Biotechnology may be applied to changes in both technology and materials,

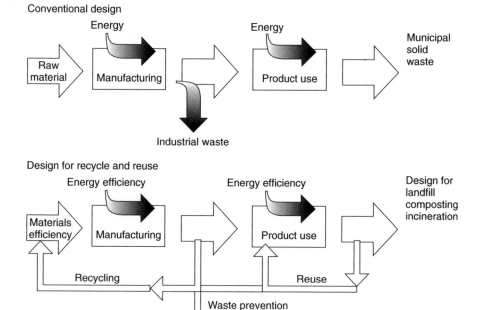

Fig. 4.1 Industrial designs for conventional processes and those incorporating recycling during manufacture and after product use (from Hill, 1997).

and some areas where the application may help to reduce waste or pollution are as follows:

- Process changes involving the replacement of chemical methods by microorganisms or enzymes, including genetically engineered organisms
- Integrated pest management (IPM) and integrated crop management (ICM) which should reduce insecticide and herbicide (agrochemicals) use
- Biological control: the use of biological materials for the control of pests and diseases, reducing the use of agrochemicals
- The production of biodegradable plastic by microorganisms
- The biological desulphurisation of coal and oil (Chapter 5)
- The production of biologically derived fuels (Chapter 6)

4.2.1 Process changes

Examples of the use of microorganisms to replace chemical processes are limited but there is great potential, particularly now that they can be genetically engineered. One example is the biological production of acetone and butanol which was developed in 1914 to replace a chemical process but was itself replaced in the 1950s by the chemical production of acetone from polypropylene. However, a better understanding of the biological process through the application of recombinant technology (Girbal and Soucaille, 1998), combined with improved process control and waste management, may see the biological system reintroduced. It has another advantage in that it utilises renewable resources.

An example of the ability of genetic engineering to adjust a microorganism's metabolism to suit a process is shown with the production of indigo which is used to dye denim (Bialy, 1997). It was discovered that a *Pseudomonas* contained an enzyme, naphthalene dioxygenase (NDO), which converted indole to indoxyl which oxidatively dimerises to indigo. The gene was cloned into *E. coli* which was then capable of synthesising indigo, but the yields were low. To improve the yield *E. coli* needed to be engineered to produce an excess of tryptophan or the indigo precursor indole. The enzymes of the pathway to chorismate were overexpressed so that chorismate accumulated. The diversion of the accumulated chorismate to tryptophan was achieved by amplifying the *trp* operon and inserting a mutant tryptophan synthase. This stimulated the formation of indole and the indole was converted to indigo at high yields. However, upon large-scale trials the indigo dye was found to contain indirubin which made the blue colour too red. The presence of indirubin was found to be due to the formation of isatin, a derivative of indoxyl. The level of isatin was controlled by adjusting the dissolved oxygen level and cloning in the enzyme isatin hydrolase which converted isatin to a colourless compound. The new *E. coli* strain containing 15 new genes was grown on a large scale and the product was found to be identical to the chemically produced indigo. To introduce 15 new genes was a very difficult process but the final process using *E. coli* was considerably cleaner than the chemical synthesis. The latter used eight operations, using highly toxic chemicals, requiring special conditions and protection for the workers. The economics of the biological process were also better than those of the chemical synthesis and the wastes formed were far easier to treat.

Enzymes can replace chemical synthesis in a number of industries, including agrochemicals, pharmaceuticals and detergent manufacture, and have the advantages of producing fewer side-products and functioning at lower temperatures. A few examples of the use of enzymes in existing processes are as follows:

- Leather processing where enzymes are used to remove hair and fat from hides.
- Textile processing where enzymes have replaced chemicals for the removal of starch and the neutralisation of bleach.
- Paper processing using enzymatic (xylanase) bleaching rather than the use of chlorine (Box 4.1).
- Detergents containing enzymes (lipase, protease) capable of functioning at the low wash temperature of 40°C, thus reducing the energy used, and a cellulase which can bring back the colour to cotton clothes by removing a layer of cellulose from cotton strands.
- Enzymes are used in a number of food processes such as the conversion of starch to sugar (amylase), thus avoiding the use of acids.

- An enzyme, phenol oxidase, has been isolated and identified as responsible for the production of adhesives in mussels. This has also been isolated from a mould and is being used to make adhesives which are stronger and safer than existing adhesives as they are water based.
- The addition of phytase to animal feed breaks down plant phytates which animals cannot digest. Phytic acid is the major storage form of phosphorus in seeds, and two-thirds of the phosphorus in cereals, legumes and oil seeds is in phytates. Pigs, poultry and humans (monogastric animals) cannot digest phytates so that much of the phosphorus is excreted, raising phosphate levels in areas of intensive farming. In addition phytates complex with metals such as iron, zinc, magnesium and calcium which decreases their availability to the animal. Phytases occur in plants, certain animals and microorganisms, and the enzyme hydrolyses phytic acid to myo-inositol and phosphoric acid which can be digested (Kim *et al.*, 1998). The addition of phytases to animal feed would increase the availability of phosphorus and metals, which could reduce the amount of feed required and the phosphorus excreted.

Box 4.1

Wood is the raw material for the production of paper and cardboard. The main constituents of wood are lignin, a polyphenol matrix surrounded by cellulose and hemicellulose. The removal of lignin is difficult as it is very inert, but by using alkaline extraction at high temperatures 90% of the lignin can be removed. The resulting product is known as kraft pulp and the remaining 10% lignin gives the pulp a brown colour, making it suitable only for the production of brown paper and cardboard. The normal method of removing the remaining 10% lignin to give a white product is chlorine bleaching and in the USA 2 million tons of chlorine are used annually for this purpose. The chlorinated lignin derivatives present a major pollution problem for the pulp and paper industry. The residual lignin is associated with hemicelluloses and this can be removed by the enzymatic degradation of the xylan component of the hemicellulose by xylanases (Chen *et al.*, 1997). Therefore, treatment with xylanases can be used as an alternative to chlorine bleaching with the resulting reduction in chlorine use and associated wastes. This method has been used for a number of years in the USA and Europe.

The discovery of bacteria capable of growing in extreme conditions such as hot springs, deep water thermal vents and salt lakes (Box 4.2) has seen the introduction of a new domain of bacteria, the Archaea. The Archaea contain extremophiles which are capable of growth in extreme conditions of pH, salinity, pressure and temperature, which has stimulated efforts to understand the physiological adaptation to these extremes. These organisms are of potential use in biotechnology. One group of Archaea, the hyperthermophiles, contain thermostable enzymes of particular interest, as thermostability in enzymes is a very desirable characteristic since it extends activity and allows the enzyme to function at higher temperatures and have a longer shelf-life. The extremophiles are difficult to isolate and grow, but a number of the enzymes have been cloned which should allow the enzymes either to be cloned into mesophiles or to act as a basis for the alteration of mesophilic enzymes to increase their stability. Genes encoding for thermophilic and hyperthermophilic enzymes have been expressed in a mesophile, and the enzyme has retained its properties (Danson and Hough, 1998). An example is the cloning of a thermostable xylanase from *Thermotoga maritima* in *E. coli* which remained thermostable upon expression (Chen *et al.*, 1997). Those genes for thermophilic enzymes which have been cloned and sequenced have not shown any dramatic difference between them and the mesophilic enzymes. Despite the similarity in structure, the basis for protein stability appears to be an increase in compactness, a reduction in internal cavities, and increased internal packing with the formation of isoleucine clusters. In addition, inter-subunit ion pairs and ion pair networks are increased in the thermostable enzyme.

Box 4.2   Archaea extremophiles

Thermophiles: grow at 55–80°C (see Fig. 4.2)
Hyperthermophiles: grow at 80–110°C
Psychrophiles: grow at <20°C
Halophiles: grow in salt concentrations near saturation
Acidophiles: grow at pH values of less than 4
Alkaliphiles: grow at pH values of more than 9
Barophiles: grow at pressures of up to 50 MPa (megapascals)

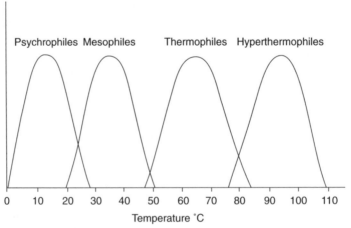

Fig. 4.2 The temperature ranges for psychrophiles, mesophiles, thermophiles and hyperthermophiles.

Table 4.1 Enzymes from hyperthermophilic species of *Thermotoga*

Enzyme	Function	Optimum temperature (°C)
Glucose isomerase	glucose → fructose	95
Xylanase	xylan hydrolysis pulp and paper bleaching	105
Amylase	starch hydrolysis	85–90
β-Glucanase	cellulose hydrolysis	95
β-Mannanase	mannan hydrolysis	92
Galactosidase	galactomannan hydrolysis	100–105
β-Glucosidase	cellobiose hydrolysis	105
Alkaline phosphatase	ELISA	85

Sources: Adams and Kelly, 1998; Dong and Zeikus, 1997.

An example of the hyperthermophilic enzymes from an Archaea species, *Thermotoga*, is shown in Table 4.1 where most of the enzymes have an optimum temperature of between 80°C and 105°C, considerably higher than that of normal mesophilic bacterial enzymes. One example of the use of thermostable enzymes is the temperature-tolerant DNA polymerase used in the polymerase chain reaction (PCR), a technique central to the recent advances in molecular biology. The PCR reaction has to go through a large number of cycles of synthesis and denaturation, and the denaturation requires a temperature of 95°C; the enzyme can tolerate 95°C and therefore new enzyme does not need to be added between cycles.

4.2.2 Integrated pest management

The use of herbicides and pesticides (biocides or agrochemicals) has been linked to the pollution of the environment and in many cases the agrochemicals are very persistent. However, the use of these biocides has been reducing over the years with a shift to less persistent and lower-dosage chemicals. Another method of reducing the application of biocides or agrochemicals is to adopt a system of Integrated Crop Management (ICM) or Integrated Pest Management (IPM). In these systems the application of agrochemicals is combined with the best biological and cultural methods to give crop protection with the minimum use of agrochemicals. The influence of biotechnology may be limited in the application of these management systems. The various factors considered in such systems are:

- Crop rotation in order to disrupt crop-specific disease.
- Cultivation techniques in order to control weeds, pests and diseases.
- The use of resistant crops. It is here that biotechnology can produce herbicide- and pesticide-resistant crops and this is described in Chapter 8.

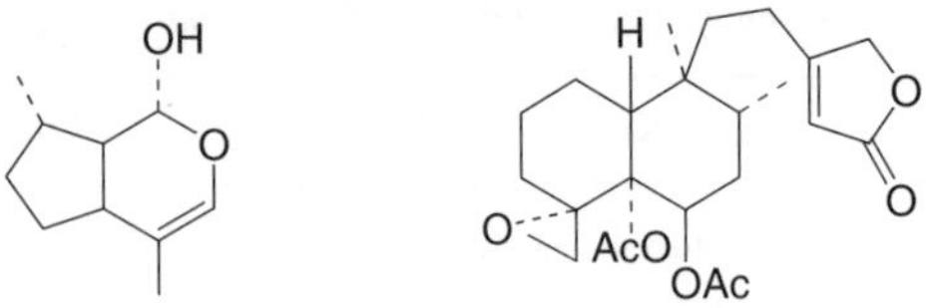

Aphid sex pheromone   Ajugarin I

Fig. 4.3 The structure of an aphid sex pheromone and the antifeedant ajugarin I from the bugle plant.

- Better prediction methods for the early detection of insect or disease attack. In this case the development of biosensors and detection systems based on recombinant technology should have an effect.
- Accurate diagnosis. Here again recombinant technology will have an effect in the development of rapid and specific tests.
- The time of addition of the agrochemicals can be important and in some cases the agrochemical is best applied at the seed stage.
- The development of more specific agrochemicals including those of natural origin. Clearly the more specific the less the damage to other species. One of the best sources of new chemicals is the higher plants. The best known example is the natural pyrethrins isolated from chrysanthemum flowers which can control a variety of insects and have directed the synthesis of more active and stable analogues known as the pyrethroids. Biotechnology can help in the screening for these types of compounds and perhaps in their production. One recent example is the interest in the active component of the neem tree which acts as an antifeedant for insects. The trees are found in Africa and India and the compound is the complex azadirachtin.
- The use of biological control (see Section 4.2.3).
- The use of semiochemicals or chemical signals.

The semiochemicals are a group of natural chemical messengers which act as signals modifying animal or plant behaviour and development. These chemicals can be used to attract or to repel the pest. Examples of attraction are the use of sex pheromones for a number of pests (Fig. 4.3). These have been used to attract male aphids to some form of trap and to attract aphid parasites. Another group is the antifeedants which interfere with the feeding of insects. An example is ajugarin found in the bugle plant *Ajuga remota*. The structure of this compound is shown in Fig. 4.3 and at low concentration it deters the feeding of Coleoptera and the Colorado beetle.

Biotechnology can have an influence on semiochemical use by the bulk production of these complex molecules which may be produced in only low levels in plants. Recombinant technology can be used to modify higher plants to produce semiochemicals. An example of a possible target is the production of Dimboa, a cyclic hydroxamic acid, in plants. Dimboa is a secondary metabolite found in maize and confers resistance to the European corn borer by interfering with feeding. There are five genes responsible for the production of Dimboa and as technology improves it may be able to transfer these genes to target plants (Chapter 8).

4.2.3   Biological control

Biological control is the use of biological material as a pest control rather than the use of chemical treatments. Biological control uses natural predators to control pests and diseases (Van Driesche and Bellows, 1996) and this can also include pheromones, resistant plants and the use of sterile insects. Biological control has the potential to reduce the use of agrochemicals and to limit their effects on the environment. Biological control has been successful in a number of cases, but the techniques used work more slowly than chemical treatments and therefore have had limited success with commercial crops.

The application of biotechnology is not central to the development of biological control which is really based on a fundamental understanding of the interactions within an ecosystem. However, biotechnology can help with biological control by producing insect-resistant plants (Chapter 8) and biopesticides. The use of biopesticides does have considerable advantages as they do not form toxic residues, pest resistance is low, and secondary pests and pest resurgence is also reduced (Bishop, 1994). One of the best examples of biopesticides is the use of *Bacillus thuringiensis* to control insect pests. This is a Gram-positive soil bacterium which can colonise living insects. *B. thuringiensis* strains are classified on serotypes and into five groups depending on their insecticidal range. Upon sporulation, *B. thuringiensis* produces a single spore and one or more large protein crystals consisting of protoxin molecules. When certain insect larvae ingest these crystals, the crystals dissolve in the midgut and the gut proteases cleave the protoxin to the active toxin which has a molecular weight of 65,000–67,000. The toxin binds to the gut epithelial and destroys the permeability of the plasma membrane; the cells swell, lyse and die. The toxin can be placed into four groups based on the type of insect affected. The groups are the Lepidoptera (CryI), Lepidoptera and Diptera (CryII), Coleoptera (CryIII) and Diptera (CryIV). A number of insect pests are sensitive to strains of *B. thuringiensis* (Table 4.2) and some of these have been approved for commercial use as biological controls. The advantage of this form of control is the stability of the preparations and their insensitivity to UV light, but the preparations have a high cost and are too specific in some cases and too slow in others compared with traditional insecticides. Other biopesticides under investigation are genetically engineered baculoviruses which cause nuclear polyhedrosis and granulosis, but the natural baculoviruses have proved difficult to clone.

Biological control has not used microorganisms to any great extent, although fungi have been used to control weeds, and fungi and bacteria have been used to suppress plant pathogens and have been shown to attack nematodes. One example is the use of bacteria which can degrade chitin, which is found in the cuticle of insects and the cell wall of some fungi. Bacteria capable of degrading chitin are common in the environment, as chitin is second to cellulose in abundance. A bacterium *Streptomyces lydicus* WYEC108 has been isolated which has chitinase activity and has been used as an antifungal agent (Mahadevan and Crawford, 1997).

Table 4.2   Insects susceptible to *B. thuringiensis*

Insect	Crops
Pieris brassicae (large white butterfly)	vegetables
Pieris rapae (cabbage looper)	vegetables
Plutella maculipennis (diamondback moth)	vegetables
Trichoplusia ni (cabbage looper)	vegetables, tobacco, cotton
Heliothis virescens (tobacco budworm)	cotton, soybean, tobacco
Heliothis zea (cotton bollworm)	cotton, soybean, tobacco
Ostrinia nubilalis (European corn borer)	corn (maize)
Manduca sexta (tobacco hornworm)	tobacco
Leptinotarsa decemlineata (Colorado beetle)	potato
Lymantia dispar (gypsy moth)	forests
Choristonecura fumiferana (spruce budworm)	forests
Malacosoma disstria (tent caterpillar)	forests
Denrolimus sibiricus (Siberian silkworm)	forests
Plodia interpunctella (Indian meal moth)	stored products
Anagasta kuhniella (Mediterranean flour moth)	stored products
Ephestia cautella (almond moth)	stored products
Culex spp., *Aedes* spp., *Anopheles* spp. (mosquito species)	malaria, yellow fever, Dengue fever
Simulium spp. (blackfly species)	African river blindness

Source: Glazer and Nikaido, 1994.

Although there are great benefits to be gained from biological control, there are concerns over the risks of biocontrol to natural diversity (Thomas and Willis, 1998) and the dangers of the introduction of exotic species to the environment. There are examples of the adverse effects of the use of biological control, but the FAO (Food and Agriculture Organisation of the United Nations) has issued a code of conduct for the import and release of exotic biological control agents. This code of conduct has suggested a number of parameters which need attention: evaluation studies before the control is applied, testing of non-target species, and post-release evaluation. Biopesticides should be used with caution since if they are overused resistance may develop in the same way as with chemical pesticides (Lewis *et al.*, 1997).

4.2.4   Microbial biopolymers

Solid domestic wastes can contain up to 29% plastics which are synthesised from petrochemicals and are not biodegradable. Therefore, plastics constitute an increasing problem of disposal, and the MARPOL agreement in 1992 banned the disposal of plastics at sea. Some microorganisms can produce a

Table 4.3 Comparison of the properties of polyethylene and poly(3-hydroxybutyrate)

Property	Polyethylene	Poly(3-hydroxybutyrate)
Molecular weight	$2.2–7 \times 10^5$	$1–8 \times 10^5$
Melting point (°C)	171–186	171–182
Density (g/cm³)	0.905–0.94	1.23–1.25
Tensile strength (MPa)*	39	40
Resistance to UV light	poor	good
Biodegradation	very poor	good

* Tensile strength is the maximum stress that the material can resist; $1\ MPa = 10^6$ Pascals.
Source: Luzier, 1992.

range of polymers, most of which are storage or reserve materials such as starch and lipids, but some of these polymers have properties similar to plastics (Daniell and Guda, 1997; Brandl *et al.*, 1990). One of the best known is poly-(R)-(3-hydroxybutyrate) or PHB which was first found in *Bacillus megaterium* but is now produced using *Acaligenes eutrophus*. The polymer has been shown to occur in more than 50 bacterial species. PHB is accumulated when the organisms are deprived of nitrogen, phosphate, magnesium or sulphate, and it can constitute up to 90% of the cell's dry weight. The polymer can be extracted from the cells by organic solvents and has a molecular weight of 2×10^6. The polymer's physical properties compare well with those of polypropylene in terms of melting point, density and tensile strength (Table 4.3), but it has the considerable advantage of being biodegradable. The polymer formed by *A. eutrophus* can also be modified if propionic acid is added, and the copolymer formed is a mixture of PHB and 3-hydroxyvalerate. The PHB plastic has a low impact strength which makes it difficult to process, but the copolymer of PHB/3-hydroxyvalerate (PHB-V) is much more amenable to processing. In addition, the higher the PHB-V content the lower the melting point. It is this type of plastic that Zeneca has marketed as Biopol. Its application has been limited because at the scale on which it is being produced it costs $5–15/kg compared with $1/kg for petroleum-based plastics. The higher costs of the microbially produced plastic are due to the costs of the medium, the bioreactor operation, and purification (Glazer and Nikaido, 1994).

The three genes responsible for the production of PHB in *A. eutrophus* have been cloned and introduced into the bacterium *E. coli* and the plant *Arabidopsis thaliana*. The *E. coli* cells produced up to 90% of their dry weight as PHB. The plant *A. thaliana* accumulated PHB granules but grew slowly and produced fewer seeds than the normal plant. The loss in growth is probably due to the drain of acetyl CoA required for PHB formation, rather than its use in numerous plant metabolic pathways. This problem may be reduced if the enzymes for PHB synthesis can be directed to specific tissues. The production of PHB in plants will certainly reduce the cost of the product considerably, as agricultural production will always be cheaper than bioreactor production.

Table 4.4 Percentage composition of domestic waste

Composition	UK	USA
Paper	35–60	32.0
Garden waste	2–35	14.8
Food waste	2–8	8.5
Metals	6–9	6.3
Glass	5–13	6.4
Plastics	1–2	11.8
Textiles/wood	1–3	
Rubber/leather	1–3	19.3
Miscellaneous	2	

Other possible biopolymers for use as plastics are the lactic acid-based polymers from *Lactobacillus* and the protein-based polymers. The protein-based polymers are not really designed to benefit the environment directly but will be biodegradable. An example of one protein-based polymer that is under investigation is the cloning of the genes for spiders' silk, which is stronger than steel and would have a number of applications if it could be made on a large scale.

4.3 Recycling

Recycling is the second option in the hierarchy of waste reduction and can involve the recycling of material produced either during the manufacturing process or from the product itself after manufacture (Fig. 4.1). Recycling makes considerable sense, bearing in mind that recycling metals and glass can save 95% of the energy that would be needed to mine new metals and make new glass containers. Most recovery and recycle systems concentrate on the reuse of metals, glass and paper, and paper is the major constituent of solid domestic waste (Table 4.4). A number of recycle systems have been developed, including the use of two or three bins to segregate the waste at collection.

4.4 Domestic wastes

Domestic solid waste is the solid refuse produced by households and institutions consisting of glass, metal, paper and organic material (Table 4.4). Trends in the treatment of domestic solid waste have changed over the years. In the USA in 1985 83% was dumped in landfill sites, 5% combusted and 12% recycled; by 1993 landfill disposal had been reduced to 62%, with 16% combusted, 4% composted and 18% recycled. Although there has been an increase in recycling and incineration, the bulk of domestic waste is still disposed of in landfill sites in the USA and UK. The elimination of domestic waste is difficult as much of the paper is produced by packaging. Domestic

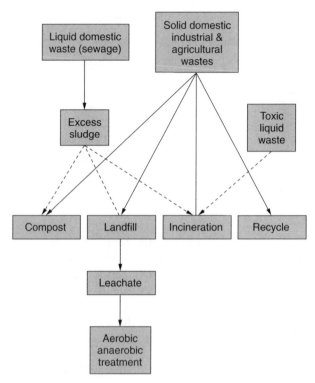

Fig. 4.4 The methods for the treatment and disposal of solid domestic waste, excess sewage sludge and toxic liquid waste.

waste could be reduced by recycling of glass, metal and paper and a reduction in packaging.

4.4.1   Landfill

Once wastes have been produced, there are a number of methods which can be used to treat or dispose of wastes, which include domestic refuse, excess sewage sludge, agricultural and industrial wastes (Fig. 4.4).

Perhaps the oldest method of disposal is burial. Initially most landfill sites were unsealed so that any leachate derived from the degradation of the contents could be dispersed in the surrounding soil, but in practice the leachate often contaminated the groundwater. The main problem of landfill disposal is finding suitable sites in terms of geology; a non-porous substratum is needed to prevent contamination of the groundwater, siting away from habitation to avoid odours, and there are now stricter regulations as to what can be disposed of in a landfill site. The most suitable site for a landfill is an abandoned quarry or opencast site, although a site can be constructed above ground by building up retaining walls. The site will need to be lined with an impermeable barrier

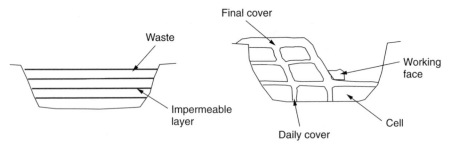

Fig. 4.5 Methods of constructing landfill sites. The use of thin layers separated by impermeable layers will not allow the easy collection of gases or the penetration of water. In the
second method the waste is laid down in compacted cells which are covered daily by soil or
ash.

to avoid contamination of the groundwater. Materials such as clay and plastics
such as polyethylene, polyvinylchloride and rubber have been used, based on
compacted soil. The site, once constructed, can be filled over a wide area or
the fill can be confined to cells or terraces (Fig. 4.5). In all cases the waste is
compacted by purpose-built vehicles and each day's waste must be covered
with soil or ash. The compaction controls the air and water transfer, reduces
the volume and reduces the possibility of spontaneous combustion by reduction of oxygen. The overall dimensions of the refuse cell will vary with the
characteristics of the waste, the cover soil, the availability of land, and the
topography of the site.

During construction permeable horizontal trenches or perforated pipes may
be installed in order to extract gas and to collect leachate (Fig. 4.6). Once the
landfill has reached its working level, the top is sealed with a layer of clay, an
impervious lining topped by a drainage layer and soil. The capping prevents
rainwater entering the site, reducing the leachate formed. Once capped the
organic content of the landfill will be degraded anaerobically in a similar
manner to the anaerobic digester (Chapter 3) and will produce methane and a
leachate. The rate of degradation is dependent on moisture content and as the
site has been capped water may have to be added. The leachate will have a
high BOD level due to the limited degradation of the organic content and
may also contain metals and toxic chemicals, particularly when industrial
waste is dumped at the same site (co-disposal); such leachates will require
treatment. An example of landfill leachates is shown in Table 4.5. The capping of the site will restrict gas extraction so that pipes or gravel vents are
inserted during construction or inserted after capping (Fig. 4.7). Landfill gas is
of variable composition but contains methane, carbon dioxide and hydrogen
and has a calorific value of about 50% of natural gas. The wells are normally
inserted 1–2 years after capping the site and give best yields of ~100 m^3 gas
per tonne of refuse (Fig. 4.8). The yield is only 25% of the possible yield, but
the rate of gas formation and migration within the site makes complete extraction difficult.

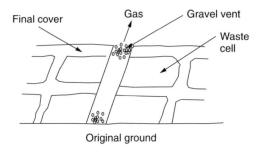

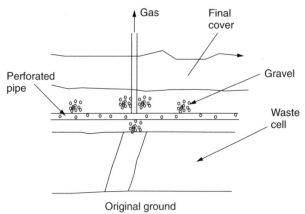

Fig. 4.6 The management of the collection of gas from landfill sites using either gravel vents or perforated pipes.

Table 4.5 Composition (mg/l) of the leachate from recent and old landfill sites

Parameter	Recent waste	Old waste
COD	23,800	1160
BOD	11,900	260
TOC	8000	465
Fatty acids	5688	5
Ammoniacal-N	790	370
Oxidised-N	3	1
Chloride	1315	2080
Sodium	960	1300
Magnesium	252	185
Potassium	780	590
Calcium	1820	250
Manganese	27	2
Iron	540	23
Nickel	0.6	0.1
Copper	0.12	0.3
Zinc	21.5	0.4
Lead	8.4	0.14

Source: data from Attewell, 1993.

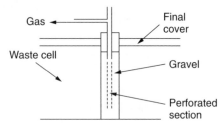

Fig. 4.7 A method of gas extraction from landfill sites. The pipe can be inserted 1–2 years after completion of the site.

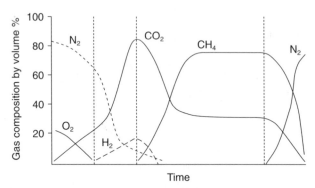

Fig. 4.8 The changes in gases in a landfill site over a number of years. The time taken to produce a steady level of methane is typically 2 years.

Despite the prevention and minimisation of waste, landfill will continue to be one of the main methods of solid waste disposal. Landfill sites under construction will be active for up to 100 years before the sites are suitable for alternative use and are issued with a Certificate of Completion. To obtain this certificate the biodegradable content of the landfill must have reached a steady state (stabilised) and metals and toxic contaminants flushed out. Thus the management of landfill sites needs modification and landfills should be regarded as anaerobic reactors rather than just sealed disposal systems. The problem with landfill is that, although the biodegradable material is broken down, the process is very slow, probably due to the lack of water and nutrients in the system. However, if the leachate, which is rich in organic materials, is recycled the degradation will be faster, more gas will be produced and the whole system will be stabilised faster. In the UK a landfill tax has just been introduced which will probably reduce landfill use. Alternatives to landfill are being investigated in Europe and the USA. If the leachate is not recycled it will require treatment before it can be released into waterways, and there are a number of technologies available. One treatment is aerobic tanks or lagoons and, as this contrasts with the anaerobic digestion in the landfill, it has been successful in reducing leachate BOD and COD levels, especially from the early leachates. Often sequencing batch reactors are used for leachate treatment where the sequence steps are feed, aerobic reaction, settle and decant, and these steps can run over a 24-hour period. Other methods of leachate treatment are anaerobic treatment, spray irrigation and reed beds.

4.4.2   Incineration

Incineration can be used for industrial, domestic and toxic wastes, and in some cases is preferable to land disposal. The critical factors for effective combustion are the temperature, the length of time at high temperature, and the effective mixing of the waste with air. There are a number of combustion systems which will operate at 1500–3000°C, the temperature required to break down organic wastes; these include rotary kilns, liquid injection, fluidised beds and multiple hearth designs. The advantages of incineration are the reduction in volume, the ability to treat toxic materials and the fact that incinerators can be constructed in areas where landfill disposal is not available. The incineration of wastes such as sewage sludge can be autocalorific so that no fuel needs to be added. The combustion is self-sustaining once started, provided the waste contains organic material.

The disadvantages of incineration are that the process can be expensive to operate and to construct, it is not a complete disposal solution as the resulting ash will need to be disposed of in a landfill site and this ash may contain high levels of metals, and incineration also produces particulates and flue gases. The flue gases from incinerators can contain hydrogen chloride, sulphur oxides, nitrogen oxides which can be removed by wet scrubbing, carbon monoxide which can be formed by incomplete combustion, and carbon dioxide which increases the level of greenhouse gases. The incineration of chlorinated compounds at low temperatures, which can happen with excess air, will allow the production of dioxins and furans which are toxic and carcinogenic. The formation of particulates is also to be avoided and electrostatic precipitation will need to be incorporated in an incinerator system.

4.4.3   Composting

One method of disposal and reuse of organic waste is composting which can be used for the organic components of domestic waste, excess activated sludge, excess straw and chaff, and some agricultural wastes.

Composting can be defined as 'the biological stabilisation of wastes of biological origin under controlled aerobic conditions' and is a process that most gardeners are familiar with. In composting the organic component of municipal waste is decomposed by a mixture of microorganisms under warm, moist and aerobic conditions (Anderson and Smith, 1987). This is in contrast to the anaerobic landfill conditions where decomposition is slow and methane is formed. In composting the matrix or conditions should be open to allow an adequate supply of oxygen. In the presence of oxygen the rapid metabolic processes produce heat. Not all the heat can be dissipated and the compost will rise in temperature to 50°C and above. The high temperatures are responsible for the inactivation of pathogens, producing a very acceptable final product.

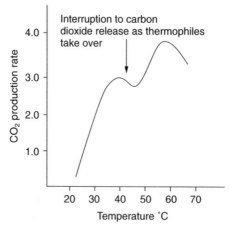

Fig. 4.9 The metabolism of the microorganisms in a compost system where the release of carbon dioxide is used as a measure of microbial activity. The dip in carbon dioxide released indicates the change from mesophilic organisms to the thermophiles, as the temperature of a compost heap rises. From Plat *et al.*,1984.

Once the compost system has been assembled, aerobic mesophilic micro-organisms start the degradation, but as the temperature rises in the compost thermophilic organisms take over. The pattern of growth can be seen in Fig. 4.9 where growth has been followed by the formation of carbon dioxide. Three days at 55°C or above is sufficient to inactivate most pathogens and viruses. The system with sufficient oxygen will be rapid (11–6 weeks) with low energy consumption, giving a hygienic standard end-product. There are a number of composting systems or processes which can be divided into two groups, open and closed systems (Table 4.6).

The simplest open system is the Windrow where the waste to be composted is piled in long heaps, often covered with straw to conserve heat, and aeration is achieved by periodic turning of the heaps. In other static systems aeration is either by blowing air in at the base of the heap (Beltsville) or by suction from the base (Rutgers). A cross-section of a typical heap is shown in Fig. 4.10 and the typical temperature cross-section for such systems is shown in Fig. 4.11.

The closed systems are normally situated in buildings and up to seven different systems have been described in which some form of mechanical means gives aeration and mixing in either continuous or discontinuous mode (Anderson *et al.*, 1984). An example is the Dano biostabiliser which is a sloping plug-flow bioreactor where mixing and aeration is carried out by rotating the cylinder. This system combines the removal and recycling of ferrous metals with composting. The residence time in the cylinder is about 1–5 days which is not enough to give complete composting, so that the partially composted material is passed onto a Windrow system for 1–6 weeks depending on conditions and starting material. The Silo system consists of a vertical plug-flow vessel where air is introduced at the base and the compostable

Table 4.6   Composting systems

Type	Features
Open systems	
Windrow	Waste piled in long rows, outdoors; aeration by periodic turning
Static pile (Beltsville process)	Elongated pile aerated by suction system
Static pile (Rutgers process)	Pile aerated by forced pressure with temperature feedback
Static pile	Aeration by alternate suction and blowing
Closed systems	
Dano system	Sloping inclined cylinder with mixing and aeration by rotating the cylinder
Tunnel system	Horizontal plug-flow with waste moved by a hydraulic ram in a rectangular concrete reactor
Metro system	Horizontal agitated solid bed system with aeration through perforated base to the rectangular tank; endless conveyor belt used as agitator/loader
Fairfield–Hardy system	Horizontal agitated solid bed system with mixing by augers in a cylindrical vessel
Silo or tower system	Vertical plug-flow reactor
Continuous system	Material composted in one large mass using forced ventilation; waste loaded at top and compost withdrawn from bottom
Discontinuous system	Digesters divided into a series of levels or floors onto which waste is sequentially transferred from top to bottom

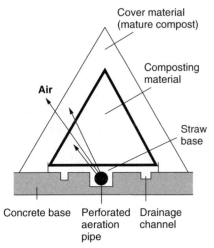

Fig. 4.10   Cross-section of a Windrow type of compost heap with aeration, adapted from Anderson and Smith, 1987. Air is pumped through the perforated pipe and out through the composting material to supply oxygen to ensure aerobic metabolism.

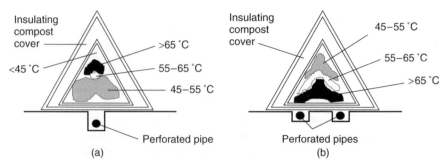

Fig. 4.11 Temperature distribution in Windrow compost heaps with aeration by (a) blowing (Rutgers) or (b) sucking (Beltsville), adapted from Stentiford *et al.*, 1985. The temperatures produced are due to the aerobic metabolism of the microorganisms growing on the composting material producing heat which cannot be lost as the heap is insulated.

material pumped in at the top, which gives both mixing and aeration. There is a facility for the recycling of the compost and the residence time in the first vessel is about 14 days. After this time the compost is moved to the curing vessel where the high temperature developed in the first vessel inactivates any pathogens present. About 25% of the curing vessel is removed after 14–20 days' incubation to be replaced by compost from the first vessel. The compost formed is used for horticulture. Composting has a lot to commend it; although it has not been popular in the UK for the treatment of domestic waste, it may be used more widely as landfill sites become more difficult to find and operate.

Some agricultural products such as chaff and straw are disposed of by composting. Straw used to be burned but as it contributes to the atmospheric particulates and CO_2 emissions this practice has been stopped.

4.5   Artificial wetlands

Plants have the ability to take up metals and degrade organic materials and therefore all types of plants can be used for waste treatment, including terrestrial plants, wetland plants, and aquatic plants and algae. The use of terrestrial plants for the removal of both synthetic organic wastes and heavy metals is discussed in Chapter 5. Recently the provision of artificial wetlands for the removal of heavy metals and organic wastes of all sorts has been under investigation. In the wetland habitat plants have a large population of microorganisms associated with their roots and it is this microbial population which is responsible for the sequestration of heavy metals and breakdown of the organic compounds.

The most common artificial wetland system uses the common reed *Phragmites* sp. which can grow in fresh or slightly brackish water (Moshiri, 1993). The reed bed is capped with clay and/or polypropylene in order to stop leakage into the subsoil and is surrounded by a wall (Fig. 4.12). The reeds, which can grow to 1.5 m in height, have the ability to pass oxygen from the leaves to the roots. The oxygen transfer encourages the development of a large aerobic

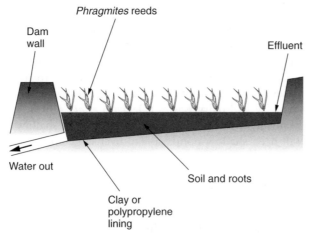

Fig. 4.12 A reed bed or artificial wetland. The *Phragmites* spp. root system provides a supply of oxygen to the microbial population associated with the roots, which allows rapid degradation of organic materials.

microbial population on the plant roots (rhizosphere). As a result the roots act like a large microbial film reactor and it is this microbial population which sequesters metals and degrades organic materials.

Reed beds have been used to clean up mine leakage containing heavy metals such as the waste from the Wheal Jane mine in Cornwall (Box 4.3). ICI have installed reed beds to remove organic waste from a methylmethacrylate plant, and reed beds have also been successfully used to reduce dairy waste from a BOD value of 1006 mg/l to 56 mg/l using a two-stage system (Biddlestone *et al.*, 1991).

Box 4.3

The Wheal Jane tin mine in Cornwall was abandoned in 1991 and subsequently flooded when the pumping of mine water ceased, although the Department of the Environment had been warned of the danger of pollution with the highly acid mine water when the pumps were turned off. On 13 January 1992 a concrete plug failed and 10 million gallons of rust-coloured water were released into the Carnon River which runs into the Fal estuary. After the initial surge the flow of water was 2 million gallons per day, containing metals such as cadmium, arsenic, iron, zinc and copper. Tests suggested that the cadmium levels in the river and estuary were 100 times higher than the accepted EU standard of 1 mg/m^3, and the estuary contains oyster beds. Sealing the mine proved difficult because of old mine workings and it was not possible to contain the mine water in a lagoon. The company initially adopted a lime treatment prior to discharge into the river but since this time a reed bed system has been successfully installed.

Aquatic plants and algae have also been used to treat a range of wastes and the best known aquatic plant is the water hyacinth *Eichhornia crassipes.* The water hyacinth is a prolific floating aquatic weed which is a major problem in waterways in a number of countries because of its rapid growth rates. It is this rapid growth rate which makes it so suitable for waste treatment. It grows luxuriantly in sewage, concentrates metals, degrades phenols and has been used to treat tannery and dairy wastes (Delgado *et al.*, 1993). The disadvantage of using water hyacinth is that it can only grow in shallow water so that any process will need shallow ponds spread over large areas.

4.6   Agricultural wastes

Agricultural wastes can be divided into solid and liquid wastes. Some 5–10% of chaff and straw waste is used to produce compost for mushroom cultivation (Gaze, 1985). Traditionally, wheat straw and horse and chicken manure are wetted, mixed and placed in a Windrow system. Aeration is normally by turning every 2–3 days. After 7–14 days outdoors, temperatures of 80°C have been reached inside the compost. The second stage is carried out indoors where the compost is incubated at 50–60°C with aeration after which the compost is packed into trays ready for mushroom seeding.

Liquid agricultural waste is mainly cattle, pig or chicken slurry, a mixture of dung and urine. The quantities are large when associated with large herds, factory farming and silage run-off. In contrast to domestic sewage, these wastes have very high BOD values of 10,000–25,000 mg/l (Table 4.7). Other liquid agricultural wastes are the run-off of nitrates and phosphates from agricultural land, and herbicides and pesticides from treatment and spraying. Farmyard slurries have traditionally been disposed of by spraying or spreading onto the land, but in the case of intensive farming far too much slurry is produced to be disposed of in this way. As a consequence large farms have installed anaerobic digesters or facultative pond systems for the disposal of the slurries.

4.7   Industrial wastes

The organic wastes from various industries can be both liquid and solid and generally have higher BOD values than domestic wastes. The degradable organic wastes are in general the products of food, drink, meat and vegetable processes along with waste from the production of yeast, citric acid and antibiotics. All these processes and industries produce strong wastes in terms of BOD (Table 4.7). If the industry is willing to pay the water company, many of these wastes can be released into the sewage system and be treated by the normal methods. In order to avoid these charges a number of biological methods of waste removal have been tested, including methods for the upgrading of the waste to an animal food.

Table 4.7 Examples of industrial and agricultural wastes

Waste	BOD$_5$ (mg/l)	COD (mg/l)	Suspended solids (mg/l)
Animal wastes			
Cow	16,000	150,000	
Pig	30,000	70,000	
Poultry	24,000	170,000	
Whey	45,000	65,000	116
Processing wastes			
Abattoir	100–3000		
Brewing	500–2000	17,000	
Sugar beet	450–2000	600–3000	800–1500
Potato processing	2000	3500	2500
Distillery	7000	10,000	
Poultry	500–800	600–1000	450–800
Wool industry	300–600	200–8000	8000

Sources: data from Gray, 1989; Glazer and Nikaido, 1994.

One solution to a strong waste is to install an anaerobic digestion system to treat the waste either fully or partially. Since such wastes are high in BOD, anaerobic digestion is very suitable. An example of this type of system was the installation of an anaerobic digester at a cheese production plant (Kemp and Quickenden, 1989). The cheese whey was anaerobically digested, producing methane which was used to run the boilers and generate electricity (Fig. 4.13). The BOD reduction was about 95% and after denitrification the effluent was of high quality and could be released directly into a nearby river.

Some of the processes that have been developed for waste treatment were attempts to apply biotechnology in the 1970s and 1980s in order to produce valuable products from industrial waste materials. Not all of the processes developed during that period are still running now, but they are included here to provide examples. Many were abandoned for economic reasons rather than because of any failure of the system. One example was the treatment of the effluent from the Bassetts confectionery factory in Sheffield which if untreated would attract a high charge if released into the River Don, as it contained high levels of sugar. In 1978 the factory installed a novel process for the reduction of the waste stream (Wheatly, 1985). The liquid waste was collected in a balance tank, continuously sterilised, and fed to a 25,000 litre bioreactor containing *Candida utilis*. The yeast used the waste sugar for growth and a continuous stream of yeast was produced (Fig. 4.14). The yeast was harvested by centrifugation, and dried, and the water with a 50% reduction in BOD was run into the river. The dried yeast was sold to food processors and this paid for the running costs of the bioreactor. However, recently the bioreactor needed to be replaced and the company has invested in an anaerobic digester as this type of treatment is much more reliable now.

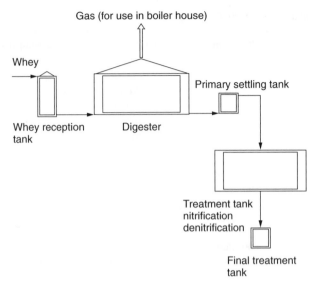

Fig. 4.13 The anaerobic digestion of whey in a South Caernarvon Creamery, adapted from Kemp and Quickenden, 1989. The anaerobic digester produces mainly methane which is used to fuel the heaters and pumps in the plant. The effluent is first settled and the liquid from the settling tank treated in an anaerobic/aerobic sequencing tank to reduce the level of ammonia and nitrate respectively. Nitrogen-containing compounds will be high in whey as there is a high protein content compared with many other wastes.

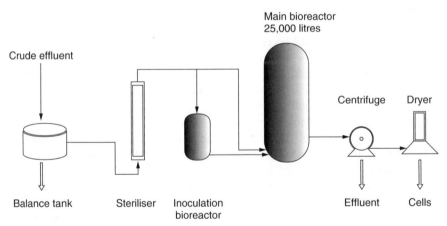

Fig. 4.14 The continuous cultivation of yeast installed at the Bassett's factory to treat sugar-containing waste (Wheatly, 1985). The waste is continuously sterilised and pumped into the bioreactor at a steady rate, and medium and cells are removed at the same rate. This maintains the cells in a condition of steady growth. The cells are harvested by centrifugation, and dried, and the final product (dried yeast) is sold as a food-grade material.

Another novel approach to waste treatment was the Symba process. The bioreactor company Chemap in conjunction with the Swedish Sugar Corporation developed the Symba process to use the waste generated from potato processing to produce an animal feed. If the product was to be sold as an animal food, the organism needed to have been approved for animal consumption and therefore the choice was *Candida utilis*. However, *C. utilis* cannot grow on starch as a substrate as it lacks an amylase, but another yeast, *Endomycopsis fibriguler*, produces amylases and can grow on starch. Therefore the two organisms were combined and the process involved the inoculation of the starch waste with *E. fibriguler*; once this was growing it should produce sufficient amylase to break down the starch to sugar. If *C. utilis* were introduced at this stage it would be capable of growth on the sugar, and as it grows faster than *E. fibriguler* on glucose a culture ratio of 10:1 *C. utilis/E. fibriguler* developed. The mixture of cells was harvested and sold. If this treatment were to be repeated in the future, it is more likely that *C. utilis* would be genetically engineered to contain an amylase. The process is not running at present, though the reasons for this are not known.

The Pekilo process was developed in Finland to utilise the material which is leached from wood pulp when bleached with sulphur dioxide. The fermentable material produced by pulp mills, if released untreated into the local rivers, would cause considerable pollution. Thus a process was developed to convert the material into animal feed. The first part of the process was to remove the residual sulphur dioxide by steam treatment, as this would inhibit the growth of most microorganisms (Fig. 4.15). The sterile material was run into bioreactors of volume 360 m^3 (300,000 litres) and phosphorus, potassium salts and ammonia added. The vessel was inoculated with a fungus, *Paecilomyces* spp., which was grown in a continuous manner, producing about 15 tonnes of biomass per hour. The biomass was harvested by filtration, as it is a filamentous mould, and dried. The product has been officially recognised as an animal food in Finland and contains about 69% protein. It is not known whether the process is still running.

4.8 Conclusions

The hierarchy of options for waste management has been reversed and little work has been carried out on waste prevention. However, attitudes to waste are changing, with a better appreciation of green issues, the introduction of legislation controlling waste disposal, and the increasing cost of disposal, all making waste reduction more attractive. In this context biotechnology will contribute in the following areas:

- Clean technology will see waste reduction by the application of enzymes in processes replacing chemical synthesis, in particular hyperthermophiles.
- There will be greater use of recombinant technology to modify microorganisms (GEMs) to form products which are normally chemically synthesised.

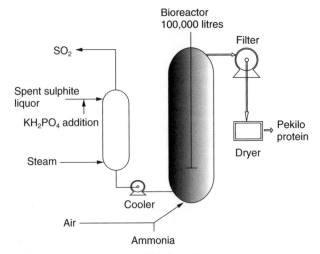

Fig. 4.15 The Pekilo process for the utilisation of wood pulp wastewater. The sulphur dioxide is removed by steam, potassium phosphate is added, and after cooling the waste is run into the bioreactor. The bioreactor is inoculated with *Paecilomyces* and aerated, and nitrogen is supplied by the addition of ammonia. At the end of the growth period the fungal mycelium is harvested by filtration and dried.

- The production of an economically viable biodegradable plastic will be given a high priority.
- It is unlikely that biotechnology will be used to upgrade wastes to single cell proteins as improvements in agriculture have made this uneconomic.
- Recombinant technology will help to determine the process of degradation in landfill and other disposal systems.
- Landfill sites will be regarded as anaerobic digesters rather than inert dumps, and leachate recycling may become common along with leachate treatment.

4.9   References

Adams, W. W. and Kelly, R. M. (1998) Finding and using hyperthermophilic enzymes. *Tibtech*, **16**, 329–332.

Anderson, J. G. and Smith, J. E. (1987) Composting, in J. M. Sidwick and R. S. Holdom (eds), *Biotechnology of Waste Treatment and Exploitation*. Ellis Horwood, Chichester, UK.

Anderson, J. G., Ponte, M., Biuso, S., Bailey, D., Kantorek, J. and Schink, T. (1984) Evaluating enclosed composting systems. *Biocycle*, **25**, 20–25.

Attewell, P. (1993) *Ground Pollution*. E & FN Spon, London.

Bialy, H. (1997) Biotechnology, bioremediation and blue genes. *Nature Biotechnol.*, **15**, 110.

Biddlestone, A. J., Gray, K. R. and Job, G. D. (1991) Treatment of dairy farm wastewater in engineered reed bed systems. *Process Biochem.*, **26**, 265–268.

Bishop, D. H. L. (1994) Biopesticides. *Current Opinion in Biotechnol.*, **5**, 307–311.

Brandl, H., Gross, R. A., Lenz, R. W. and Fuller, R. C. (1990) Plastics from bacteria and for bacteria: poly(b-hydroxyalkanoates) as natural, biocompatible, and biodegradable polyesters. *Adv. Biochem. Engin./Biotechnol.*, 41, 77–93.

Chen, C. C., Adolphson, R., Dean, J. F. D., Eriksson, K.-E. L., Adams, M. W. W. and Westpheling, J. (1997) Release of lignin from kraft pulp by a hyperthermophilic xylanase for *Thermatoga martima. Enzyme Microb. Technol.*, 20, 39–45.

Daniell, H. and Guda, C. (1997) Biopolymer production in microorganisms and plants. *Chemistry & Industry*, July, 555–558.

Danson, M. J. and Hough, D. W. (1998) Structure, function and stability of enzymes from the Archaea. *Trends Microbiol.*, 6, 307–313.

Delgado, M., Bigeriego, M. and Guardiola, E. (1993) Uptake of Zn, Cr and Cd by water hyacinths. *Water Research*, 27, 269–272.

Dong, G. and Zeikus, J. G. (1997) Purification and characterization of alkaline phosphatase from *Thermotoga neapolitana. Enzyme Microb. Technol.*, 21, 335–340.

Gaze, R. H. (1985) Cultivation systems and their evolution, in P. B. Flegg, D. M. Spencer and D. A. Wood (eds), *The Biology and Technology of the Cultivated Mushroom.* John Wiley & Sons, Chichester, UK.

Girbal, L. and Soucaille, P. (1988) Regulation of solvent production in *Clostridium acetobutylicum. Tibtech*, 16, 11–16.

Glazer, A. N. and Nikaido, H. (1994) *Microbial Biotechnology.* Freeman, New York.

Gray, N. F. (1989) *Biology of Waste Water Treatment.* Oxford University Press, Oxford.

Hill, M. K. (1997) *Understanding Environmental Pollution.* Cambridge University Press, Cambridge.

Kemp, D. L. and Quickenden, J. (1989) Whey processing for profit – a worthy alternative, in R. Greenshields (ed.), *Resources and Applications of Biotechnology: The New Wave.* Macmillan, London.

Kim, Y. O., Kim, H. K., Bae, K. S., Yu, J. H. and Oh, T. K. (1998) Purification and properties of a thermostable phytase from *Bacillus* sp. DS11. *Enzyme Microb. Technol.*, 22, 2–7.

Lewis, W. J., Van Lenteren, J. C., Phatak, S. C. and Tomlinson, J. H. (1997) A total system approach to sustainable pest management. *Proc. Nat. Acad. Sci.*, 94, 12243–12248.

Mahadevan, B. and Crawford, D. L. (1997) Properties of the chitinase of the antifungal biocontrol agent *Streptomyces lydicus* WYEC108. *Enzyme Microb. Technol.*, 20, 489–493.

Moshiri, G. A. (1993) *Constructed Wetlands for Water Quality Improvement.* CRC Press, Boca Raton, FL.

Plat, J. Y., Sayag, D. and Andre, L. (1984) High-rate composting of wool industry waste. *Biocycle*, 25, 39–42.

Stentiford, E. I., Mora, D. D. and Taylor, P. L. (1985) Forced aeration co-composting of domestic refuse and sewage sludge in static piles, in J. K. R. Gasser (ed.), *Composting of Agricultural and Other Wastes.* Elsevier, London.

Thomas, M. B. and Willis, A. J. (1998) Biocontrol – risky but necessary? *Trends Environ. Ecol.*, 13, 325–328.

Van Driesche, R. G. and Bellows, T. S. (1996) *Biological Control.* Chapman and Hall, New York.

Wheatly, A. D. (1985) Wastewater treatment and by-product recovery. *Critical Reports in Applied Chemistry*, 11, 68–106.

4.9.1   Recommended reading

Greenshields, R. (ed.) (1989) *Resources and Applications of Biotechnology*: *The New Wave*. Macmillan, London.

Hill, M. K. (1997) *Understanding Environmental Pollution*. Cambridge University Press, Cambridge.

Moshiri, G. A. (1993) *Constructed Wetlands for Water Quality Improvement*. CRC Press, Boca Raton, FL.

Theodore, L. and McGuinn, Y. C. (1992) *Pollution Prevention*. Van Nostrand Reinhold, New York.

Chapter 5

Bioremediation

5.1 Introduction

The types of pollutants found in the environment that are outlined in Table 1.3 in Chapter 1 are present as a result of industrial effluents, outfalls, mine waters, landfill run-offs, waste tips and accidental spillages. These pollutants can be found in all regions of the environment: marine, estuaries, lakes and soil. In this chapter the application of biotechnology to inorganic, synthetic organic (xenobiotic), petrochemical and gaseous pollutants will be discussed in terms of both clean-up and prevention. The types of contaminated site and the nature of some of the contamination are listed in Table 5.1.

The biological removal of contaminants from contaminated sites is known as **bioremediation**. Bioremediation can be defined as the natural or managed biological degradation of environmental pollution. Bioremediation is normally carried out by the indigenous microorganisms and their activity can be enhanced by the supply of nutrients or by enhancing the microbial population in a process known as bioaugmentation.

5.2 Inorganic waste

Metals and other inorganic compounds are discharged into the environment from a number of activities, including mining, smelting, electroplating and farming. Many metals are required by living organisms for their normal function but at high concentrations these can become toxic. Table 5.2 lists some of the sources and effects of inorganic wastes. One example is copper which is an essential micronutrient (trace element) for plants, but excess copper can cause inhibition of photosynthesis, pigment synthesis and damage to plasma membranes (Marschner, 1995; Ouzouridou, 1994). The damage by copper is caused by the generation of superoxide anions, hydrogen peroxide and hydroxyl radicals due to incomplete oxidation of oxygen during respiration. The free radicals and hydrogen peroxide will attack lipids, proteins and DNA, causing mutation and death (Halliwell and Aruoma, 1993). An example of the toxicity of metals to humans was the mercury poisoning at Minamata in Japan which killed 43 people and disabled many others. The mercury originated from a factory producing vinyl chloride and acetaldehyde which released low

Table 5.1   Industrial sites and contaminants*

Industry	Sites	Contaminants
Chemicals	Acid/alkali works Dye works Fertilisers and pesticides Pharmaceuticals Paint works, wood treatment	Acids, alkalis, metals, solvents, phenols, organic compounds
Petrochemicals	Oil refineries Fuel storage depots Tar distilleries	Hydrocarbons, phenols, acids, alkalis and asbestos
Metals	Iron and steel works Foundries, smelters Electroplating and galvanising works Engineering works Shipbuilding Scrap plants	Metals, especially Fe, Cu, Ni, Cr, Zn, Cd, Pb; asbestos
Energy	Gasworks Power stations	Phenols, cyanides, sulphur compounds, coal and coke dust
Mineral extraction	Mines and spoil heaps Land restoration Quarries	Metals, especially Cu, Zn, Pb; gases, leachates
Water supply, sewage treatment	Waterworks Sewage works	Metals in sludge, sludge, microorganisms
Miscellaneous	Docks, wharves Tanneries Rubber works Military sites	Metals, organic compounds, methane, toxic, flammable or explosive substances, microorganisms

* Ubiquitous contaminants include hydrocarbons, PCBs, asbestos, sulphates and many metals. These may be present on almost any site.
Source: derived from Rowley, 1993.

levels of methyl mercury into the sea. Marine organisms adsorbed and concentrated the mercury, and consumption of the fish passed on the mercury contamination to the local population at very high concentrations in a process of biomagnification.

Because of the toxicity of some metals, national and international standards have been set for metal levels in drinking water (Mason, 1996). Metals released from some industrial processes often far exceed the levels set for drinking water values (Table 5.3), but these wastes are often greatly diluted when added to waterways or sewage systems. Although these metal levels are low, metals can accumulate in plants, animals and microorganisms in a process known

Table 5.2 Sources and effects of inorganic contaminants

Inorganic waste	Source	Effect
Arsenic	Smelting, refining, pesticides	Poisoning
Asbestos	Insulation	Asbestosis, carcinogenic effects
Cadmium	Electroplating, battery production	Kidney disease, joint pain
Lead	Leaded petrol, batteries	Impairs nervous system
Mercury	Chlor-alkali production, slimicides, fungicides	Impairs central nervous system, paralysis, death
Nitrates/nitrites	Agricultural run-off, meat preservation	Production of carcinogenic nitrosamines, methemoglobinemia
Sulphur dioxide	Combustion	Irritant, formation of acid rain
Phosphates	Agriculture	Eutrophication

Table 5.3 Levels of metal contamination from domestic and industrial sources (all values in mg/l)

Metal	Drinking water standard	Domestic waste	Industrial wastes			
			Food	Meat	Plating	Textiles
Cadmium	0.005	0.01	0.006	0.01	1	0.03
Chromium	0.05	0.08	0.150	0.15	11	0.80
Lead (secondary standards)	0.05	0.10	0	0	0	0
Copper	1.0	0.17	0.29	0.09	6	0.03
Zinc	5.0	0.29	1.08	0.43	9	0.47

as **bioaccumulation**. Metals cannot be degraded by chemical or biological processes, so that any process for the treatment of metal must concentrate the metal so that it can be contained or recycled.

5.2.1 Biosorption

Biological material can adsorb a variety of metals. The response of microbial cells to high concentrations of metals can be one or more of the following, which in some cases can confer a degree of tolerance to that metal:

- exclusion of the metal from the cell
- energy-dependent efflux of metals taken into the cell
- intracellular sequestration by specific proteins, some of which are known as metallothioneins
- extracellular sequestration, either on cell wall or on extracellular polysaccharides
- chemical modification of the metal.

The internal and external sequestration of metals means that biological material can bind metals to high levels of up to 30% of the dry weight (Volesky and Holan, 1995). The use of biological material to remove metals from wastes can take two forms. The first is the detoxification of the wastewater stream, and the second is the recovery of valuable metals such as gold (Vilchez *et al.*, 1997).

The uptake of metals from wastewater by living material can be active or passive or both. Passive uptake is independent of cellular metabolism and involves the binding of metals to the polyanionic cell wall or by ion exchange with ions in the cell wall. Microbial extracellular polysaccharides are also known to bind metals (Richau *et al.*, 1997). Passive uptake is rapid, reaching completion in 5–10 minutes, and is unaffected by metabolic inhibitors, but is affected by physical conditions such as pH and ionic strength. Passive binding is reversible and can occur with both living and dead material (Lovley and Coates, 1997). The active uptake of metals is slower than passive uptake, dependent upon the cellular metabolism, and is affected by metabolic inhibitors, uncouplers and temperature. In active uptake the metals are complexed with specific proteins, such as metallothioneins, or contained in the vacuole. Both passive and active uptake can occur at the same time and the adsorption of metals is relatively non-specific in terms of the metal taken up.

Biosorption has been evaluated as a method for the removal of metals from waste streams and in addition a small-scale treatment of mine drainage has been reported (Ledin and Pedersen, 1996). It has been shown that biosorption may be economically competitive with chemical techniques (Eccles, 1995), particularly when the biomass used is inexpensive, such as waste biomass from the fermentation industry, excess sewage sludge and easily harvested marine algae. The ability of marine macroalgae (seaweed), both living and dead material, to adsorb metals has been well documented (Volesky and Holan, 1995) and has been used in multiple cycles of adsorption and desorption (Chitguppe *et al.*, 1997). Immobilised non-living microalgae in a permeable matrix are available commercially as AlgaSORB (Vilchez *et al.*, 1997). This material has properties similar to ion exchange resins and has been used to remove cadmium. In another case a marine brown macroalga, *Ecklonia radiata*, has been used to bind copper (Matheickel *et al.*, 1997). Another response of organisms to high levels of metals is the production of metal-binding proteins such as metallothioneins which bind the excess metal in the cells. Various attempts have been made to over-express metallothioneins in bacteria in order to increase metal binding. In an attempt to increase the specificity of the metal binding of biological material, peptides were expressed on the surface of bacteria which had the ability to bind metals by forming a sphere around the metal ion. *Escherichia coli* cells expressing one or two hexahistidine clusters on the surface were able to bind 11 times as much cadmium as non-engineered cells (Sousa *et al.*, 1996).

The process formats for the removal of heavy metals using biological materials can take the form of immobilised material in packed-bed, fluidised-bed and rotating-disc reactors as shown in Fig. 5.1. The process of regeneration of the biomass is also shown.

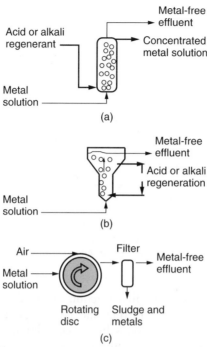

Fig. 5.1 Some of the processes for the removal of heavy metals: (a) a packed-bed bioreactor containing immobilised biomass, where the operation was continuous, with *in situ* regeneration using acid or alkali; (b) a fluidised-bed reactor where the biomass is immobilised in or on an inert substrate and operated as the fixed-bed reactor; (c) a rotating-disc bioreactor where the biomass forms a film on the rotating discs and aeration occurs when the discs are out of the liquid. Any excess biomass sloughs off to be collected in a filter or settling tank for disposal. Adapted from Gadd and White (1993).

5.2.2 Extracellular precipitation

A number of industrial and mining effluents contain not only metals but sulphates, and processes have been developed for their removal. In the presence of sulphate, heavy metals can be removed by the action of anaerobic, sulphate-reducing bacteria such as *Desulfovibrio* and *Desulfotomaculum* strains. Under the anaerobic conditions the bacteria use simple carbon sources, such as lactic acid, to generate hydrogen sulphide from sulphate:

$$3SO_4^{2-} + 2 \text{ lactic acid} \rightarrow 3H_2S + 6HCO_3^-$$

The hydrogen sulphide reacts with any metals present, forming insoluble metal sulphides:

$$H_2S + Cu^{2+} \rightarrow CuS + 2H^+$$

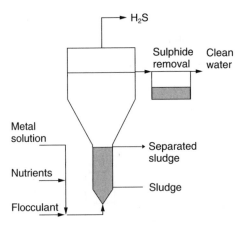

Fig. 5.2 A sludge blanket bioreactor for the anaerobic precipitation of heavy metals as sulphides. Hydrogen sulphide is produced along with the metal sulphides and the excess hydrogen sulphide can be vented off and burnt. Adapted from Gadd and White (1993).

The bicarbonate formed in the first reaction breaks down to carbon dioxide and water, increasing the pH further and encouraging the precipitation of sulphides. The production of excess hydrogen sulphide is a problem as this is poisonous and corrosive, but it can be burnt off or controlled by limiting the supply of organic carbon, although it is not always possible to balance the two. In some cases the excess hydrogen sulphide can be oxidised to sulphur by oxygen or by colourless, green or purple sulphur bacteria (Kolmert *et al.*, 1997).

The production of insoluble metal sulphides has been used in a number of bioreactor formats, including an upflow sludge system as seen in Fig. 5.2 (Gadd and White, 1993), or with the biomass immobilised in a reactor filled with spent mushroom compost which acts as a support (Dvorak *et al.*, 1992). A comparison of bioreactor formats suggested that a packed-bed system was better than suspended carrier systems (Kolmert *et al.*, 1997).

5.2.3 Other inorganic wastes

Inorganic pollutants other than the metals include nitrates, nitrites, phosphates, sulphates, cyanides and arsenic. Phosphates and nitrates are derived mainly from sewage treatment, and run-off from agriculture and industry, and if well diluted, as in a river, cause little problem. However, if they accumulate to high levels in lakes they can cause eutrophication. Eutrophication can be defined as 'the nutrient enrichment of waters which results in the stimulation of an array of symptomatic changes among which increased production of algae and macrophytes, deterioration of water quality and other symptomatic changes, are found to be undesirable and interfere with water uses' (Ryding and Rast, 1989). The removal of nitrates and phosphates by the sewage system has been discussed in Chapter 3. However, other biological systems are under investigation for the removal of high levels of nitrate. A bacterium, *Klebsiella oxytoca*, has been isolated which can tolerate high levels of nitrate up to 1M and at the same time remove the nitrate. This organism has been tested successfully at pilot-plant level (40 litres) (Pinar *et al.*, 1997). Another approach to the removal of both nitrate and phosphate has been the use of the photosynthetic cyanobacterium *Phormidium bohneri* in a simple photobioreactor (Sylvestre *et al.*, 1996). *Phormidium laminosum* immobilised in polyurethane foam has also been used to remove nitrate (Garbisu *et al.*, 1991). In these cases the advantage of using a photosynthetic bacterium is that the medium is simple and the energy is derived from sunlight, avoiding the addition of a carbon and energy source. *Chlamydomonas reinhartii* immobilised in alginate beads has been used to remove nitrite from water (Vilchez and Vega, 1994), while others have used *Chlorella vulgaris* immobilised in alginate and carrageenan beads to remove both nitrate and phosphate (Lau *et al.*, 1997).

Sulphide-containing waste streams are usually treated chemically but a cheaper, biologically based method of disposal has been developed. This is based on the ability of colourless sulphur bacteria to oxidise sulphide to elemental sulphur under aerobic conditions (Visser *et al.*, 1997).

The largest source of cyanide in industry is gold extraction but cyanide can be produced by a number of other industries. Cyanide can be removed by oxidation with chlorine or peroxide, but biological methods are under investigation, including the use of biosorption by the mould *Fusarium lateritium*.

5.3 Petroleum-based wastes

Crude oil is an extremely complex and variable mixture of organic compounds. The majority of the compounds in crude oil are hydrocarbons, which can range in molecular weight from the gas methane to the high molecular weight tars and bitumens. These hydrocarbons can also come in a wide range of molecular structures: straight and branched chains, single or condensed rings, and aromatic rings. The two major groups of aromatic hydrocarbons are monocyclic, such as benzene, toluene, ethylbenzene and xylene (BTEX), and the polycyclic hydrocarbons (PAHs) such as naphthalene, anthracene and phenanthrene. The proportion of each individual compound can vary greatly between crude oil sources and this variation in composition affects the properties of the oil. Oils with a high proportion of low molecular weight material are known as 'light' oils and flow easily, while 'heavy oils' are the reverse. In addition to the hydrocarbons, crude oil contains 0.05–3.0% of heterocyclic compounds, containing sulphur, nitrogen and oxygen, and some heavy metals. Crude oil is refined, after extraction, in a number of processes which convert most of the polyaromatic hydrocarbons into monocyclic aromatic compounds. Typically naphthalenes can constitute 5–35% of the crude oil, which can be reduced to 1–7% after refining. Refined oil can be split into petroleum, diesel, heating oil and many other products.

5.3.1 Crude oil

Crude oil has accumulated underground as a result of the anaerobic degradation of organisms over a very long time. Under the conditions of high temperature and pressure the organic material has been converted to natural gas,
liquid crude oil, shale oil and tars. At the underground temperatures shale oils
and tars do not flow, but the crude oil is liquid, and unless contained will
escape to the surface, where the volatiles evaporate forming a tar bed. Apart
from this release of crude oil, the main source of crude oil and oil products,
such as BTEX and PAHs, released into the environment comes from the
leaking of storage tanks, spillages and accidents during its transport. Estimates
suggest that there are between 100,000 and 300,000 leaking petroleum or
petroleum-based product tanks in the USA (Mesarch and Nies, 1997; Lee and
Gongaware, 1997). The petroleum leaks are of particular interest as petroleum
can contain up to 20% BTEX and these are on the hazardous list. These
BTEX compounds, although not miscible with water, are mobile and can
contaminate the groundwater (Bossert and Compeau, 1995). Figure 5.3 shows
the possible fate of a crude oil or petroleum product leak or spill on land. The

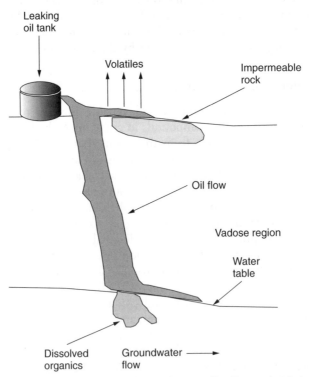

Fig. 5.3   The distribution of hydrocarbons in soil from an oil spill on or just below the surface
(adapted from Bossert and Compeau, 1995).

volatile components can be lost to the atmosphere if the leak is on the surface, but if the leak is below soil level the mobile components can migrate down through the soil to the water table. Any compounds which are water soluble can also migrate down through the soil and into the groundwater. The higher molecular weight components are mostly insoluble and immiscible and may move slowly through the soil or remain on or near the surface, depending on the soil structure. Insoluble compounds may also be absorbed very tightly onto the soil particles. If the water-immiscible components do migrate through the soil and reach the water table they will form a layer on the surface of the water and spread out in this manner.

The most spectacular spillages have been the marine oil spills from tankers such as the *Torrey Canyon*, *Amoco Cadiz*, *Exxon Valdez*, *Braer* and *Sea Empress*. Although these spills gain public attention, taken over a period of time the amount spilled is about the same as that released by natural seepage (Prince, 1997; MacDonald, 1998).

5.3.2   Bioremediation of marine oil spills

Crude oil when released at sea will not mix with sea water and will float on the surface, allowing the escape of the volatile components, those of 12 carbons and below. The floating oil, if it does not reach the shore, will be dispersed due to the action of waves. The dispersion will allow naturally occurring hydrocarbon-degrading organisms to break down the oil. Oil breakdown will occur at the interface between the oil and water and therefore the better the oil dispersion, the greater the area, the faster the degradation. Crude oil is a naturally occurring product and as such is regarded as biodegradable, and it is perhaps no surprise that hydrocarbon-degrading microorganisms are distributed widely in nature.

Box 5.1

The term 'biodegradable' implies that the compound can be degraded or transformed by a biological process. The term does not, however, give any indication of the extent of degradation. Complete degradation to carbon dioxide, water and other inorganic compounds is referred to as **mineralisation**, and partial degradation refers to some intermediate stage. **Persistent** organic compounds do not undergo degradation under certain circumstances, whereas **recalcitrant** compounds are not degraded under any conditions.

The rate of dispersion of the oil will depend on the wave action which in turn is dependent on the weather. In the case of the oil tanker *Braer*, which ran aground in a gale in 1993 carrying light crude oil, the oil was dispersed in a matter of hours. The more complex and less soluble oil components will be degraded much more slowly than the lighter oils, and it is these high molecular weight components that will persist on the sand and rocks if the spill reaches shore.

The first stage in the recovery and clean-up of an oil spill is to stop the release and contain the spill. Once this has been done the surface oil can be removed mechanically with skimmers and other machines (Fingas, 1995). The process of recovery of the oil will depend on the location, the volume of the spill, the weather conditions, and the nature of the oil. If the oil reaches the shore mechanical removal is possible on sandy areas, but on rocky shores washing the oil back into the sea is usually attempted. Chemical dispersants can be used on both floating oil and oil which has reached a rocky shore, but care has to be taken as the detergents can be as harmful to the environment as the oil. Although both physical and chemical methods are efficient, not all the oil can be removed and it is the remaining high molecular weight oil that may need to be removed by some form of bioremediation. Crude oil can be degraded by the indigenous microbial population in the sea and on the shore, as microorganisms capable of using hydrocarbons as a source of carbon compounds and energy are widely found (Button *et al.*, 1992). However, it is thought that the supply of utilisable phosphorus and nitrogen compounds is limiting in most marine environments, so that to encourage degradation slow-release fertilisers have been added to oil slicks at a nitrogen to oil ratio of 1:100.

A better approach has been to treat the oil slick with a nitrogen- and phosphate-containing dispersant, which also contains a surfactant which directs the salts to the oil droplet surfaces. In the case of the *Exxon Valdez* spill, the Alaskan shore was so free of nitrogen and phosphate compounds that addition of fertilisers was particularly effective. In coastal areas which receive waste streams, such as sewage outfall, there is little effect on the addition of further nitrogen and phosphate compounds as the levels are already high. The *Exxon Valdez* oil tanker spillage provided the opportunity to study the effect of nutrient addition on oil removal from the rocky shore, and three different forms of nitrogen and phosphate fertiliser were tried. The first was a soluble fertiliser with a ratio of 23:2 nitrogen to phosphorus, the second was a slow-release encapsulated fertiliser, and the last was an oleophilic fertiliser, which would concentrate in the oil droplets. All three fertilisers were tried on the oil-contaminated rocky shore, where the oleophilic fertiliser gave the best results, cleaning the rocks of oil after only 10 days' treatment (Atlas, 1991).

5.3.3 Bioremediation of soils

Soils contain a very large number of microorganisms which can include a number of hydrocarbon-utilising bacteria and fungi (Sutherland, 1992), representing 1% of the total population of some 10^4–10^6 cells per gram of soil. In addition, cyanobacteria and algae have also been found to degrade hydrocarbons. Hydrocarbon-contaminated soils have been found to contain more microorganisms than uncontaminated soils, but the diversity of the microorganisms was reduced (Bossert and Compeau, 1995; Mesarch and Nies, 1997).

The fate of organic compounds in the environment is affected by a number of factors, which can be grouped into those factors affecting the growth and metabolism of the microorganisms and those affecting the compound itself. Factors affecting the growth of microorganisms are as follows:

- presence of other biodegradable organic material
- presence of nitrogen- and phosphorus-containing inorganic compounds
- oxygen levels
- temperature
- pH
- presence of water, soil moisture
- number and types of microorganisms present
- presence of heavy metals.

Factors affecting degradation of the compound are as follows:

- bacterial growth and metabolism
- chemical structure of the organic compound
- availability and/or solubility
- photochemistry.

The biodegradation of the hydrocarbons is associated with microbial growth and metabolism and therefore any of the factors affecting microbial growth will influence degradation. If the microorganisms cannot use the hydrocarbons as their sole source of energy and carbon skeletons, some other growth substrate will be needed. In some cases if another substrate is present the microorganisms may use this in preference to the hydrocarbons. The microorganisms may also require supplementation with nitrogen- and phosphorus-containing compounds as demonstrated in marine conditions. Aerobic degradation of hydrocarbons is considerably faster than the anaerobic process (Holliger and Zehnder, 1996), so that a supply of oxygen will be needed to maintain aerobic conditions if rapid degradation is required. A soil with an open structure will encourage oxygen transfer and a waterlogged soil will have the reverse effect. The temperature affects microbial growth, so that at low temperatures the rate of degradation will be slow. Nutrient addition to soils at temperatures of 4–10°C has been shown to have little effect as the low temperature has reduced growth to such a low level. The pH of the soil will affect both the growth and the solubility of the compound to be degraded. The presence of large numbers of hydrocarbon-degrading microorganisms in the soil will clearly be of advantage at the start, but as most soils contain these types of organisms growth will soon increase the numbers, so that seeding with specific hydrocarbon-degrading organisms will probably not be needed. Hydrocarbon contamination may also be associated with high levels of heavy metal which may inhibit microbial growth, depending on the concentration and type of metals.

The rate of degradation of the hydrocarbon will also be dependent on the structure of the compound. The simpler aliphatics and monocyclic aromatics are readily degradable, but more complex structures such as PAHs are not easily degraded and may persist for some time. The persistence will be increased if the compound is also toxic or its breakdown products are toxic. Another crucial factor is the availability of the compound for degradation within the soil. Availability will be affected by the soil structure, its porosity and composition, and the solubility of the compound itself. Some compounds can be adsorbed to clays and are thus rendered invulnerable to degradation. To overcome this problem surfactants have been added to contaminated soils to improve the availability of hydrocarbons (Mihelcic *et al.*, 1993).

5.3.4   Pathways of degradation

Petrochemicals, PAHs and BTEX compounds are degraded by soil microorganisms, which use them as a source of both energy and carbon compounds for cell synthesis. Hydrocarbons are stable reduced compounds and therefore degradation generally proceeds by oxidation under either aerobic or anaerobic conditions. Microbial degradation of monocyclic and polycyclic aromatic hydrocarbons has been extensively studied (Cerniglia, 1993). Aliphatic hydrocarbons are converted into alcohols and then oxidised sequentially to carboxylic acids which are β-oxidised.

Monocyclic aromatics, as in the case of benzene, are first hydroxylated by a dioxygenase enzyme to *cis*-1,2-dihydroxy-1,2-dihydrobenzene, which is then converted to catechol (Fig. 5.4). The subsequent metabolism of catechol can take one of two pathways: *ortho* cleavage yields *cis,cis*-muconate, whereas *meta* cleavage yields 2-hydroxymuconic semialdehyde. Both pathways lead to compounds which can enter the Krebs cycle (Fig. 5.4). The first two stages of the degradation of benzene are common for the breakdown of many other monocyclic and polycyclic aromatic hydrocarbons (Fig. 5.5).

In general aromatic ring hydroxylation is followed by ring cleavage, and both of these reactions are carried out by oxygenases (Fukuda, 1993). The incorporation of two oxygen molecules causes the introduction of two hydroxyl groups which can undergo either *meta* or *ortho* cleavage. Incorporation of a single oxygen molecule is catalysed by monooxygenases and both enzymatic systems can be used to degrade polycyclic aromatic hydrocarbons (Fig. 5.5).

Many of the monocyclic aromatic hydrocarbon-degrading bacteria have chromosomal genes coding for the enzymes of the pathway for the degradation of hydrocarbons, but plasmids have been found that code for the degradation of compounds such as camphor, octane, toluene, naphthalene, and some herbicides and pesticides. Some plasmids code only for some part of the pathway. It is clearly an advantage in the soil to be able to transfer the degradative ability between bacteria, as this allows the rapid adaptation of the population to a particular compound. The best studied plasmid-based pathway has been the toluene degradation by the bacterium *Pseudomonas putida* mt-2 and the

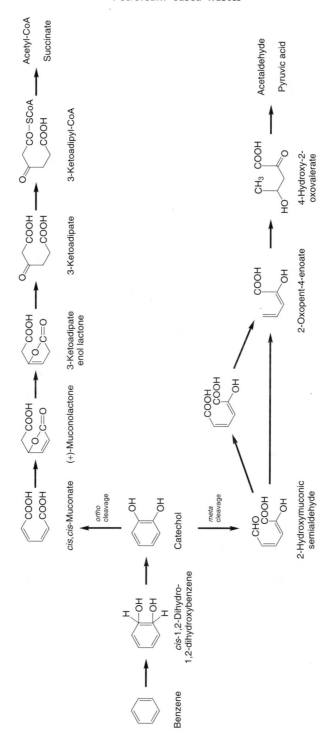

Fig. 5.4 The pathway for the degradation of benzene, showing both *ortho* and *meta* cleavage pathways (from Glazer and Nikaido, 1994).

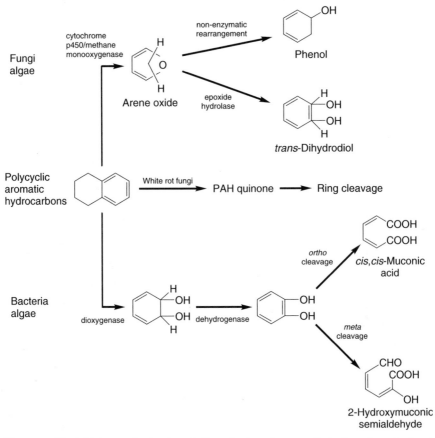

Fig. 5.5 The initial steps in the degradation of polycyclic aromatic hydrocarbons by fungi, bacteria and algae (adapted from Cerniglia, 1993).

plasmid TOL (Fig. 5.6) (Glazer and Nikaido, 1994). The TOL plasmid has been shown to confer the ability to degrade toluene and other benzene derivatives. The genes involved are the xyl genes which are arranged into two groups or operons: the xylCAB code for the degradation to benzoic acid, and the other group xylXYZLEGFJIH code for the breakdown of benzoate into pyruvate and acetaldehyde. Table 5.4 lists the enzymes involved.

The bioremediation of hydrocarbon-contaminated soil cannot always be maintained under aerobic conditions due to waterlogging, the fine particle structure of the soil and blocking of the soil pores with the biomass itself. However, aliphatic, monocyclic and polycyclic aromatic hydrocarbons can be degraded anaerobically provided oxygen can be obtained from water under methanogenic conditions, from nitrate under nitrifying conditions and from sulphate under sulphur-reducing conditions. The hydrocarbons are converted to central metabolic intermediates by hydration, dehydration, reductive

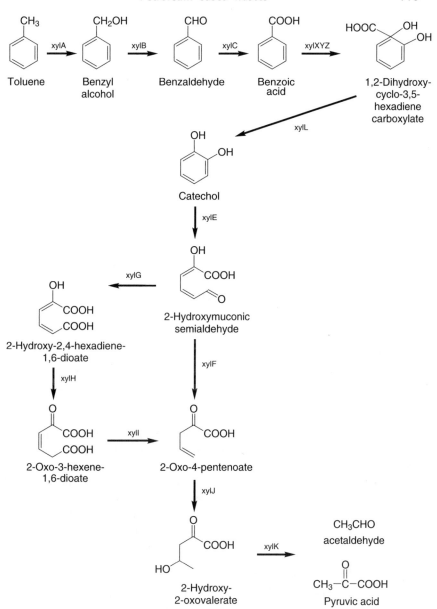

Fig. 5.6   The pathway for the degradation of toluene (from Glazer and Nikaido, 1994).

dehydroxylation, nitroreduction and carboxylation. The central intermediates are benzoyl CoA and sometimes resorcinol which are reduced and hydrolysed and finally transformed to compounds which can enter the Krebs cycle (Holliger and Zehnder, 1996). The only disadvantage with anaerobic degradation is that the process is much slower than the aerobic pathway.

Table 5.4   Enzymes encoded by genes on the TOL plasmid

Gene	Enzymes
Initial part of pathway	
xylA	Xylene oxygenase
xylB	Benzyl alcohol dehydrogenase
xylC	Benzaldehyde dehydrogenase
Later part of pathway	
xylX,Y,Z	Toluate dioxygenase
xylE	Catechol 2,3-dioxygenase
xylF	2-Hydroxymuconic semialdehyde hydrolase
xylG	2-Hydroxymuconic semialdehyde dehydrogenase
xylH	4-Oxalocrotonate tautomerase
xylI	4-Oxalocrotonate decarboxylase
xylJ	2-Oxopent-4-enoate hydratase
xylK	2-Oxo-4-hydroxypentenoate aldolase
xylL	Dihydroxycyclohexadiene carboxylate dehydrogenase
xylR	Regulatory protein
xylS	Regulatory protein

Source: Glazer and Nikaido, 1994.

One of the features of the degradation of both hydrocarbons and other organic molecules is the ability of some enzymes to function with compounds other than their normal substrate. This condition, often known as **gratuitous metabolism**, is probably a result of broad enzyme specificity. Another feature is known as **co-metabolism** which describes the metabolism of a substrate not required for growth in which no apparent benefit is derived by the organism (Semprini, 1997). Wackett (1996) regards co-metabolism as an undefined term describing the imprecise specificity of enzyme systems and their induction systems. However, whatever the precise definition, *in situ* aerobic co-metabolism has been demonstrated for trichloroethylene with the co-metabolic substrates of phenol and toluene (McCarty, 1993).

5.4   Synthetic organic compounds

In addition to the petrochemical-derived products, the environment is also open to contamination by sundry other organic compounds, many of which are on the priority pollutant lists (Tables 2.1 and 2.2, Chapter 2). Unlike the products from crude oil, many of these organic compounds do not occur naturally. These essentially new organic compounds are often referred to as xenobiotic, from the Greek *xenos*, meaning new. Many thousands of compounds have been synthesised and some of these find their way into the environment. Some of the most commonly found are the pesticides (biocides), herbicides and preservatives and an outline of their structures is given in Table 5.5. Most

Table 5.5 Pesticides, herbicides and preservatives

Structure	Biocide
Non-aromatic	Carbon tetrachloride (fumigant)
	Trichloroethylene (fumigant)
Cyclic non-aromatic	Lindane (insecticide)
Biphenyls	DDT (insecticide)
Phenol	Pentachlorophenol (fungicide)
Phenoxy acid	2,4-D (herbicide)
Phenylurea	Diuron (herbicide)
Organophosphate	Glyphosphate (herbicide)
Amides	Aroclor (herbicide)
Tetrazines	Atrazine (herbicide)

Table 5.6 Production of herbicides

Product	Production (ktonnes/year)
Atrazine	39
Cyanazine	13
Diuron	3
2,4-D	30
Aroclor	50
Glyphosphate	12

biocides and herbicides are released into the environment by direct use. Others such as polychlorobiphenyls (PCBs), which are used as hydraulic fluids, plasticisers, adhesives, lubricants, flame retardants, and dielectric fluids in transformers, are released into the environment during production, from spillages and disposal. Another group of compounds found frequently to contaminate groundwater are the chlorinated solvents such as trichloroethene, carbon tetrachloride and tetrachloroethene. Trichloroethene is a priority pollutant (Table 2.2) and contamination is found at industrial, commercial and military sites as a result of disposal and spillage. Other contaminants such as dibenzo-p-dioxins and dibenzofurans can be formed during the combustion of PAHs. The release of some of these xenobiotics into the environment can occur on a very large scale as can be seen by the scale of herbicide use given in Table 5.6, which lists six widely used herbicides.

Many of the xenobiotic compounds released into the environment can be degraded microbially, but others are removed only slowly, and in some cases so slowly as to render them effectively permanent. Table 5.7 gives the half-lives of some halogenated pesticides, which can be seen to be very long,

Table 5.7   Persistence of some halogenated pesticides

Pesticide	Approximate half-life
Chlorine	2–4 years
DDT	3–10 years
Dieldrin	1–7 years
Heptachlor	7–12 years
Toxaphene	10 years

Source: Alexander, 1977.

for example up to 10 years in the case of DDT. The persistence of organic molecules in the environment has a number of unwanted consequences, including protracted exposure to the compound by organisms in the environment, which can increase its toxic effect. The very low rates of degradation mean that organisms tend to accumulate the compound, in a process known as **biomagnification**. In this case the first organism may be the prey of another and as a consequence the concentration of the compound will be increased in the second organism. Thus a very low level of compound in the environment, under certain circumstances, can be magnified to a high and toxic level. An example of this is the accumulation of DDT in grebes (fish-eating water birds) which were at the top of the food chain on a lake treated with 0.01–0.02 ppm DDT to control gnats. The levels found in the grebes were some 100,000 times the DDT level applied. Another problem with these persistent compounds is that in many cases there is little information on their toxicity and long-term effects.

The persistence of xenobiotics in the environment is influenced by the structure and properties of the molecules, their toxicity to microorganisms, and the environmental conditions. Natural complex polymeric molecules, such as lignin, will be slow to degrade. Many of the xenobiotic compounds are also complex in structure and therefore slow to degrade. For many of the xenobiotics their activity and persistence are also linked to the presence of halogens in the compound. The toxicity and persistence of the organohalogen are influenced by the number of halogen molecules, their position, and the type of halogen. The first commercial production of organochlorines was in 1907 with carbon tetrachloride and later in 1920 with trichloroethane. It was found that adding three or more chlorines to phenolic herbicides increased their efficiency. Organochlorines are effective biocides due to their hydrophobic properties, allowing them to pass through or into membranes, disrupting activity; they are also effective because of their ability to inhibit oxidative phosphorylation. The solubility of organochlorines decreases as the chlorine content increases, which often increases their toxicity. Degradation of these organochlorines by microorganisms has to overcome their increased toxicity, and their low solubility in the aqueous phase (Table 5.8). The problem may also be increased as

Table 5.8 Solubility and toxicity of polycyclic aromatic hydrocarbons

Compound	Solubility (mg/l)	Carcinogenicity
Naphthalene	31.7	No
Anthracene	0.07	No
Phenanthrene	1.3	No
Fluoranthene	0.26	Weak
Pyrene	0.14	No
Benz[a]anthracene	0.002	Yes
Benzo[a]pyrene	0.003	Yes

some organochlorine compounds are a mixture of isomers, as found with PCBs, which decreases the rate of degradation.

The rate of degradation of xenobiotics in soil and water is also dependent on the presence of microorganisms with the enzymatic capability to degrade the molecule. As xenobiotics are not normally found in nature, the level of the degrading microorganism may be very low. In many cases a period of adaptation is required before degradation occurs. The environmental conditions which affect the degradation of xenobiotics are essentially the same as those which affect the degradation of hydrocarbons.

5.4.1   Pathways of degradation

Organisms capable of degrading xenobiotics have been found in soil and sediment, particularly from contaminated sites, and include bacteria, fungi and algae. The degradation pathways for some of the chloroaromatics have been determined (Fukuda, 1993) under both aerobic and anaerobic conditions (Wolforth and Dickert, 1997). The chloroaromatics are normally cleaved by monooxygenases and dioxygenases similar to those found with the degradation of PAHs. Superimposed on the degradation is the process of dehalogenation which can be by four mechanisms:

- oxidative dehalogenation – the halogen is removed and replaced by two hydroxyl ions
- eliminative dehalogenation – the simultaneous removal of the halogen and an adjacent hydrogen ion
- hydrolytic (substitutive) dehalogenation – the substitution of the halogen with a hydroxyl ion
- reductive dehalogenation – the halogen is replaced by a hydrogen ion.

The following are examples of the degradation of organochlorines illustrating individual pathways and general processes.

Pentachlorophenol (PCP) is a herbicide and fungicide used for the preservation of wood and is a priority pollutant (Table 2.2). Because of its toxicity its manufacture has all but ceased in Europe, although treated wood is still imported. A number of microorganisms have been isolated which can degrade PCP under aerobic and anaerobic conditions, including *Flavobacterium, Arthrobacter, Rhodococcus* (Lo *et al.*, 1998) and the white rot fungus *Phanerochaete chryososporium* (Bryant *et al.*, 1991). Most pathways for the breakdown of chlorophenols consist of the dechlorination and hydroxylation of the aromatic ring followed by ring cleavage. Both hydroxylation and ring cleavage are catalysed by oxygenases similar in nature to those found in PAH metabolism (Focht, 1995). The first step appears to be the rate-limiting step in PCP degradation (Fig. 5.7) where aerobic degradation starts with reductive dehalogenation.

The use of polychlorinated biphenyls (PCBs) has been banned for over 20 years due to their toxicity, but as their use was extensive, contaminated sites and sediments remain. PCBs can be degraded aerobically and the first step is similar to that for monocyclic aromatics involving a dioxygenase, which is similar in nature to the dioxygenases for naphthalene and toluene (Focht, 1995). The pathway is shown in Fig. 5.8.

Atrazine is the most widely used triazine herbicide and is effective against broadleaved weeds. It had been employed for some 40 years and was considered to be recalcitrant. However, pure cultures of bacteria have been isolated which can degrade atrazine (De Souza *et al.*, 1998), although bacterial consortia have also been reported to degrade atrazine. Atrazine is converted to cyanuric acid in three steps (Mandlebaum *et al.*, 1995) and the cyanuric acid can be converted to CO_2 and NH_2. Cyanuric acid can also be metabolised by soil

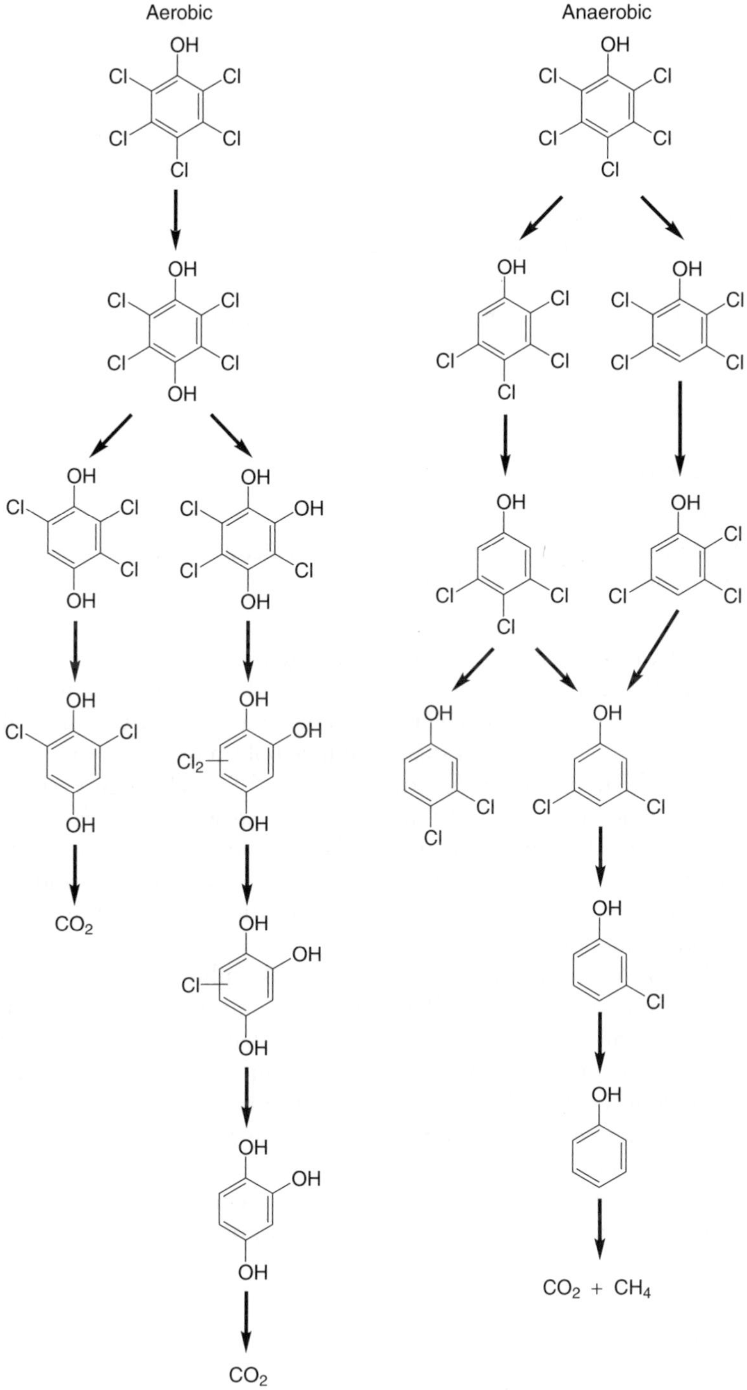

Fig. 5.7 The aerobic and anaerobic degradation of pentachlorophenol.

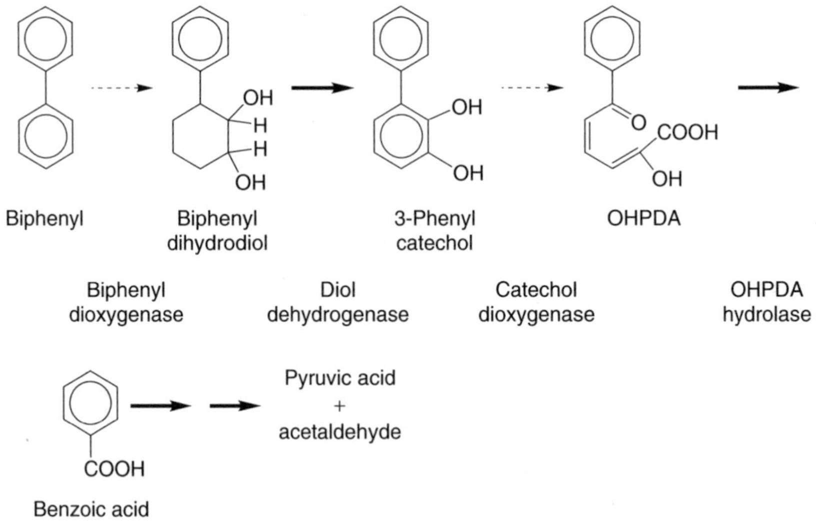

Fig. 5.8 The degradation of polychlorinated biphenyls (PCBs), from Focht (1995). OHPDA is 2-hydroxy-6-oxo-6-phenylhexa-2,4-dienoic acid.

bacteria that cannot degrade atrazine. Three genes are involved in coding for the enzymes that convert atrazine to cyanuric acid. In *Pseudomonas* spp. these genes are found on a plasmid. The isolation of these three enzymes has allowed the determination of the form of sharing of metabolism that occurs in a bacterial consortium which can degrade atrazine (Fig. 5.9). The figure shows the contribution made by *Clavibacter* and *Pseudomonas* where the *Clavibacter* are responsible for the first two steps and the *Pseudomonas* for the remaining steps.

Synthetic organophosphorus compounds are used as domestic and agricultural pesticides. The usual methods of detoxification are chemical treatment, landfill and incineration. Soil microorganisms such as *Pseudomonas diminuta* MG and *Flavobacterium* can degrade organophosphorus using a hydrolase enzyme (Richins *et al.*, 1997). Purified organophosphate hydrolase enzyme has been immobilised to various supports and has been shown to detoxify organophosphates, but the costs are too high due to the need to purify the enzyme. If whole cells can be used the need for purification would be removed, thus reducing the costs. One approach to this has been to clone the gene for the hydrolase and express it on the surface of the cell (Chen and Mulchandani, 1998). A surface-expressed hydrolase has been developed which will eliminate the problems of enzyme purification and the transport of the organophosphates into the cells.

5.4.2   Bioremediation technology

The bioremediation of hydrocarbon- and xenobiotic-contaminated soils can be carried out either *in situ* or *ex situ*. The trend in the USA is for removal as

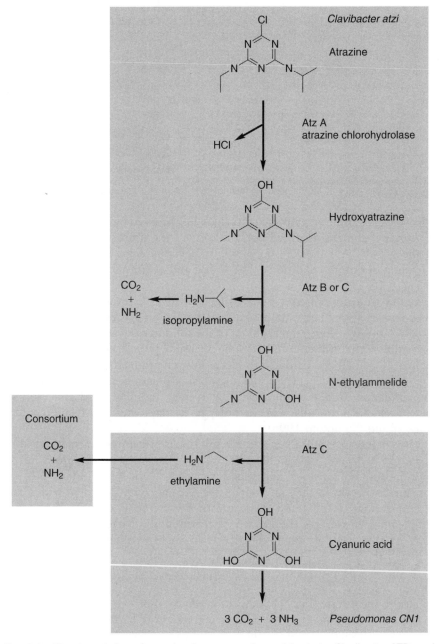

Fig. 5.9 The degradation of atrazine by a consortium of bacteria, *Clavibacter* ATZ1 and *Pseudomonas* CN1 (from De Souza *et al.*, 1998).

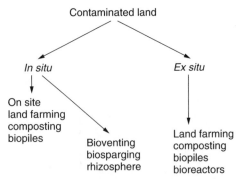

Fig. 5.10 The types of bioremediation technologies for *in situ* and *ex situ* processes.

this avoids litigation over any contamination not removed by an *in situ* treatment. Whatever treatment is carried out, the basis of the process is the stimulation of the growth and metabolism of the indigenous degrading population by providing optimum conditions. The *in situ* and *ex situ* processes are outlined in Fig. 5.10.

Ex situ treatment of contaminated land involves excavation of the soil for treatment or disposal elsewhere. One bioremediation process is land treatment or land farming, where regular tilling of the soil increases aeration and supplementation with fertiliser encourages the microbial population. Often the treatment area is lined and dammed to retain any contaminants that leak out. The rate of degradation depends on the microbial population, the type and level of contamination, and the soil type. The average half-life for degradation of diesel fuel and heavy oils is in the order of 54 days with this type of system (Bossert and Compeau, 1995).

The composting process is another solid-phase treatment carried out after extraction. Composting material such as straw, bark and wood chips is mixed with the contaminated soil and piled into heaps, as for the Windrow process. The process works in the same way as the normal compost system with a rise of temperature to 60°C and above caused by microbial activity. The higher temperature encourages the growth of thermophilic bacteria. The increased costs of this type of system restrict it to highly contaminated materials, although the process is more rapid than land farming.

In the biopile process the soil is heaped into piles within a lined area to prevent leaching. The piles are covered with polythene and liquid nutrients applied to the surface (Fig. 5.11). Aeration can be improved by applying suction to the base of the pile as in a composting system (Chapter 3). Any leachate formed is collected by pipes at the base and can be recycled if necessary. This type of system can be used when space is limited, and when vapour emissions need to be restricted some form of biofilter can be added to the system.

Soil extracted from a contaminated site can also be treated as a solid waste (slurry) or as a liquid leachate in bioreactors of various designs. The use of bioreactors gives control of parameters such as temperature, pH, mixing and

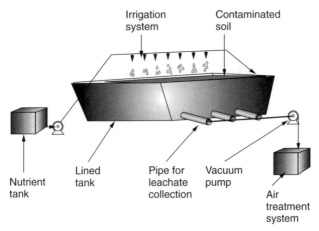

Fig. 5.11 The biopile process for the treatment of contaminated land either *in situ* or after excavation.

oxygen supply, which can improve degradation rates. A wide range of bioreactor designs can be used and these include prepared bed reactors, slurry reactors, biofilter (fixed film) or anaerobic digesters.

The processes of land farming, composting, biopiles and bioreactors can be carried out on site as well as on a site removed from the contaminated land. The *in situ* treatments of contaminated soil are bioventing, biosparging, extraction and phytoremediation. Bioventing is an *in situ* process which combines an increased oxygen supply with vapour extraction. A vacuum is applied at some depth in the contaminated soil which draws air down into the soil from holes drilled around the site and sweeps out any volatile organic compounds (Fig. 5.12). Nutrient supplementation can be provided by running nutrients into trenches dug across the site. The increased supply of air will increase the rate of natural degradation by the aerobic microorganisms. Clearly this is effective only for reasonably volatile compounds and where the soil is permeable. However, the vapour extracted may need some form of treatment and one biological solution is the use of biofilters.

Biosparging is a process to increase the biological activity by increasing the supply of oxygen to the soil by sparging air or oxygen into the soil. Air injection was tried at first but was replaced by pure oxygen in order to increase the degradation rates. The expense of this type of treatment has limited its application to highly contaminated sites, but on-site generation of oxygen has reduced the costs. Hydrogen peroxide has been used on a number of sites, but even at low concentration it can be toxic to microorganisms. This process is similar to soil vapour extraction which can be used for volatile contaminants.

In bioventing and biosparging the structure of the soil can be the predominant factor in its success. The major engineering consideration with *in situ* bioremediation is the delivery of the additions and supply to the contaminants, which is affected by conditions in the soil. The fate of contaminants in soil

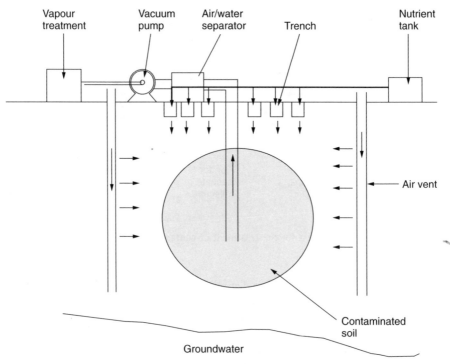

Fig. 5.12 The process of bioventilation where a vacuum is applied to the contaminated site drawing in air and removing volatiles (from Bossert and Compeau, 1995).

is affected by channels and pores in the soil structure, diffusion into closed pores and soil organic matter. Other features are adsorption onto mineral surfaces and partitioning into organic matter.

Other *in situ* processes that can be applied are the extraction of the contaminants and their treatment on the surface in bioreactors, the stimulation of microbial growth *in situ* by providing extra nutrients, and the supplementation of the microbial population.

The addition of nitrogen- and phosphorus-containing substrates has been shown to stimulate the indigenous microbial population. Another course of action is the addition of a second carbon source to stimulate co-metabolism. Over the years a number of *in situ* aerobic co-metabolism processes have been demonstrated (Semprini, 1997). The major problem with this process is to ensure that the substrates added are distributed through the soil and not just close to the injection bore. To reduce recirculation, systems have been investigated for trichloroethylene removal where oxygen and methane, the co-metabolic substrate, were added to the subsoil.

The addition of microorganisms is a process known as **bioaugmentation**. It has been suggested that the best approach is to stimulate the indigenous microbial populations, but this is not suitable for all occasions. Some degradative pathways can produce intermediates which are trapped in dead-end pathways, or transform the pollutants into toxic compounds. Thus there may be situations which can be improved by bioaugmentation with selected or genetic manipulated organisms. A number of fungal inocula have been used to bioaugment soils contaminated with PCP and this procedure removed 80–90% within 4 weeks (Lestan and Lamar, 1996). A selected strain, *Methylosinus trichosporium*, was used in a field study where the organism was selected for its high TCE transformation rate under low copper conditions. Once the organism had been injected, 50% of the cells attached to the soil, forming a biofilter which was efficient for the transformation of TCE (Erb *et al.*, 1997).

Not all soil contaminants are easy to remove or readily available for degradation. Many are insoluble in the aqueous phase so that a number of methods have been used for their extraction. One solution has been to apply biosurfactants, which are surface-active molecules which solubilise, emulsify, disperse, and act as detergents. These surfactants represent a spectrum of structures and are generally more complex than chemical surfactants (Finnerty, 1994). The addition of biosurfactants to oil-contaminated soil has resulted in an increased rate of degradation. Biosurfactants have been used to solubilise oils, and xenobiotics such as PCBs and organophosphates. These biosurfactants can be produced *in situ* by added microorganisms, added as an extracted chemical, or produced by stimulation of the indigenous population. Another method of extraction has been the use of liquid carbon dioxide for the removal of compounds. The method has been successfully used for diesel removal (Lee and Gongaware, 1997). Soil washing has been used to remove pollutants such as pentachlorophenol. The soil is generally removed and washed by a series of scrubbing and physical separation techniques. In this technique the contaminants are partitioned into the liquid phase and the fine particles which were collected for biotreatment or disposal. The water can be treated in a number of bioreactors which can be run in sequence.

5.5 Phytoremediation

Phytoremediation is the use of plants for the removal of contaminants and metals from soil. Phytoremediation can cover the following processes:

- phytoextraction – the removal of contaminants and metals from the soil and its storage or degradation in the plant
- phytovolatilisation
- rhizofiltration
- phytostabilisation, the transformation of one species of molecule to a less toxic species, e.g. Cr^{6+} to Cr^{3+}.

Phytoextraction is possible because of the ability of certain plants to take up metals and accumulate them at high levels in leaves and stems. These types of plants are known as hyperaccumulators and can accumulate 50–100 times more metal than normal plants (Chaney *et al.*, 1997; Brooks *et al.*, 1998). Examples are *Thaspi caerulescens* and *Cardaminopsis halleri* which accumulate zinc and cadmium, and *Alyssum lesbiacum* which accumulates nickel. The properties of high accumulators are as follows. The plants must be able to tolerate high levels of metal in their roots and shoots and this is possible by the concentration of the metal in the vacuole or by chelation of the metal (Ortiz *et al.*, 1995). The plant must also be able to take up the metal from the soil at high rates and transfer the metal from the roots to the shoots at a high rate.

Some plants can convert metal ions to more volatile species in a process known as phytovolatilisation which can reduce the toxicity of the metal and aid disposal. Examples are the conversion of selenium to dimethylselenide and of methyl mercury to mercury vapour. Rhizofiltration is the removal of contaminants from flowing water; this can be achieved by the plant itself or the microorganisms associated with the roots (rhizosphere). The contaminants removed can include organic compounds as well as metals and an example has already been given in Chapter 4 with the reed bed system. Plants have been shown to degrade a number of synthetic organic compounds, although the mechanisms involved are still under investigation. Poplar trees have been used to remove trichloroethylene from contaminated water which was applied to their roots, and other plants have been used to remove contaminating explosives from other sites (Boyajian and Carreira, 1997). Recently plant cell cultures have been shown to be capable of degrading nitroglycerin and PCBs (Goel *et al.*, 1997; Mackova *et al.*, 1997) which suggests that some plants could be isolated that are capable of degrading a number of environmental contaminants.

In many respects plants are ideal for the remediation of contaminated soil as they are a low-cost system, are easy to apply, require the minimum of maintenance and have an excellent degree of public acceptance.

5.6   Gaseous wastes

Gaseous contaminants can be volatile organics (VOCs), sulphur dioxide, nitrous oxides, CFCs, and greenhouse gases such as carbon dioxide and methane, apart from particulates. These contaminants can originate from a number of sources. VOCs come from the vaporisation of compounds such as hydrocarbons. Sulphur dioxide and nitrous oxides are derived from the combustion of sulphur-containing oils and coal, and carbon dioxide from the combustion of fossil fuels.

One method of removing VOCs is biofiltration, where living microorganisms are used to degrade the volatile compounds (Deshusses, 1997; Kiared *et al.*, 1997). The simplest design is to use a bed of soil where the VOCs are piped into the base of the bed some 1 metre down; as they pass through the soil to the surface the organisms present degrade them. A more sophisticated biofilter is a reactor containing packing with a high surface area which supports an active microbial biofilm (Fig. 5.13). The support material can be simple, such as peat or wood bark, or a more complex high-porosity plastic material. The biofilm is maintained by a continual supply of nutrients and high humidity, which is maintained by either humidifying the inlet air or

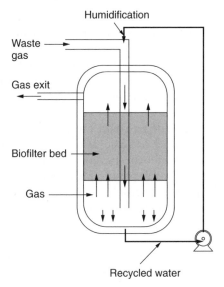

Fig. 5.13 The outline of a biofilter. The microorganisms are attached to an inert support in the filter bed which is kept wet by the recirculation of the liquid to humidify the inlet gas.

recirculating the medium through the reactor. Other parameters which can be controlled are temperature and pH. These filters are beginning to be installed to treat waste gases from industrial processes and have been shown to be capable of removing volatiles such as dichloromethane, styrene and toluene (Cox *et al.*, 1997).

Microbial systems can also be used to remove hydrogen sulphide from flue gases. There are a number of physical processes for the removal of hydrogen sulphide from exit gases (Jensen and Webb, 1995) but there is increasing interest in the use of bacteria such as *Thiobacillus* to oxidise hydrogen sulphide to sulphate. The sulphate can be removed upon neutralisation.

5.7   Desulphurisation of coal and oil

Coal and oil contain a variety of sulphur compounds and their combustion yields sulphur dioxide. Sulphur dioxide is a pulmonary irritant and has been linked to the formation of acid rain. The Clean Air Act of 1956 removed much of the atmospheric pollution caused by the industrial and domestic burning of coal in cities. Present concerns are associated with the use of coal and oil in power stations and the use of high-sulphur oils as the stocks of low-sulphur oil become depleted. The sulphur dioxide released is readily converted to sulphuric acid and this appears to be the main source of acid rain. The sulphuric acid formed lowers the pH of the rain which lowers the pH of soils and waters, leading to the death of trees and a decline in fish stocks. In addition, acid conditions solubilise metals and inhibit essential soil microbial activity. Acid rain is defined as water with a pH of less than 5.65, though values as low as 2.3 have been recorded. Emission of nitrous oxides, from the combustion of both oil and coal, also contributes to acid rain. The generation of electricity in power stations is responsible for 60% of the sulphur dioxide emissions, with industry contributing the remaining 40%. Industrial countries are developing regulations for the reduction of sulphur dioxide. In the case of the USA the Clean Air Act would require the removal of 90% of the sulphur from coal (Kilbane, 1989).

Reduction in sulphur dioxide emission can be achieved by either reducing the sulphur content of the fuel or removal of sulphur dioxide from the flue gases. There are a number of conventional techniques for the removal of sulphur dioxide from the flue gases of power stations. Flue gas desulphurisation (FGD) is accomplished by wet scrubbing of the flue gases, converting the sulphur dioxide to an insoluble calcium salt, calcium sulphite:

$$CaCO_3 + SO_2 \rightarrow CaSO_3 + CO_2$$

The calcium sulphite can be removed as a slurry and discarded as it has no commercial value. If an oxidation step is included the sulphite is oxidised to calcium sulphate:

$$2CaSO_3 + O_2 + 4H_2O \rightarrow 2CaSO_4 \cdot 2H_2O$$

The calcium sulphate or gypsum has a commercial value as it is used for the production of plasterboard. There are other processes under development such as dry absorbant injection into the flue gas, but the wet process is more efficient and cheaper at present, even with the high installation costs. At present, the cost of removing the sulphur dioxide from the flue gases is about a fifth of the cost of removing the sulphur from the fuel prior to burning (Moses and Moses, 1995). However, as stocks of low-sulphur fuels become depleted, high-sulphur fuels will have to be used and at this stage it may become more economic to remove the sulphur from the fuel.

The level of sulphur in coal can be up to 6%, with low-sulphur coals having below 1% sulphur. The sulphur content of oil is very variable depending on the type of oil and its source. Heavy oils and bitumens generally have a high sulphur content. The sulphur content of coal can be reduced by physical treatments such as washing if the coal is pulverised. The emission of sulphur dioxide can be reduced by fluidised-bed combustion where pulverised coal is fluidised by an air stream, which ensures that the coal is completely burnt. Limestone is added to trap the sulphur as a molten slag which can be run off. This process requires advanced combustion designs and is not applicable to all power stations.

The biological removal of sulphur from coal and oil is an alternative to the physical methods (Kargi, 1986). Coal is a heterogeneous solid containing a variety of organic and inorganic compounds which will vary with source. Sulphur occurs as both inorganic and organic compounds. The inorganic compounds are mainly iron sulphides (pyrites) and sulphates, which can comprise up to 6% of the total weight in bituminous coals. The dominant organic constituents are the thiophenes such as dibenzothiophene (DBT). Crude oil is a complex mixture of aliphatic, monocyclic and polycyclic aromatic hydrocarbons. Sulphur is present as elemental sulphur, metal sulphides and thiosulphites and the organic content is a mixture of thiols, thiophenes and substituted dibenzothiophenes.

Coal mines and coal storage are known to produce acid drainage water which is due to the formation of sulphuric acid by microbial activity. It is clear that both coal and oil can act as a microbial substrate, but coal is a solid and oil is immiscible so that intimate contact between the organisms and the substrate is essential. Thus the structure and state of the substrate is of particular importance. Coal has a porous structure separated by fissures, where the pores can range from 5 mm to 2 nm, which at the lower range can restrict microbial access.

The inorganic sulphur in coal can be oxidised by chemolithotrophs such as *Thiobacillus ferrooxidans, T. thiooxidans* and *Sulfolobus acidocaldarius,* and it is these that are responsible for acid mine drainage. These species of *Thiobacillus* have been used to desulphurise coal and are aerobic, acidophilic (pH 2–3) chemolithotrophs. These organisms can remove inorganic sulphur compounds by both direct and indirect processes. *T. ferrooxidans* generates energy by the direct oxidation of ferric sulphide to ferrous sulphate:

$$2FeS_2 + 7O_2 + 2H_2O \rightarrow 2FeSO_4 + 2H_2SO_4$$

The ferrous sulphate is further oxidised to ferric sulphate:

$$4FeSO_4 + O_2 + 2H_2SO_4 \rightarrow 2Fe_2(SO_4)_3 + 2H_2O$$

Microbial action can also directly convert elemental sulphur:

$$2S + 3O_2 + 2H_2O \rightarrow 2H_2SO_4$$

The indirect process is the conversion of ferric sulphide by ferrous sulphate to sulphuric acid which is a non-biological process but has the advantage of keeping the pH low. The process will remove 90% of the inorganic sulphur in a slow process requiring 4–5 days' continuous exposure. Thermophilic *Sulfolobus* species which can grow at 65–80°C are being investigated with a view to improving the rate of the process.

The main organic sulphur compounds in coal are the dibenzothiophenes (DBT) and these have been used as a model compound. The organic sulphur compounds are an integral part of the coal matrix and therefore much more difficult to remove than the pyrites. The enzyme needed to remove these organic compounds will need to cleave the C-S bond rather than the C–C bond. Various microorganisms have been found which are capable of degrading dibenzothiophenes, including *Rhodococcus* sp. (Gray *et al.*, 1996), *Pseudomonas* sp. TG232 (Kilbane, 1989), *Brevibacterium* sp. (McEldowney *et al.*, 1993) and *Aspergillus niger.* The potential of particular species to cleave the C-S and C–C bonds differs from species to species, the C-S bond cleavage being the best option as it does not degrade the coal and therefore

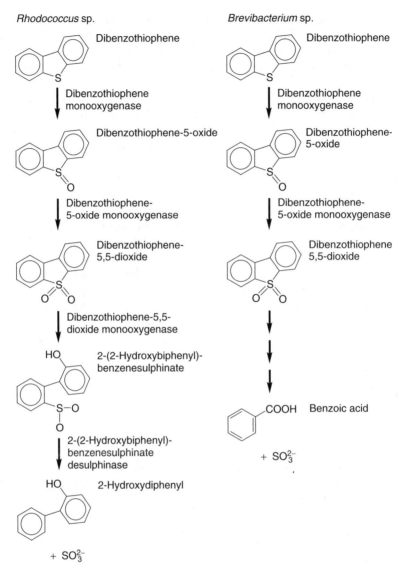

Fig. 5.14 Two pathways for the oxidation of dibenzothiophene, the major organic sulphur-containing compound in coal and oil.

retains its calorific value (Fig. 5.14). The oxidation of dibenzothiophenes by *Brevibacterium* sp. is shown in Fig. 5.14 where monooxygenase converts dibenzothiophenes to dibenz-5,5-dioxide and this is eventually cleaved to benzoic acid and sulphite. The sulphite is converted non-biologically to sulphate which can be washed out of the coal. An example of the biological removal of sulphur from coal is shown in Table 5.9. The enzymes involved in the cleavage to benzoic acid are under investigation but the result is a

Table 5.9 Desulphurisation of coal by a mixture of bacteria

Sulphur type	Percentage of coal		
	Untreated coal	Treated coal	% Reduction
Sulphate	0.38	0.10	74
Pyritic	0.22	0.12	45
Organic	2.25	0.20	91
Total	2.85	0.42	85

Source: Kilbane, 1989.

loss of carbon material. The degradation by *Rhodococcus* again gives 2-(2-hydroxybiphenyl)-benzenesulphinate from three oxidations, which is then cleaved by a desulphinase to yield sulphide which is converted to sulphate.

5.8 Conclusions

- It is clear that the potential for bioremediation is immense as public health and safety legislation and the need for sites for housing and commerce increase.
- The processes and pathways involved in bioremediation are still under investigation and recombinant DNA technology will help greatly.
- The effect of environmental conditions on the rates of bioremediation requires further investigation, as do methods of bioremediation.

5.9 References

Alexander, M. (1977) Pesticides, *Introduction to Soil Microbiology*, 2nd edition. John Wiley & Sons, Chichester, UK, pp. 428–456.

Atlas, R. M. (1991) Microbial hydrocarbon degradation-bioremediation of oil spills. *J. Chem. Tech. Biotechnol.*, **52**, 149–156.

Bossert, I. D. and Compeau, G. C. (1995) Cleanup of petroleum hydrocarbon contamination in soil, in L. Y. Young and C. E. Cerniglia (eds), *Microbial Transformation and Degradation of Toxic Organic Chemicals*. Wiley-Liss, New York, and John Wiley & Sons, Chichester, UK, pp. 77–125.

Boyajian, G. E. and Carreira, L. H. (1997) Phytoremediation: a clean transition from laboratory to marketplace? *Nature Biotechnol.*, **15**, 127–128.

Brooks, R. R., Chambers, M. F., Nicks, L. J. and Robinson, B. H. (1998) Phytomining. *Trends in Plant Science*, **3**, 359–362.

Bryant, F. O., Hale, D. D. and Rogers, J. E. (1991) Regiospecific dechlorination of pentachlorophenol by dichlorophenol-adapted microorganisms in freshwater, anaerobic sediment slurries. *Appl. Environ. Microbiol.*, **57**, 2293–2301.

Button, D. K., Robertson, B. R., McIntosh, D. and Juttner, F. (1992) Interactions between marine bacteria and dissolved-phase and bleached hydrocarbons after the Exxon Valdez oil spill. *Appl. Environ. Microbiol.*, **58**, 243–251.

Cerniglia, C. E. (1993) Biodegradation of polycyclic aromatic hydrocarbons. *Current Opinion in Biotechnol.*, **4**, 331–338.

Chaney, R. L., Malik, M., Li, Y. M., Brown, S. L., Brewer, E. P., Angel, J. S. and Baker, A. J. M. (1997) Phytoremediation of soil metals. *Current Opinion in Biotechnol.*, **8**, 279–284.

Chen, W. and Mulchandani, A. (1998) The use of live biocatalysts for pesticides detoxification. *Tibtech,* **16**, 71–76.

Chitguppe, R., Chu, K. H. and Hashim, M. A. (1997) Reusability of seaweed bioadsorbent in multiple cycles of cadmium adsorption and desorption. *Biotechnol. Techniques,* **11**, 371–373.

Cox, H. H. J., Moerman, R. E., Van Baalen, S., Van Heiningen, W. N. M., Doddema, H. J. and Harder, W. (1997) Performance of a styrene-degrading biofilter containing the yeast *Exophiala jeanselmei. Biotechnol. Bioeng.*, **53**, 259–266.

Deshusses, M. A. (1997) Biological waste air treatment in biofilters. *Current Opinion in Biotechnol.*, **8**, 335–339.

De Souza, M. L., Newcombe, D., Alvey, S., Crowley, D. E., Hay, A., Sadowsky, M. J. and Wackett, L. P. (1998) Molecular basis of a bacterial consortium: interspecies catabolism of atrazine. *Appl. Environ. Microbiol.*, **64**, 178–184.

Dvorak, D. H., Hedin, R. S., Edenborn, H. M. and McIntire, P. E. (1992) Treatment of metal-contaminated water using bacterial sulfate reduction: results from pilot-scale reactors. *Biotechnol. Bioeng.*, **40**, 609–616.

Eccles, H. (1995) Removal of heavy metals from effluent streams – why select a biological process? *Intern. Biodeter. Biodegrad.*, 5–16.

Erb, R. W., Eichner, C. A., Wagner-Dobler, I. and Timmis, K. N. (1997) Bioprotection of microbial communities from toxic phenol mixtures by genetically designed pseudomonad. *Nature Biotechnol.*, **15**, 378–382.

Fingas, M. (1995) Oil spills and their cleanup. *Chemistry & Industry*, December, 1005–1008.

Finnerty, W. R. (1994) Biosurfactants in environmental biotechnology. *Current Opinion in Biotechnol.*, **5**, 291–295.

Focht, D. D. (1995) Strategies for the improvement of aerobic metabolism of polychlorinated biphenyls. *Current Opinion in Biotechnol.*, **6**, 341–346.

Fukuda, M. (1993) Diversity of chloroaromatic oxygenases. *Current Opinion in Biotechnol.,* **4**, 339–343.

Gadd, G. M. and White, C. (1993) Microbial treatment of metal pollution – a working biotechnology. *Trends Biotechnol.*, **11**, 353–359.

Garbisu, C., Gil, J. M., Bazin, M. J., Hall, D. O. and Serra, J. L. (1991) Removal of nitrate from water by foam-immobilised *Phormidium laminosum* in batch and continuous-flow bioreactors. *J. Appl. Phycol.*, **3**, 221–234.

Glazer, A. N. and Nikaido, H. (1994) *Microbial Biotechnology.* Freeman, New York.

Goel, A., Kumar, G., Payne, G. F. and Dube, S. K. (1997) Plant cell biodegradation of a xenobiotic nitrate ester, nitroglycerin. *Nature Biotechnol.* **15**, 174–177.

Gray, K. A., Pogrebinsky, O. S., Mrachko, G. T., Xi, L., Monticello, D. J. and Squires, C. H. (1996) Molecular mechanisms of biocatalytic desulphurisation of fossil fuels. *Nature Biotechnol.*, **14**, 1705–1709.

Halliwell, B. and Aruoma, O. I. (1993) *DNA and Free Radicals.* Ellis Horwood, Chichester, UK.

Holliger, C. and Zehnder, A. J. B. (1996) Anaerobic biodegradation of hydrocarbons. *Current Opinion in Biotechnol.*, **7**, 326–330.

Jensen, A. B. and Webb, C. (1995) Treatment of H_2S-containing gases: a review of microbiological alternatives. *Enzyme Microb. Technol.*, **17**, 2–10.

Kargi, F. (1986) Microbial methods for desulfurization of coal. *Tibtech*, November, 293–297.

Kiared, K., Wu, G., Beerli, M., Rothenbuhler, M. and Heitz, M. (1997) Application of biofiltration to the control of VOC emissions. *Environ. Biotechnol.*, **18**, 55–63.

Kilbane, J. J. (1989) Desulphurisation of coal: the microbial solution. *Tibtech*, 7, 97–101.

Kolmert, A., Henrysson, T., Hallberg, R. and Mattiasson, B. (1997) Optimization of sulphide production in an anaerobic continuous biofilm process with sulphate reducing bacteria. *Biotechnol. Letters*, **19**, 971–975.

Lau, P. S., Tam, N. F. Y. and Wong, Y. S. (1997) Wastewater nutrients (N and P) removal by carrageenan and alginate immobilized *Chlorella vulgaris*. *Environ. Technol.*, **18**, 945–951.

Ledin, M. and Pedersen, K. (1996) The environmental impact of mine wastes – role of microorganisms and their significance in treatment of mine wastes. *Earth-Sci. Rev.*, **41**, 67–108.

Lee, C. M. and Gongaware, D. F. (1997) Optimization of SFE conditions for the removal of diesel fuel. *Environ. Technol.*, **18**, 1157–1161.

Lestan, D. and Lamar, R. T. (1996) Development of fungal inocula for bio-augmentation of contaminated soils. *Appl. Environ. Microbiol.*, **62**, 2045–2052.

Lo, K. V., Zhu, C. M. and Cheuk, W. (1998) Biodegradation of pentachlorophenol by *Flavobacterium* species in batch and immobilised continuous reactors. *Environ. Technol.*, **19**, 91–96.

Lovley, D. R. and Coates, J. D. (1997) Bioremediation of metal contamination. *Current Opinion in Biotechnol.*, **8**, 285–289.

MacDonald, I. R. (1998) Natural oil spills. *Scientific American*, November, 30–35.

Mackova, M., Macek, T., Kucerova, P., Burkhard, J., Pazlarova, J. and Demnerova, K. (1997) Degradation of polychlorinated biphenyls by hairy root culture of *Solanum nigrum*. *Biotechnol. Letters*, **19**, 787–790.

Mandlebaum, R. T., Wackett, L. P. and Allan, D. L. (1995) Isolation and characterization of a *Pseudomonas* sp that mineralizes the s-triazine herbicide atrazine. *Appl. Environ. Microbiol.*, **61**, 1451–1457.

Marschner, H. (1995) *Mineral Nutrition of Higher Plants*. Academic Press, London.

Mason, C. F. (1996) *Biology of Freshwater Pollution*, 3rd edition. Longman Scientific and Technical, Harlow, UK.

Matheickel, J. T., Yu, Q. and Feltham, J. (1997) Cu(II) binding by *E. radiata* biomaterial. *Environ. Technol.*, **18**, 25–34.

McCarty, P. L. (1993) *In situ* bioremediation of chlorinated solvents. *Current Opinion in Biotechnol.*, **4**, 323–330.

McEldowney, S., Hardman, D. J. and Waite, S. (1993) *Pollution: Ecology and Biotreatment.* Longman Scientific and Technical, Harlow, UK.

Mesarch, M. B. and Nies, L. (1997) Modification of heterotrophic plate counts for assessing the bioremediation potential of petroleum-contaminated soils. *Environ. Technol.*, **18**, 639–646.

Mihelcic, J. R., Lueking, D. R., Mitzell, R. J. and Stapleton, J. M. (1993) Bioavailability of sorbed- and separate-phase chemicals. *Biodegradation*, **4**, 141–153.

Moses, V. and Moses, S. (1995) *Exploiting Biotechnology*. Harwood Academic, Chur, Switzerland.

Ortiz, D. F., Ruscitt, T., McCue, K. F. and Ow, D. W. (1995) Transport of metal binding peptides by HMTI, a fission yeast ABC-type vacuolar membrane protein. *J. Biol. Chem.*, **270**, 4721–4728.

Ouzouridou, G. (1994) Copper-induced changes in growth, metal content and photo-synthetic functions of *Alyssum montanum* L plants. *Envir. Exp. Bot.*, **34**, 165–172.

Pinar, G., Duque, E., Haidour, A., Oliva, J.-M., Sanchez-Barbero, L., Calvo, V. and Ramos, J. L. (1997) Removal of high concentrations of nitrate from industrial wastewaters by bacteria. *Appl. Environ. Microbiol.*, **63**, 2071–2073.

Prince, R. C. (1997) Bioremediation of marine oil spills. *Tibtech*, **15**, 158–159.

Richau, J. A., Choquenet, D., Fialho, A. M., Moreira, L. M. and Sa-Correia, I. (1997) The biosynthesis of the exopolysaccharide gellan results in the decrease of *Sphingomonas paucimobilis* tolerance to copper. *Enzyme Microb. Technol.*, **20**, 510–515.

Richins, R. D., Kaneva, I., Mulchandani, A. and Chen, W. (1997) Biodegradation of organophosphorus pesticides by surface expressed organophosphorus hydrolase. *Nature Biotechnol.*, **15**, 984–987.

Rowley, A.G. (1993) Time to clean up the act? *Chemistry in Britain*, November, 959–963.

Ryding, S.-O. and Rast, W. (eds) (1989) *The Control of Eutrophication of Lakes and Reservoirs*. Parthenon Publishing Group, Carnforth, UK.

Semprini, L. (1997) Strategies for the aerobic co-metabolism of chlorinated solvents. *Current Opinion in Biotechnol.*, **8**, 296–308.

Sousa, C., Cebolla, A. and deLorenzo, V. (1996) Enhanced metalloadsorption of bacterial cells displaying poly-His peptides. *Nature Biotechnol.*, **14**, 1017–1020.

Sutherland, J. B. (1992) Detoxification of polycyclic aromatic hydrocarbons by fungi. *J. Ind. Microbiol.*, **9**, 53–62.

Sylvestre, S., Lessard, P. and de la Noue, J. (1996) Removal performance of nitrogen and phosphorus compounds by a photobioreactor using a biomass of Cyanobacteria *Phormidium bohneri*. *Environ. Technol.*, **17**, 697–706.

Vilchez, C. and Vega, J. M. (1994) Nitrate uptake by *Chlamydomonas reinhardtii* cells immobilised in calcium alginate. *Appl. Micro. Biotechnol.*, **41**, 137–141.

Vilchez, C., Garbayo, I., Lobato, M. V. and Vega, J. M. (1997) Microalgae-mediated chemicals production and waste removal. *Enzyme Microb. Technol.*, **20**, 562–572.

Visser, J. M., Robertson, L. A., Verseveld, H. W. V. and Kuenen, J. G. (1997) Sulfur production by obligately chemolithoautotrophic *Thiobacillus* species. *Appl. Environ. Microbiol.*, **63**, 2300–2305.

Volesky, B. and Holan, Z. R. (1995) Biosorption of heavy metals. *Biotechnol. Progress*, **11**, 235–250.

Wackett, L. P. (1996) Co-metabolism: is the emperor wearing any clothes? *Current Opinion in Biotechnol.*, **7**, 321–325.

Wolforth, G. and Dickert, G. (1997) Anaerobic dehalogenases. *Current Opinion in Biotechnol.*, **8**, 290–295.

5.9.1 Recommended reading

Crawford, R. L. and Crawford, D. L. (1996) *Bioremediation Principles and Applications*. Cambridge University Press, Cambridge.

Freedman, B. (1995) *Environmental Ecology*, 2nd edition. Academic Press, New York.

Ray, B. T. (1995) *Environmental Engineering*. PWS Publishing, Boston, MA.

Young, L. Y. and Cerniglia, C. E. (eds) (1995) *Microbial Transformation and Degradation of Toxic Organic Chemicals*. John Wiley & Sons, Chichester, UK.

Chapter 6

Energy and biofuel

6.1 Introduction

The global use of energy has been increasing steadily since the industrial revolution; for example, it increased fivefold from 1937 to 1988, and this growth is expected to continue into the foreseeable future. The global increase in energy demand was 1.85% in 1995, but if the former USSR is excluded, the growth in energy demand was 2.9% due to the increased demands of the developing Asian countries (Anon., 1997). It is clear that energy demand varies from country to country depending on their state of development, as there is a close correlation between energy consumption and improvements in living conditions measured by life expectancy and infant mortality. The present annual global demand for energy is 398 EJ (398 × 10^{18} J) and the sources of this energy are given in Fig. 6.1 (Boyle, 1996). Oil, gas and coal are the main sources of energy, supplemented by biomass, hydroelectric and nuclear power.

This chapter outlines the world's demand for energy and the alternatives to fossil fuels that are available, concentrating on biologically based fuels such as biogas, biomass and ethanol.

At present some 75% of the world's energy is derived from fossil fuels, and consumption of these fuels is expected to rise by 50–60% by 2010 (Fulkerson

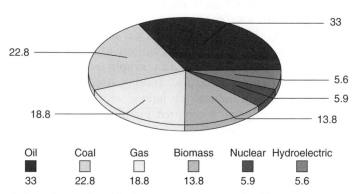

Oil	Coal	Gas	Biomass	Nuclear	Hydroelectric
33	22.8	18.8	13.8	5.9	5.6

Fig. 6.1 Estimated annual world primary energy consumption. The segments represent percentages of a total of 398 EJ (exajoules) (398 × 10^{18} J) (from Boyle, 1996 by permission of Oxford University Press).

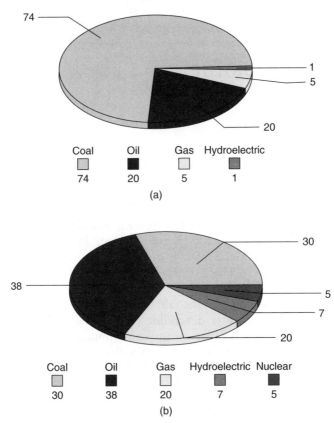

Fig. 6.2 Changes in world energy consumption excluding that from biomass from (a) 1937 to (b) 1988. The total in 1937 was 60 quads and in 1988 it was 321 (1 quad = 1.055×10^{18} J) (from Fulkerson *et al.*, 1990).

et al., 1990). The main fossil fuels are coal, oil and natural gas. Figure 6.2 shows the changes in the sources of energy from 1937 to 1988. Nuclear power was introduced during this time and natural gas and oil have replaced coal in many cases. The reasons that fossil fuels continue to be used are that they are found throughout the world, require only simple technology to extract the energy, and can be transported easily. Another feature which is important is that crude oil and oil products are liquid, which makes their transport convenient, and this property is required for their use as automotive fuels. However, despite their continued use there are problems associated with the use of fossil fuels:

- finite supply
- production of greenhouse gases (global warming)
- production of other pollutants (air pollution, acid rain).

Over the years the use of coal has reduced as a proportion of the overall power supply and the bulk of coal is now used for the generation of electricity

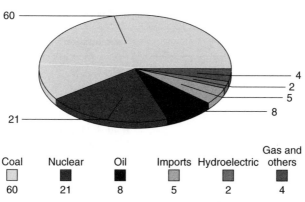

Fig. 6.3 The fuels used for electricity generation in the UK (from Boyle, 1996 by permission of Oxford University Press).

Table 6.1 Oil and gas demand, Mbbl/d*

	1993	1994	1995	1996	1997
Former USSR	5.73	4.83	4.77	4.55	4.50
Other non-OECD[†]	22.79	23.98	24.97	26.05	27.40
OECD[†]	39.04	40.00	40.30	41.20	41.70
Total	67.56	68.81	70.04	71.80	73.60

* Million barrels per day, where 1 barrel = 159 litres.
† OECD: Organisation for Economic Cooperation and Development.
Source: Euro Energy Information, 1997.

(Fig. 6.3). Thus deep coal mining has been reduced and has been replaced by opencast extraction. However, as opencast coal stocks are exhausted, deep mining may have to be restarted if coal is still required. It has been estimated that coal stocks will last until 2180 (Fulkerson *et al.*, 1990). Natural gas is replacing coal for the generation of electricity, as it is a cheaper and cleaner fuel and produces more energy on combustion. However, natural gas is less abundant and not evenly distributed and stocks are said to last only until 2047.

Improved combustion efficiencies and continued exploration and detection of oil sources have extended the estimates of how long oil stocks will last. Nevertheless it has been estimated that oil supplies will last only until 2080, though the price of crude oil has remained stable and has even decreased. However, the demand for oil continues to increase (Table 6.1) and as a consequence the extraction of oil has to be attempted in increasingly hostile and difficult conditions, such as Alaska and the North Sea. This will eventually increase the costs and reduce the supply of crude oil. At present many of the alternatives to oil-based fuel are not competitive on cost, but eventually this will change and alternative power sources will be required.

Table 6.2   Composition of emissions from a coal-fired power station

Chemical	Concentration
Air (oxygen depleted)	~80%
Water	~4.5%
Carbon dioxide (CO_2)	~12%
Carbon monoxide (CO)	40 ppm*
Sulphur dioxide (SO_2)	1000–1700 ppm
Sulphur trioxide (SO_3)	1–5 ppm
Nitric oxide (NO)	400–600 ppm
Nitrogen dioxide (NO_2)	~20 ppm
Nitrous oxide (N_2O)	~40 ppm
Hydrochloric acid (HCl)	250 ppm
Hydrofluoric acid (HF)	< 20 ppm
Particulates	< 115 mg/m^3
Mercury (Hg)	3 ppb*

* ppm, parts per million; ppb, parts per billion.
Source: Roberts *et al.*, 1990.

The combustion of fossil fuels, whether coal, oil or gas, results in the production of a number of combustion products. As can be seen from Table 6.2,
the burning of coal, of which 60% is used in power stations, generates carbon
dioxide, sulphur dioxide from the sulphur compounds in the coal, nitrous
oxides from the nitrogenous compounds, and a range of particulates. The
combustion of oil-based products such as diesel and petrol also produces similar
gases, including carbon monoxide. Some of these combustion products are
known as greenhouse gases. Greenhouse gases, apart from chlorofluorocarbons
(CFCs), occur naturally and include:

● water vapour
● ozone
● carbon dioxide
● methane
● nitrous oxide
● chlorofluorocarbons (CFCs).

These gases affect the global climate, as short-wave solar radiation can pass
through the atmosphere and, although some is reflected, much is adsorbed by
the earth's surface, warming the atmosphere. Long-wave radiation is emitted
by the warm surface of the earth and on average the outgoing radiation
balances the incoming solar radiation. However, some of the outgoing radiation is partially adsorbed by the greenhouse gases in the atmosphere which
radiate the energy back to the surface (Fig. 6.4), and as a consequence the
earth's surface is warmer than it would be by direct heating.

Human activities such as deforestation and the burning of fossil fuels have
increased the concentration of greenhouse gases. Table 6.3 shows the concen-

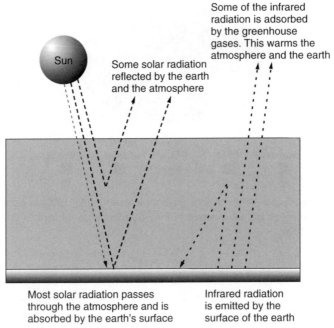

Some of the infrared radiation is adsorbed by the greenhouse gases. This warms the atmosphere and the earth

Some solar radiation reflected by the earth and the atmosphere

Sun

Most solar radiation passes through the atmosphere and is absorbed by the earth's surface

Infrared radiation is emitted by the surface of the earth

Fig 6.4 The effect of greenhouse gases on the distribution of the radiation from the sun. Most solar radiation passes through the atmosphere, warming the earth's surface. The warm surface of the earth radiates the solar radiation at a longer wavelength in the infrared. Much of this infrared radiation will escape from the earth but some will be adsorbed by the greenhouse gases and reflected back to the surface, causing an increase in global temperature.

Table 6.3 Greenhouse gases affected by human activities*

Parameter	CO_2	CH_4	CFC-11	CFC-12	N_2O
Pre-industrial concentrations (1750–1800)	280 ppmv[†]	0.8 ppmv	0	0	288 ppbv[†]
Current concentrations (1990)	353 ppmv	1.72 ppmv	280 pptv[†]	484 pptv	310 ppbv
Current rate of accumulation	0.5%	0.9%	4%	4%	0.25%

* Ozone has not been included due to lack of data.
[†] ppmv, parts per million by volume; ppbv, parts per billion by volume; pptv, parts per trillion by volume.
Source: Houghton *et al.*, 1990.

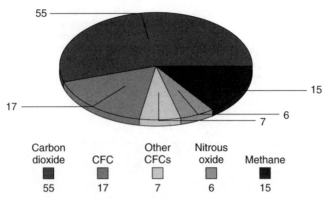

Fig. 6.5 The contribution of the various greenhouse gases (1980–1990) to global warming. Water vapour and ozone are not included as their contribution is difficult to estimate (from Houghton *et al.*, 1990).

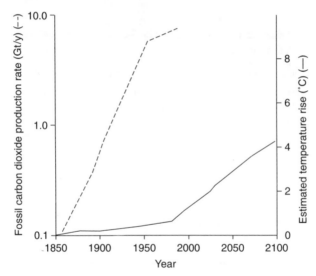

Fig. 6.6 The increase since 1860 in the annual production rate (gigatonnes per year) of carbon dioxide derived from fossil fuels (dashed line); and the estimated temperature rise (°C) for global warming caused by greenhouse gases (solid line) (from Houghton *et al.*, 1990).

trations and changes in some greenhouse gases since the industrial revolution (Houghton *et al.*, 1990). Water vapour and ozone are not included in Table 6.3. Water vapour has the largest greenhouse effect but its level is not affected by human activities, although it will change in response to global warming. Ozone levels have been changed due to human activity, but it is difficult to estimate ozone concentration and therefore it has been omitted. The contributions to the remaining greenhouse gases are given in Fig. 6.5. The combustion of fossil fuels and deforestation have increased the carbon dioxide concentration by 26% since the start of the industrial revolution (Fig. 6.6).

Table 6.4 Sources and sinks for methane

	Annual release (million tonnes)
Sources	
Natural wetlands	115
Rice paddies	110
Enteric fermentation	80
Gas drilling, venting	45
Biomass burning	40
Termites	40
Coal mining	40
Oceans	10
Freshwaters	5
CH_4 hydrate distillation	5
Sinks	
Removal by soils	30
Reaction with OH in the atmosphere	500
Atmospheric increase	44

Source: Houghton *et al.*, 1990.

Annual carbon dioxide emissions are now at 7 billion tonnes which could rise to 20 billion tonnes by 2010. By increasing the greenhouse gases and adding new greenhouse gases such as CFCs, human activity is raising the global temperature, and the predicted increases in temperature are given also in Fig. 6.6. At this rate a global increase of 2.5°C can be expected by 2100 (Houghton, 1996). This is the most rapid change in temperature for the last 10,000 years and will increase sea level by 0.5 m due to expansion of the sea and melting ice. This will directly affect people living in low-lying areas such as delta regions in Egypt, China and Bangladesh where 6 million people live below the 1 m contour.

Methane levels are twice what they were in pre-industrial times (Table 6.3) and have been increased by human activities such as rice cultivation, natural gas (including leaks), and coal mining. The contributions of the various sources are given in Table 6.4. The principal removal pathway for methane is through its reaction with hydroxyl radicals in the atmosphere, where it is a significant source of stratospheric water vapour. However, the quantitative importance of the various sources is not known as yet.

CFCs are new to the environment, having been introduced in the last 30 years. The concentration of these halocarbons has increased more rapidly than that of other greenhouse gases, and CFCs have been shown to deplete ozone in the stratosphere. Ozone, as well as being a greenhouse gas, acts as a filter for ultraviolet radiation. Reduction of the ozone layer will allow more ultraviolet radiation to reach the surface, causing skin damage (sunburn) and with

Table 6.5   Global emissions of sulphur compounds into the atmosphere

Source	Annual flux (million tonnes S)
Anthropogenic (fossil fuel burning)	80
Biomass burning	7
Oceans	40
Soils and plants	10
Volcanoes	10
Total	147

Source: Houghton *et al.*, 1990.

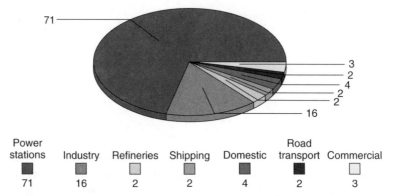

Power stations	Industry	Refineries	Shipping	Domestic	Road transport	Commercial
71	16	2	2	4	2	3

Fig. 6.7   The sources of atmospheric sulphur dioxide in the UK (from Boyle, 1996 by permission of Oxford University Press).

constant exposure an increase in skin cancers. The Montreal Protocol in 1987 sought to limit the production and consumption of halocarbons and many of the developed nations have switched to alternative chemicals.

Nitrous oxide is now 8% above pre-industrial levels. The sources of nitrous oxide are difficult to quantify, but human activities have increased the levels. The major loss of nitrous oxide is the photochemical decomposition in the stratosphere.

The burning of fossil fuels also produces gases other than greenhouse gases, such as sulphur dioxide and oxides of nitrogen (NO_x). The burning of fossil fuels accounts for 54% of the atmospheric sulphur dioxide (Table 6.5). The sources of sulphur dioxide in the UK are shown in Fig. 6.7; fossil fuel emissions are from the inorganic and organic sulphur compounds in both coal and oil. The emissions of sulphur dioxide and to some extent those of nitrous oxides are responsible for the formation of acid rain and urban smog.

In order to reduce the problems associated with the combustion of fossil fuels, a number of measures can be taken, including the following:

- an increase in the sinks for carbon dioxide, such as forests
- reduction in the emission of greenhouse gases and other gases by increases in efficiency of existing energy systems
- removal of carbon dioxide from fossil fuel emissions
- the use of alternative energy sources that do not produce greenhouse gases.

The problems of the reduction in supply of fossil fuels, their contribution to global warming and other forms of air pollution have encouraged the investigation of alternative power sources, particularly those which can mitigate the release of greenhouse gases. In reality a switch to alternative forms of energy will take many decades and therefore the appropriate action must be taken now (Houghton, 1996).

6.1.1   Removal of carbon dioxide

The removal of carbon dioxide or the capture of carbon dioxide from fossil fuel emission is very much in the development stage. The planting of forests to absorb carbon dioxide seems an easy process, but it has been calculated that to absorb the carbon dioxide emitted by the burning of fossil fuels in the USA, 23% of the land area of the USA would have to be forested (Fulkerson *et al.*, 1990). This is clearly not possible, but some programme of reafforestation would help to make up for the forest losses in areas such as the Amazon. Other schemes have proposed separating the carbon dioxide from exhaust gases and piping it to the deep ocean or to depleted natural gas reservoirs. These schemes will probably not be developed on account of their cost. One process which does show promise is the removal of carbon dioxide from exhaust gases using microalgae. Microalgae have been used as sources of food and chemicals and for waste removal (Vilchez *et al.*, 1997) and systems for the large-scale cultivation of microalgae have been developed (Richmond, 1990). In this case the process uses microalgae to fix the carbon dioxide in the exhaust gases from a fossil-fuel power station. In one case a marine microalga, *Tetraselmis suecica*, was grown outdoors with the addition of pure carbon dioxide or stack gases and achieved carbon dioxide utilisation of 96% (Laws and Berning, 1991). Other workers have addressed the problem of the inhibition of algal growth by high carbon dioxide levels (similar to those found in stack gases) and low pH values by isolating strains which can tolerate such conditions. A marine green alga, *Chlorococcum littorale*, has been isolated which can fix CO_2 at a daily rate of 4 grams per litre from flue gases (Kurano *et al.*, 1995). These systems look promising but, unless some method is available to fix the algae, they will degrade and return the carbon dioxide to the atmosphere.

6.1.2   Increases in efficiency of existing energy generation

In conventional power stations pulverised coal is burnt in a boiler to produce steam which drives a turbine to produce electricity at an efficiency of around 37%. The emission of sulphur dioxide in the flue gases can be reduced either by using low-sulphur coal, or by removing the sulphur from the coal prior to burning (see Chapter 5). In oil-powered electricity generation low-sulphur oils can be used, and natural gas contains only low levels of sulphur compounds. Nitrous oxides can be removed from flue gases by catalytic reduction using ammonia mixed with the exhaust gases. The use of advanced combustion systems such as atmospheric fluidised-bed combustors (AFBC) or pressurised fluidised-bed combustors (PFBC) allows coal to be burnt with limestone, which removes about 90% of the sulphur as a slag. The efficiency also allows a lower temperature to be used, which reduces the formation of nitrous oxides. Other advanced systems involve the conversion of coal to gas where the sulphur can be removed prior to burning. All these systems reduce sulphur dioxide emissions but still produce carbon dioxide.

6.2   Alternative non-fossil energy sources

Alternative systems for the supply of all forms of energy are being sought (ETSU, 1994; World Energy Council, 1994). Those now being used or under development are:

- nuclear power
- hydroelectric power
- tidal power
- wave power
- wind power
- geothermal energy
- solar energy
- biological processes.

6.2.1   Nuclear power

The process of fission of uranium is the basis of the production of large amounts of energy in nuclear power stations. The process of fission is nuclear power's main advantage and disadvantage. The fission process releases large amounts of energy, about 50 million times that of coal on a weight basis. This means that very little uranium fuel is required, which reduces the problems of transport and storage of fuels, and as no combustion is involved the process forms none of the fossil fuel gases. However, the uranium fuel is expensive to produce and requires the mining of considerable quantities of ore. The ore contains about 0.7% uranium-235 which needs to be enriched to 3% before it can be used in the fission process. The greatest disadvantage of nuclear power is that fission generates radioactive materials, some of which have very long half-lives, which have to be contained during production and disposal. The volume for disposal is small compared with fossil fuel wastes, but radioactive materials are very difficult to deal with. Radiation at high levels can cause injury and death and, if insufficient to cause an immediate effect, can cause cell transformation and mutation, showing up as cancers some years later. Thus nuclear power generation requires considerable attention to the protection of the public and of plant operators from the effects of radiation and radioactive materials. There are considerable problems in the reprocessing and disposal of spent fuel, the possibility of leaks or accidents, and the decommissioning of the power stations at the end of their working life. The accidents at the nuclear generating plants at Three Mile Island and Chernobyl have shown that despite very stringent safety arrangements accidents can occur. This has made the public wary of nuclear power and more likely to accept alternative sources of power.

6.2.2   Hydroelectric power

The production of hydroelectric power is a clean, non-polluting, long-lasting, renewable source. Large-scale hydroelectric plants are responsible for about 17% of the electricity supply in developed countries and for 31% in developing countries. The power is derived indirectly from solar radiation as this evaporates water from the oceans and land which returns as rain which forms rivers and lakes. Hydroelectricity (hydropower) represents a proven technology and has the advantage that it is not linked to CO_2 or other gas emissions. However, no energy generation process is without its environmental impact. In the case of hydropower, the environmental impact, although site specific, can engender resistance where villages are flooded and river flow patterns changed. The danger of the dam collapsing due to earthquakes also causes concern. The building of dams and power stations is very capital intensive, and another limiting factor is the availability of suitable sites. For these reasons, the expansion of hydropower has been restricted.

6.2.3   Tidal power

The regular rise and fall of water level due to tides can be harnessed to generate electricity. Like hydropower the process is clean, reliable, long-lasting and renewable. The tidal amplitude in bays or estuaries over the area involved gives an estimate of the potential energy of a site. The normal construction is to trap the tidal flow behind a barrier or dam, releasing the water through turbines as the tide drops and in some cases as the tide flows in. Sites with a sufficient tidal range and area which can be practically enclosed by a barrier are limited, and tidal power represents about 10% of the energy that is available from hydroelectricity. A barrier system has been functioning for 20 years at the Rance estuary in Brittany, producing some 240 kW. There have been proposals for the construction of a barrier on the Severn estuary, producing 8.6 GW (8.6×10^9 watts) of power, and for others in the Bay of Fundy (Canada) and at St Malo in France. The Severn estuary proposal would represent a huge project, with a barrier 15.9 km long and construction costs estimated (at 1988 figures) as $8280 million (Boyle, 1996). The environmental impact on the local ecology would be enormous, with changes in tidal and current patterns which would affect both fish and birds. Other practical problems of barrier construction are silting up and fouling of the turbines.

6.2.4   Wave power

Schemes for the harnessing of the rise and fall of waves are under investigation in a number of countries. Devices for the conversion of wave energy to shaft power or compression have been proposed and a number have been tested. The problem at present appears to be related to the efficiency and the strength of construction to be able to withstand winter conditions, and the initial costs and results suggest that the best location would be offshore rather than in coastal locations.

6.2.5   Wind power

Harnessing the power of the wind is one of the most promising alternative methods of electricity generation as it has the potential to generate substantial amounts of energy without pollution. Over 7000 MW of wind power electricity generation has been installed worldwide. The wind can also be used to drive water pumps in order to store energy, to charge batteries in remote regions, or as off-grid power sources. The potential for wind power has been recognised and programmes have been initiated in 15 countries, including Brazil, China, Denmark, Spain, India, the USA and the UK, with the OECD funding $45 million of research and development in 1996 (Milborrow, 1998). Most wind turbines are horizontal-axis rotors with the ability to rotate as the wind direction changes. The typical rotor is up to 66 m in diameter, with three blades constructed from glass-reinforced plastic. These rotors turn at about 25 rpm, generating 100–700 kW per 55 m rotor. Bulk generation requires 10–100 machines in a 'wind farm'. These need to be sited in exposed locations and care needs to be taken in their installation as they can be intrusive in the landscape and can produce noise. The obvious disadvantage of wind power is that it is reliant on the wind, which can be variable even in windier areas, and although land disturbance is small there have been complaints about the noise generated by the turbines. One method of reducing the impact on the landscape is to site the rotors offshore, which also has the advantage of a steadier wind velocity. The first example of this form of farm was at Vindely in Denmark. This was constructed in 1991 and consists of eleven 459 kW turbines sited 1.5–3 km offshore. In the UK wind farms containing a large number of turbines each generating up to 100 kW of power have been built in Cornwall and Yorkshire and recently another was opened in South Wales. The economics of this form of electricity generation depend on local conditions and the price of fossil fuels. Development is capital intensive but in Denmark the price has seen an 8% drop each year for the last 10 years (Milborrow, 1998).

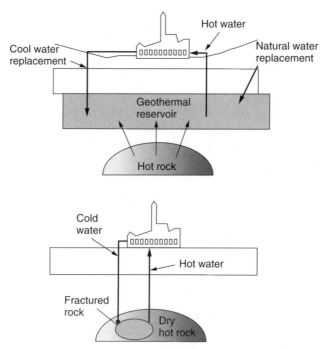

Fig. 6.8 The generation of electricity using geothermal heat. At the top hot water, prefer-
ably above 150°C, is removed from a reservoir of hot water heated by permeable hot rocks.
The water is replaced naturally or cold water is pumped back to replace that removed. At the
bottom hot dry rocks are fractured, often by hydraulic pressure, which allows water to be
introduced to extract the heat.

6.2.6   Geothermal energy

The earth's centre is very hot at about 4000°C and this combined with heat
generated by the decay of radioactive material means that heat is conducted to
the surface. This heat transfer drives the geological processes of plate tectonics,
volcanoes, earthquakes and mountain formation (Wright, 1998). Most heat
which reaches the surface cannot be utilised, but in areas of volcanic activity
high-grade heat is retained in molten or hot rocks at a depth of 2–10 km.
Most volcanic activities are limited to the main plate tectonic areas where the
plates spread apart.

The heat from these hot or molten rocks can be extracted in two ways. The
first method of heat extraction is that which occurs naturally when these rocks
come in contact with groundwater. This results in water at up to 300°C
forming hot springs or geysers when it reaches the surface. If the temperature
of the water is above 150–170°C it can be used to run steam turbines directly
for the generation of electricity (Fig. 6.8). If the water is below 150°C it can
be used as a supply of hot water for industrial or domestic heating. This can
be seen in Iceland where the whole of the capital city is heated by geothermal

hot water. Electricity can also be generated if the water is used to heat a second liquid which has a lower vaporisation temperature than water (isobutane or isopentane), and this can be used to drive the turbines. In cases where the rocks are not accessible to water, if these dry hot rocks can be fractured to allow water to be pumped into the region then the heat could be extracted (Fig. 6.8). It has been proposed that hot rocks, mainly in granite regions, as these represent a large fraction of the upper crust and were formed from the magma, be fractured and wells used to supply water and to extract hot water. The principal cost is the drilling of the wells through hard crystalline rock and the fracture of the rock by water pressure. Experimental wells have been drilled at Fenton Hill, New Mexico, and the industry is optimistic about the progress (Boyle, 1996). In the UK the programme involved drilling bore holes up to 2 km in depth in Cornwall, but after the initial work it was decided in 1997 not to continue.

6.2.7 Solar energy

The sunlight collected can be used either directly or indirectly for:

- solar panels for hot water generation
- solar collectors for steam generation
- solar architecture for heating buildings
- solar thermal–electric, steam linked to electricity generation
- photovoltaic, direct generation of electricity
- solar hydrogen generation.

The use of solar panels and solar architecture to provide hot water and to heat buildings is well proven in many countries and is regarded as cost effective. The provision of solar collectors for the generation of electricity based on parabolic mirrors or collector fields has been investigated in very sunny conditions but may not function in countries such as the UK which are too cloudy. Photovoltaic generation of electricity is perhaps beyond the scope of this book, but a considerable effort is being made to improve photovoltaic production of electricity and to use this to form hydrogen as an energy store.

6.3 Biological energy sources

Biological materials have always been used as a source of energy, for example the burning of wood, but recently the use of biological materials to provide a renewable source of energy has attracted considerable attention (Kendall *et al.*, 1977 and Palz *et al.*, 1985). The use of renewable biological materials to replace fossil fuels has a number of advantages – reduction in coal and oil use, reduction in the emission of greenhouse and other gases – and this supply of energy is inexhaustible and renewable. In the UK the Ministry of Agriculture, Fisheries and Food (MAFF) has encouraged the planting of energy crops with the Arable Area Payments Scheme, and the UK also has the Non-Fossil Fuel

Table 6.6   Possible sources of biofuels

Biomass	Source	Fuel
Wood/grass	Woody plants Short-rotation coppice Perennial grasses	Wood chips Charcoal Methanol/ABE*
Starch	Cereals Cassava Maize Potato	Ethanol/ABE
Sugar	Sugarcane Sugarbeet Jerusalem artichoke Grain sorghum	Ethanol/ABE
Oil	Rape Sunflower *Euphorbia* Algae	Transesterified oils Oils
Whole plant	Water hyacinth Algae	Biogas Direct use
Bacteria	Cyanobacteria	Hydrogen

* ABE is the acetone/butanol/ethanol fermentation.

Obligation (NFFO) where regional electricity companies must purchase some of their electricity derived from a non-fossil source and this supply commands a premium price. Biomass is already supplying some 15% of the world's energy needs, i.e. 55 EJ (55×10^{18} J) per year (25 million barrels of oil per day) (Scurlock *et al.*, 1993).

Energy can be produced from biological material either by direct combustion of wood or crop residues or by its conversion to another fuel such as methane or ethanol. Table 6.6 outlines the possible sources of biofuels and the types of fuel formed. The energy sources can be as follows:

- combustion of biomass
- production of biogas (methane)
- plant-derived oils
- production of ethanol
- acetone/butanol/ethanol fermentation (ABE)
- production of hydrogen.

6.4   Combustion of biomass

Biomass is the term for organic matter both living and dead, such as trees, crops, grasses, roots and plant process waste. The types of biomass are therefore very diverse and a number of methods of extracting energy from biomass are currently being investigated in a number of countries. The conversion of biomass into heat or power can take a number of options: direct combustion, gasification and pyrolysis. The direct combustion of biomass in the form of wood has been with us for thousands of years as a source of heat, but in order to produce other forms of energy such as electricity it needs to be burnt in boilers to produce steam in order to run turbines. Some 90% of the biomass energy is held in trees and in developing countries timber is used not only for energy but for a number of other industries. At the same time the trees are not being replaced at the same rate as they are being harvested so that the resource is being depleted and carbon dioxide added to the atmosphere. Another problem of using wood in boilers is that, although combustion technology is advanced for coal and oil, the combustion of wood is not well understood. Gasification is a process where the biomass is reacted with steam and oxygen to produce a gaseous fuel. The resulting gas is a mixture of carbon monoxide, hydrogen, methane, carbon dioxide and nitrogen. There are a number of gasification methods operating at various temperatures. The value of the gasification process is that it produces a cleaner fuel, which as a gas is more versatile, as it can be burnt in boilers, internal combustion engines and gas turbines. Under some conditions gasification can produce synthesis gas which is a mixture of carbon monoxide and hydrogen and can be used to synthesise hydrocarbons. Pyrolysis is the heating of the biomass in the absence of air at temperatures of 300–500°C. Under these conditions the solids which remain are charcoal, and the volatiles if collected can, after treatment, be used as fuel oil. The production of charcoal has been known for centuries; as a fuel it has twice the energy density of wood and burns at a higher temperature.

The sources of biomass for the above processes can be agricultural wastes, domestic and industrial wastes and purpose-grown crops. The energy content of the wastes or crops is given in Table 6.7 and compared with petrol. The residues from forestry and timber processing are obvious sources but are often discarded. Straw burning has been stopped in the UK, and straw represents a considerable source of energy. At present some 200,000 tonnes of straw, less than 1% of the total produced in the UK, are burnt in boilers. In tropical countries wastes like bagasse (sugarcane), rice husks and old cotton plants are under investigation as boiler fuels. Domestic and industrial wastes also contain combustible material and this can be used as fuel. Most of the domestic waste in the UK goes to landfill sites, but there are a few solid-waste burners operating in the UK and these sell non-fossil-fuel generated electricity. The disadvantage of wastes is that they have to be treated to remove non-combustible materials prior to combustion.

The growth of crops specifically for the production of energy has attracted attention in particular in the EU, with the provision for renewable material for bioenergy generation. The bioenergy systems have the advantages of being renewable and carbon dioxide neutral, and utilising the excess land in the EU, but the main limitations are the costs of harvesting, delivery, drying and

Table 6.7 Average energy content of fuels

Fuel	Energy (GJ/tonne)
Wood (20% moisture)	15
Paper	17
Dung (dried)	16
Straw (dried)	14
Sugarcane	14
Domestic refuse	9
Commercial wastes	16
Grass	4
Oil (petroleum)	42
Coal	28
Natural gas	55

Source: Boyle, 1996 by permission of Oxford University Press.

storage and the combustion technology. If these crops are to replace coal or gas as a fuel they need to be able to compete on a cost basis. One of the main parameters influencing cost is productivity as measured in terms of dry weight of biomass per hectare per year. Three main crops have been considered as possible candidates: forestry (wood chips), short-rotation coppice, and perennial grasses. Forestry has long been recognised as an economic crop, with annual yields of up to 20 t/ha, and can be used directly as wood chips or for the production of charcoal and oil via pyrolysis. Short-rotation coppice of willow (*Salix*) and poplar (*Populus*) appears to be the most promising crop, with annual yields of 9–20 t/ha (Table 6.8). The third group are the perennial grasses such as *Miscanthus*, napier grass (*Pennisetum*) and limpograss (*Hemmthria*). These are not native to the UK or Europe but have a fast growth rate and give high yields (Table 6.8). *Miscanthus* can be grown in Europe and is under trials at present within the EU. When considering a large-scale bioenergy programme the following need to be considered:

● land availability
● productivity of species
● environmental sustainability
● social factors
● economic feasibility.

6.5 Biogas

Anaerobic digestion has been developed for the treatment of high BOD organic wastes (Chapter 3) and produces biogas, consisting of 50–75% methane. In developed countries this biogas is used to power the sludge pumps and heat the anaerobic reactors in sewage treatment plants. A digester can produce 200–400 m³ of gas at 11 GJ (11×10^9 J) which yields two-thirds of the original

Table 6.8 Biomass yields for potential biofuel plants

Plant	Dry wt/ha/yr
Woody plants	
Populus	10–17
Salix dasyclodo	6–15
Eucalyptus grandis	15
Oil plants	
Rapeseed	2–3 (oil yield 0.4)
Hydrocarbon plants	
Calotropis	10.8–21.9
Euphorbia lethyris	3–10
Grasses	
Sugarcane	38–70
Sorghum	20–37
Miscanthus	20
Limpograss (*Hemmthria*)	7–22
Napiergrass (*Pennisetum*)	34–55
Maize	26
Aquatic	
Water hyacinth (*Eichornia*)	52–100
Cattails (*Typha*)	8–34
Root and herbaceous	
Sweet potato (*Ipomoea*)	5–21
Jerusalem artichoke (*Helianthus*)	2.8–9
Sugarbeet	7.8–15.4
Cassava (*Manihot*)	6.1–13.2

Sources: Klass, 1981; Lewis, 1985; Martin, 1991.

energy in the dung or sewage. In other cases the biogas has been used to generate electricity, as in some cases it commands a non-fossil-fuel premium as part of the NFFO agreement. In developing countries, anaerobic digesters have been linked to on-site treatment of waste and the production of gas. Both India and China have seen extensive development of these small biogas plants where the feedstock is mainly pig or cattle waste. In some areas water hyacinth has been specifically grown on wastes in lagoons for digestion to produce biogas. A typical design is shown in Fig. 6.9. The digester is run at ambient temperature, which is fine in many parts of India and China in summer, but in winter in areas with low temperatures gas production may be greatly reduced. In these systems 90% of the gas is used for cooking and lighting. The loading rates are in the region of 10 kg cattle dung per cubic metre per day, producing gas at 0.15 m^3/d per m^3 of tank volume.

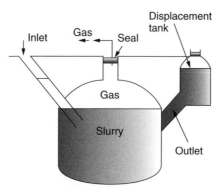

Fig. 6.9 An example of an anaerobic digester for the conversion of animal dung into biogas. The gas is collected and provides low-pressure gas for cooking and heating in countries such as India and China.

Another source of biogas is landfill sites which produce a mixture of carbon dioxide and methane. In the UK a large proportion of domestic waste is placed in landfill sites. Although the contents of a landfill site are very mixed, the conditions are anaerobic and with a sufficient concentration of organic material biogas will be formed. In early sites the build-up of the gas constituted a hazard as a potentially explosive mixture. However, increasingly landfill sites which are provided with the means of collecting the biogas are being used for power generation.

6.6 Oils

One of the problems of developing fuels from renewable resources is the development of a liquid fuel which will replace the petrol and diesel used in motor vehicles. Rudolf Diesel's first engine ran for the first time on 10 August 1893 and the patent when filed suggested that the fuel could be either powdered coal or a petroleum-based fuel. It was also reported that he also tried groundnut oil as a fuel, and later castor oil was also used (Shay, 1993). Thus the use of plant-derived oil in the internal combustion engine is not new, and such engines were probably not developed due to the availability of cheap petroleum-based fuels. On a short-term basis plant oils can be used directly in a diesel engine, but the differences between the oils stops their long-term use and thus they need modification before extended use is possible. Plant-derived fuels have the advantage that they produce little sulphur dioxide on combustion and are easily biodegradable. Plant oils are normally extracted from seeds where the plant uses oil rather than starch as an energy store for the developing plantlet. Seed oil can be extracted from a wide range of crops which can be grown in most climates and locations. A list is given in Table 6.9 where it is clear that perennial crops give a higher yield. Despite this fact, annual crops such as rape and soyabeans have commanded most interest, probably because there is already a market for their oil (Coghlan, 1997).

Table 6.9   Oil yields from oilseed crops

Plant	Approximate yields (kg/ha/yr)
Perennials	
Elaeis guineensis (oil palm)	3000–5000
Cocos nucifera (coconut)	800
Orbignya spp. (Babassu palm)	1100
Sapium sebiferum (tallow tree)	300
Jatropha curcas (physic nut)	200–800
Annuals	
Helianthus annuus (sunflower)	600–750
Arachis hipogaea (groundnut)	1350–1700
Glycine max (soybean)	442
Brassica napus (rapeseed)	640–1388
Cuphea spp.	288–720
Salicornia bigelovii	600

Source: Shay, 1993.

The principal problems with using unmodified oils in diesel engines are that residuals such as waxes and gums clog the fuel lines, high viscosity causes poor atomisation and therefore poor combustion, and polymerisation of unsaturated components in the combustion chamber causes deposits on the cylinders. Therefore, unless degummed filtered oils are used, some form of oil modification is required.

There are four methods of modifying plant oils: blending, microemulsification, pyrolysis and transesterification. Plant oils can be blended with diesel oil to form a mixture which can be used in unmodified engines with a mixture containing up to 20% plant oil. This is cheap and allows unmodified oil to be used, but on storage the two oils separate. Microemulsification is the blending of diesel with short-chain alcohols and surfactants to form a microemulsion. Mixtures of methanol and triolein have given good results, but the economics of this process are probably not satisfactory. Pyrolysis is a heating process (300–500°C) which breaks the triglyceride structure. Soyabean oil has been treated in this way and has yielded an oil with properties close to diesel. However, the yields of pyrolysis are poor and the conditions expensive so that this may not be adopted. Transesterification of plant oils with methanol or ethanol in the presence of an acid catalyst yields fatty acid esters and glycerol (Fig. 6.10). Oils such as soyabean, canola and particularly rapeseed oil have formed oils which were similar in properties to diesel oil (Table 6.10).

Other plant sources of oils are herbaceous plants, trees and algae. A number of herbaceous plants produce hydrocarbons (terpenes), particularly those in the Euphorbiaceae such as *Hevea brasiliensis*, *Euphorbia lathyris* and *Calotropis procera*. The hydrocarbons are produced as a latex which consists largely of a

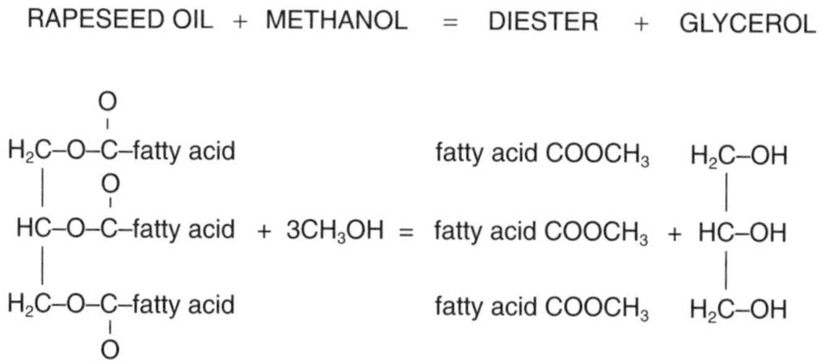

RAPESEED OIL + METHANOL = DIESTER + GLYCEROL

O
‖
H_2C–O–C–fatty acid   fatty acid COOCH$_3$ H_2C–OH
| O
| ‖
HC–O–C–fatty acid + 3CH$_3$OH = fatty acid COOCH$_3$ + HC–OH
|
H_2C–O–C–fatty acid   fatty acid COOCH$_3$ H_2C–OH
‖
O

Fig. 6.10 The formation of biodiesel by the transesterification of rapeseed oil to form esters and glycerol.

Table 6.10 The properties of biodiesel

Property	Biodiesel	Diesel fuel	Heating fuel
Specific gravity	0.88	0.83–0.86	0.83–0.86
Calorific value (MJ/litre)	33.2	35.3–36.3	35.3–36.3
Viscosity (cSt)	7.2	9.5	7.5
Flash point (°C)	185	55	55–120

Source: Staat and Vallet, 1994.

C_{30} triterpenoid which can be cracked (pyrolysed) to form petrol. The herbaceous plants can be grown in various parts of the world and give quite good yields in terms of dry weights per hectare (Table 6.7). Annual plants do have a problem of soil erosion and the expense of annual planting which is not found for trees.

Trees such as *Eucalyptus globus*, *Pittosporum resiniferum* and *Copaifera multijuga* produce oils, often in the fruit as in *P. resiniferum*, but with the Brazilian tree *C. multijuga* the trunk can be tapped and the oil used directly as a diesel replacement. The plant-derived oils have an advantage over ethanol as they have a higher energy composition similar to diesel and petrol (Table 6.11), and they have a number of other advantages:

- reduce the use of fossil fuels
- liquid
- high viscosity at low temperatures
- low sulphur content
- oxygenated nature means low NO$_x$ formation
- carbon dioxide neutral
- higher energy content than ethanol
- biodegradable.

Table 6.11   Energy content of plant oils, algae and petroleum-based fuels

Fuel	Energy content (MJ/kg)
Petrol	47.3
Diesel	43.0
Crude oil	42.3
Ethanol	29.4
Methanol	22.4
Rapeseed oil	39.5
Castor oil	37.0
Sunflower oil	36.9
Euphorbia oil	39.3
Chlorella vulgaris	28.0

Much development has concentrated on rapeseed oil as this is a crop which can be easily grown in Europe and North America. Transesterified rapeseed oil is at present being used in buses in the UK and Europe. At present the price of plant-derived oil cannot compete with diesel, as the best yield of oil comes from palm oil at 3.4 t/ha and from rapeseed with a biomass yield of 2–3 t/ha and an oil yield of 0.4 t/ha.

The accumulation of storage lipids does occur at high levels in a limited number of microorganisms, notably the algae and yeasts (Ratledge, 1989) under specific conditions. Algae have the advantage that they do not require a substrate for growth and as they fix carbon dioxide they are carbon dioxide neutral on combustion. Microalgae can accumulate up to 75% dry weight of their cells as lipid (Table 6.12), often under conditions of nitrogen depletion, which has been shown to stimulate lipid accumulation by yeasts (Moreton, 1988). The triglycerides cannot be used directly as a fuel but can be trans-esterified to low melting point esters (Fig. 6.10) or catalytically converted into hydrocarbons which can be used as petrol substitutes. Oil from *Chaetocera muelleri* and *Monoraphidium minutum* show similarities with transesterified vegetable oils, but processing the whole cells gave problems with a high ash content. One of the most promising algae is *Botyrococcus braunii* where brown resting cells can produce up to 86% of their weight as two polyunsaturated terpenoid hydrocarbons. Catalytic cracking of these hydrocarbons yields 67% petrol, 15% aviation fuel, 15% diesel and 3% residual oil (Calvin, 1985). However, the productivity rate for hydrocarbon accumulation is too low to be economic at 0.12–0.15 grams per litre per day.

Algal cells can be used directly without the extraction of the oil as a fuel for diesel engines, replacing up to 85% of the diesel. The algae can be regarded as a fine powder which like pulverised coal will burn rapidly. *Chlorella vulgaris* has a calorific value of 21 kJ/g, but this can be increased to 28 kJ/g when the lipid content of the cells is increased from 21% to 58% by growing the cells in low nitrogen medium. The elimination of the oil extraction step should improve the economics of the process.

Table 6.12 Lipid content of some algae

Species	Maximum lipid content (%w/w)
Monalanthus salina	72
Botryococcus braunii	53–75
Dunaliella primolecta	54
Dunaliella bardawil (salina)	47
Navicula pelliculsa	45
Radipsphaera negevensis	43
Biddulphia aurita	40
Chlorella vulgaris	40–58
Nitzschia palea	40
Ochromonas dannica	39–71
Chlorella pyrenoidosa	36
Peridinium cinctum	36
Neochloris oleabundans	35–54
Oocystis polymorpha	35
Chrysochromulina spp.	33–48
Phaeodactylum tricornutum	31
Stichococcus bacillaris	32

Sources: Kosaric and Velikonja, 1995; Scragg and Leathers, 1988.

6.7 Ethanol

The ability of microorganisms to produce alcohol from sugars has been known since Ancient Egyptian times and could be regarded as one of the first uses of biotechnology. Apart from its use in the brewing, wine and spirits industries, ethanol is widely used in the chemical industry and was used as a motor fuel in the early days of motoring. Petrol engines will run on mixtures containing up to 20% ethanol without major modification. Table 6.13 shows that ethanol is not very different from petrol in the areas important in automotive fuels. The octane rating of ethanol is higher than that of petrol, as is the latent heat of vaporisation. The octane rating is a measure of the resistance of the fuel to pre-ignite when compressed in the cylinder of the engine. Lower-octane petrol will pre-ignite, causing 'pinking' and loss of power. The higher heat of vaporisation of ethanol means that as the fuel is vaporised in the carburetter the mixture is cooled to a lower temperature than for petrol. This means that more fuel enters the engine, in part compensating for the lower energy content. To avoid separation of an aqueous layer in cold weather the ethanol needs to be anhydrous. The heat of combustion (or gross energy) is lower than that of petrol, which leads to some reduction in performance and a 15–25% increase in fuel consumption. Ethanol has some disadvantages in that it mixes with water and this type of mixture will corrode steel tanks. Blending ethanol with petrol (gasohol) has advantages, but if water is present the ethanol and petrol will separate.

Table 6.13 Comparison of the characteristics of petrol and ethanol

Characteristics	Ethanol	Petrol
Boiling point (°C)	78	35–200
Density (kg/litre)	0.79	0.74
Gross energy (MJ/kg)	27.2	44.0
Latent heat of vaporisation (MJ/kg)	855	293
Flashpoint (°C)	45	13
Octane number	99	90–100

The use of ethanol as a fuel started in the 1930s in the USA where ethanol produced from maize was used at a concentration of 20% to produce gasohol called 'Agrol'. In the UK gasohol was marketed by the Cleveland Oil Company under the name of 'Discol' in the 1930s and this continued until the 1960s. In the USA gasohol was dropped by 1945 due to the availability of cheap fuel. A major change in ethanol use started in the 1970s, initiated by the oil crisis. Ethanol was a possible extender of petrol as a 10–20% mixture, or a complete replacement for petrol. Two countries, Brazil and the USA, initiated the production of biomass-derived ethanol and each had different approaches. In the USA dependence on imported oil was regarded as a problem. In the 1970s chemically produced ethanol was selling at $0.145 per litre but in the 1980s the increase in the feedstock increased ethanol prices to $0.53 per litre which was the same price as biologically produced ethanol. An additional reason for the production of alcohol as a fuel was the low prices that the farmers were getting for their maize and this could be an alternative market. Production was also stimulated by the removal of a 4 cents per gallon tax from ethanol by the Carter Administration's Energy Act in 1979. Congress set a goal of 10% of total petrol consumption to be replaced by ethanol by 1990.

6.7.1 Production of ethanol in the USA

The main source of renewable material available in the USA for fermentation was starch extracted from maize or other starchy crops (sorghum, cassava, barley), and perhaps wastes such as cane or citrus molasses, cheese whey, sulphite liquor and potato wastes. It was thought that there would be both small and large producers of ethanol. In 1988 51 plants were operating of which 12 used waste material and the one situated in Hawaii used molasses. However, some 78% of the ethanol was produced by eight plants as maize was the main source of starch, and in the 1990s only one waste-utilising plant remained. Maize is normally wet milled to yield not only starch but oil, gluten and high protein material (Fig. 6.11). The main organism used in fermentation

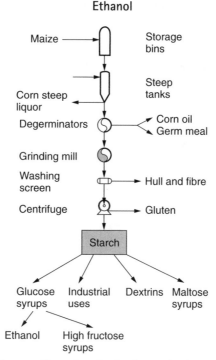

Fig. 6.11 The use of wet milling of maize in the production of glucose syrups for the production of ethanol. Other products are also indicated.

Table 6.14 Ethanol-producing bacteria and yeasts

Yeasts	Substrates
Saccharomyces cerevisiae	Glucose, fructose, galactose, maltose, maltotriose, xylulose
S. carlsbergensis	Glucose, fructose, galactose, maltose, maltotriose, xylulose
Kluyveromyces fragilis	Glucose, galactose, lactose
Candida tropicalis	Glucose, xylose, xylulose
Bacteria	
Zymomonas mobilis	Glucose, fructose, sucrose
Clostridium thermocellum (thermophilic)	Glucose, cellobiose, cellulose

is *Saccharomyces cerevisiae*, and although this is efficient in the formation of ethanol the substrates that it can use are somewhat limited (Table 6.14). *Saccharomyces* spp. cannot use either starch or cellulose so that if these are to be utilised some form of pretreatment in needed. The starch is converted to sugar by heating to 150–169°C to gelatinise the starch granules and this is followed by hydrolysis by amylases or acid. Often an amylase is added before

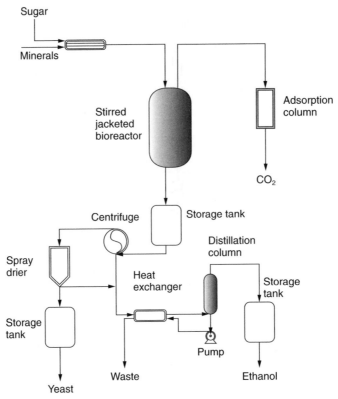

Fig. 6.12 An outline of the process for the production of ethanol from sugar as often found in US production systems.

heating to reduce the viscosity of the gelatinised starch. The enzyme is inactivated by the high temperature but is active during the heating process. The gelatinised starch, called the mash, is cooled to $90°C$ and more amylase added and incubated for 30–60 minutes. This is the liquefaction stage where the starch is converted to long-chain dextrins. The dextrins are converted to glucose by the addition of an *Aspergillus niger* amyloglucosidase and incubation at $50–60°C$ for 60–120 minutes. The sugar mix is then cooled to $30°C$ and the yeast added to start the fermentation (Fig. 6.12).

S. cerevisiae converts glucose to ethanol via the glycolytic pathway which leads to pyruvate which is converted to acetaldehyde with the release of carbon dioxide and then to ethanol (Fig. 6.13). The overall equation is given below:

$$C_6H_{12}O_6 \rightarrow 2C_2H_5OH + 2CO_2$$

The theoretical yield of ethanol from this equation is 51% of the substrate glucose, but some of the ATP formed in glycolysis is used for cell growth, which reduces the yield to 86% of the maximum. Yields of 90% and above have been obtained. This increase in yield is due to the use of ATP for cell maintenance,

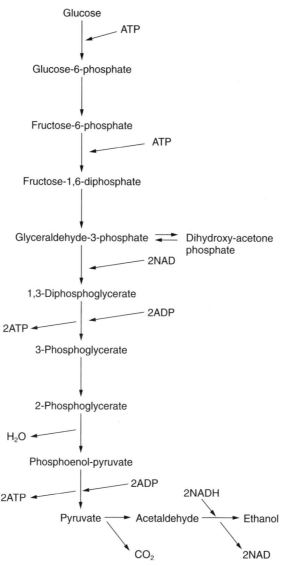

Fig. 6.13 The enzymatic steps in the formation of ethanol.

which increases as the ethanol content of the medium increases, at the expense of cell growth. The allows more of the sugar to be converted to ethanol.

The fermenter (bioreactor) is run at 30–35°C for 42–72 hours until a final concentration of 8–12% ethanol is obtained. This type of bioreactor operation is called batch but other forms of bioreactor operations exist: fed-batch, continuous, and multi-vessel continuous. The productivities of the various systems are given in Table 6.15. The traditional method of microbial growth

Table 6.15   Productivities of ethanol by batch and continuous fermentation

System	Ethanol productivity (grams per litre per hour)
Continuous, vacuum recycle	80
Continuous, recycle	40
Batch, recycle	15
Continuous, multi-stage	12
Continuous	5
Batch	2

Source: Kosaric and Velikonja, 1995.

has been batch culture in which the medium is inoculated with the organism and growth proceeds over a period of time. In some cases all the medium or carbon source is not added at the beginning of the culture but is added in aliquots during the growth of the microorganism in what is known as fed-batch culture. In batch culture the composition of the medium is constantly changing and therefore steady-state growth is not possible. Continuous culture is a system for the growth of microorganisms maintained at a steady growth rate by continuously removing medium and replacing it with fresh medium. There are essentially two types of continuous culture – chemostat and turbidostat – but only the former is used on an industrial scale and so discussion will be restricted to this system.

Fresh medium is pumped into the bioreactor at a constant flow rate and the vessel is mixed as well as possible. The culture volume is maintained constant by removing culture at the same rate as medium is pumped in. One of the simplest methods of achieving this is from a weir system. The rate of flow of the new medium (F) and the vessel volume (V) combine to form the parameter, the dilution rate D:

$$D = \frac{F}{V}$$

Under these conditions the rate of change in cell number or mass will be equal to the rate of growth of the cells, minus the cells lost as the medium is removed from the vessel:

$$\frac{dx}{dt} = \mu x - Dx$$

or

$$\frac{dx}{dt} = x(\mu - D)$$

At a steady state dx/dt is zero as there is no net growth. Thus the equation simplifies to

$$\mu = D$$

The system is self regulating as the dilution rate controls the rate of substrate supplied and the cells will consume the substrate at such a rate that the concentration in the vessel will decrease along with the growth rate, until a balance is reached.

Continuous culture is regarded as a more efficient way of cultivating cells as it does not entail the loss of time due to the lag phase of growth, cleaning, refilling and sterilising the vessel, which makes for a more efficient and higher-yielding process. The disadvantages of the continuous process are the need to maintain sterility over a long period of time and the throughput of large volumes. The batch process is much more adaptable for bioreactor runs which are different each time, and for simple processes the loss due to cleaning, refilling and sterilisation is small. In the multi-vessel continuous process one vessel is used to grow the cells rapidly and the cells from the first vessel are run into a larger vessel. As the flow rate is the same in the second vessel as in the first vessel, but the volume is larger, the dilution factor is smaller and hence the growth rate slower, especially as the substrate has already been depleted in the first vessel. The slower growth rate allows product to accumulate. However, as ethanol is formed during growth a slow growth rate is not required for ethanol accumulation and thus the low values in Table 6.15 can be explained. The recycling of cells, whether in batch or continuous, means the removal of the cell from the culture either at the end of growth in batch or from the culture removed in the continuous system. The cells can be removed by centrifugation or filtration and returned to the culture. This maintains a high level of cell (biomass) in the vessel, thus increasing productivity as can be seen in Table 6.15.

The final concentration of ethanol in a *S. cerevisiae* fermentation is generally 8–12% above the concentration at which the yeast metabolism is arrested, although other yeasts can tolerate higher ethanol concentrations. The reason for the loss of viability as the ethanol concentration increases is that ethanol is a solvent and disrupts the cell's lipid–protein membrane, making it increasingly leaky. Yeast strains with a higher tolerance to ethanol have membranes containing a higher proportion of longer-chain unsaturated fatty acids.

To be used as a fuel ethanol has to be more than 96% pure and therefore has to be separated from the fermentation medium and concentrated, usually by distillation. The distillation column can be used in a continuous manner or in a two-stage process where the first column is the stripping and the second the rectifier. The final ethanol concentration is usually 96%, and if water-free ethanol is required a second distillation is carried out in which benzene is mixed with the ethanol.

6.7.2 Production of ethanol in Brazil

The reasons for the development of ethanol as a fuel in Brazil were to reduce the imports of petrol as Brazil had few oil fields, opening up areas of the country for cultivation, to provide employment, to increase the industrial base, and to develop ethanol exports of plant and expertise. In addition Brazil is one of the largest producers of sugar from sugarcane so that a good substrate was readily available which did not require processing. Sugarcane also has one of the highest yields of potential biofuel crops (Table 6.8). The development started in 1975 and by 1984/85 about 95% of the cars were run on ethanol or gasohol. This number has declined to about 50% in 1990 due to pressure from cheap petroleum but this still represents a considerable saving in petrol use.

The processes used for the production of ethanol were on a smaller scale than in the USA. The sugar extracted from the sugarcane is fermented in bioreactors of $100-200$ m^3 which are often able to yield 8–12% ethanol. The bagasse, the fibre and cellulose remaining after the juice is removed is often burnt to provide heat for the distillation.

6.7.3　Economics of ethanol production

It has been calculated that with maize the energy input to grow the crop is about 30% of the energy contained within the crop. If the crop is used to produce ethanol the output is less than required to grow and process the crop (Table 6.16) and this is also true for sugarcane. However, if the fossil fuel is replaced by bagasse for the distillation then the input/output energy ratio rises to 1.29 for maize and 2.03 for sugarcane.

There are fixed costs in biological energy production. In the case of the Brazilian ethanol programme there is some disagreement about the economics of ethanol production. Some authors have suggested that the cost of ethanol was as low as $0.185 per litre in the 1980s, at which price it could compete with fossil fuels. However, the continued low prices for oil appear to make ethanol in Brazil an expensive alternative.

6.7.4　Future developments

Possible alternative microorganisms for the production of ethanol are shown in Table 6.14. To replace *S. cerevisiae* they will need to have the following characteristics:

- ability to ferment a range of carbohydrates rapidly
- ethanol tolerance and ability to produce high levels of ethanol
- low levels of by-products
- osmotolerance, ability to use high concentrations of sugars
- high cell viability for recycle
- flocculation and sedimentation characteristics for downstream processing and recycle.

Zymomonas mobilis, a Gram-negative bacterium, has been isolated from fermenting sugary materials. It grows faster than *Saccharomyces* and produces ethanol more rapidly, but, like yeasts, grows on only a limited number of sugars. *Z. mobilis* can also tolerate high sugar concentrations and a higher final

Table 6.16 Energy input required to produce 1000 litres of ethanol from maize and sugarcane

Input	Maize (10^3 kcal)	Sugarcane (10^3 kcal)
Maize	3259*	—
Sugarcane	—	1945[†]
Transport	325	400
Water	90	70
Steel	228	91
Cement	60	15
Coal	4617	—
Bagasse[§]	—	7600
Total input	8579	10,121
Output	5130[‡]	5130[‡]
If the costs of the fuels, coal and bagasse are removed, total input energy is	3961	2521
Ratio output/input	1.29	2.03

* 2700 kg of maize is required to produce 1000 litres ethanol and represents 3259 kcal energy.

[†] 14,000 kg of sugarcane are needed to produce 1000 litres ethanol which represents 1945 kcal energy input.

[‡] 1000 litres ethanol = 5130 kcal.

[§] Bagasse is the fibrous material left after the sugar has been extracted from the sugarcane, which will burn well.

Source: Primental et al., 1988.

ethanol concentration but to date has not replaced the yeasts. The reason for this is due to the pathway used by Z. mobilis to accumulate ethanol. Z. mobilis metabolises glucose via the Entner–Doudoroff pathway (Fig. 6.14) which produces two moles of NADH and only one mole of ATP compared with two formed in glycolysis. However, when fructose and sucrose are metabolised the products formed are different. Fructose tends to encourage the formation of dihydroxyacetone, mannitol and glycerol. In the presence of sucrose Z. mobilis forms levans, high molecular weight sugar polymers. Thus although Z. mobilis has many of the attributes required for ethanol formation, it cannot be used as it produces unacceptably high levels of by-products.

The direct conversion of cellulose to ethanol would produce a much cheaper process if this were possible. Three clostridial strains – C. thermocellum, C. thermosaccharolyticum and C. thermohydrosulfuricum – are Gram-positive thermophilic anaerobes which are capable of degrading cellulose to ethanol, as well as using a number of other carbohydrates. However, lignocellulose and cellulose require physical disruption before they can be degraded by cellulases

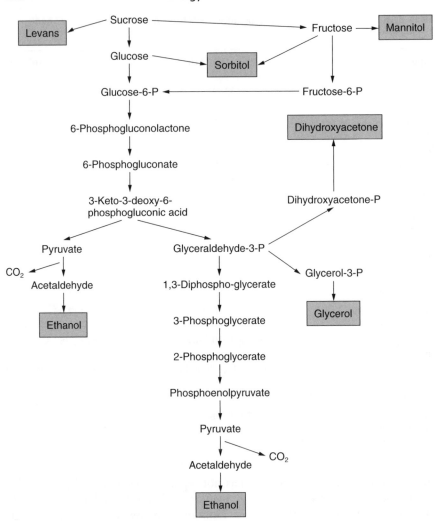

Fig. 6.14 The Entner–Doudoroff pathway.

and the rate of breakdown is slow. The clostridial strains are less tolerant to ethanol than *S. cerevisiae* and produce a number of organic acids as by-products. These features have meant that the clostridial strains and lignocellulase have not been adopted for ethanol production to date. The ideal situation would be a thermophilic bacterium which could convert cellulose to ethanol at a temperature which would distil off the ethanol formed.

6.7.5   Other alcohols

Butanediol has a similar heating value to ethanol but is more expensive than ethanol. Before it can be used, butanediol needs to be either dehydrated to

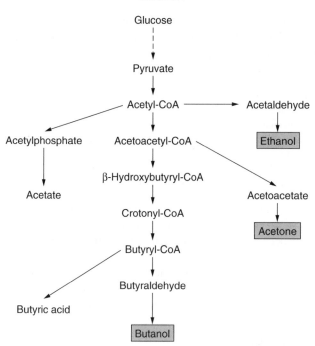

Fig. 6.15 Metabolic pathways involved in the production of solvents in clostridia.

methyl ethyl ketone (MEK), as this has a lower boiling point, or condensed to yield components for aviation fuels. Butanediol can occur in two forms and these are formed by bacteria such as *Bacillus polymyxa, Klebsiella pneumoniae, Bacillus subtilis* and *Serratia marcescens* (Kosaric and Velikonja, 1995). The yields are low, below 1 gram per litre per hour, and product recovery is difficult due to butanediol's high boiling point of 180°C. Although the cost of butanediol may be higher than that of ethanol, if production was combined with waste utilisation it may form an attractive product.

Another possible fuel is butanol which has a calorific value of 32 MJ/kg and is fully miscible with diesel oil. The commercial production of butanol started in 1915 with the discovery by Weismann that some clostridia could produce a mixture of butanol, acetone and ethanol. At this time there was a great demand for acetone as this was used in the production of cordite, an explosive, which was in great demand in World War I. Prior to this time acetone was prepared from calcium acetate which was produced by the pyrolysis of wood, with some 100 kg of wood needed to form 1 kg of calcium acetate. *Clostridium acetobutylicum, C. butylicum* and *C. butyricum* were the main strains used and these would produce different proportions of acetone, butanol and ethanol (6:3:1) when cultured on sugars. The pathways to the formation of these compounds are given in Fig. 6.15. The laboratory-based observations were rapidly converted to large-scale industrial processes producing up to 13×10^6

kg acetone per year, and 26×10^6 kg butanol per year. The processes continued until the 1950s when they were replaced by the production of acetone from propylene which was produced by the petrochemical industry. The biological process could not compete because of:

- low solvent yields (30–35% of carbon source)
- low solvent concentration (20–25 g/litre)
- loss of strain activity
- high cost of distillation, due to low solvent concentration
- rise in substrate costs (molasses)
- large quantities of effluent
- competition from petrochemical production.

However, the process does have the advantage in that the clostridia can ferment a large range of treated substrates. In addition, over the years considerable information has been obtained on the genetics and regulation of solvent accumulation. It is clear that there are two different mechanisms for alcohol formation and the elucidation of the molecular mechanisms will open up the possibilities of genetic engineering to give high yields. The problem of large quantities of effluent can also be addressed more efficiently today.

6.8   Hydrogen production

In contrast to fossil fuels, hydrogen is an ideal fuel as on combustion the only product is water, making it a very clean fuel which adds no other greenhouse gases to the environment. Hydrogen can be used as an automotive fuel as well as a fuel for the generation of electricity. The suggestion that hydrogen could be an alternative fuel was initiated by the energy crisis in the 1970s. Hydrogen can be produced by photovoltaic or other energy-generating systems by the electrolysis of water or by biological systems.

Basic research some 100 years ago had shown that algae and bacteria produced hydrogen (Benemann, 1996). The blue-green cyanobacterium *Anabena cylindrica* was shown to produce hydrogen *in vivo*. However, a large number of biological and engineering problems have to be solved before the biological production of hydrogen can be realised and biotechnology may have some solutions to these problems. The biological production of hydrogen can take place in the light using energy from solar radiation or in the dark using energy stores formed during photosynthesis. There are six possible pathways for the generation of hydrogen (Fig. 6.16).

In the light, the direct photobiological production of hydrogen uses the same pathways that are used in photosynthesis. Photosynthesis involves the absorption of light by light-harvesting complexes of photosystem II which is used to split water, producing oxygen. A second photosystem I generates the reducing power to reduce carbon dioxide. In green plants only carbon dioxide is reduced but in some microalgae, both eukaryotes and prokaryotes, hydrogenase enzymes are also present which under some conditions form

1. Direct photolysis

2. Heterocysts of nitrogen-fixing *Cyanobacterium*

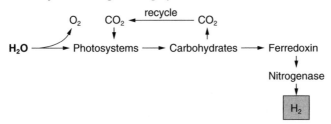

3. Indirect photolysis

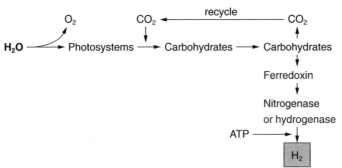

4. Photofermentation, photosynthetic bacteria

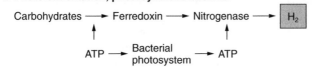

5. Microbial shift reaction, photosynthetic bacteria

$$CO + H_2O \longrightarrow \boxed{H_2} + CO_2$$

6. Dark fermentations

Carbohydrates $\longrightarrow$ Ferredoxin $\longrightarrow$ Hydrogenase $\longrightarrow$ $\boxed{H_2}$

Fig. 6.16 The possible processes for the biological production of hydrogen (from Benemann, 1996).

hydrogen. The reaction is shown in Fig. 6.17. However, the rates of hydrogen production are much lower than that of carbon dioxide fixation and this is caused by the inhibition of the hydrogenase by oxygen which is also produced in the process of splitting water during photosynthesis. Thus the direct process

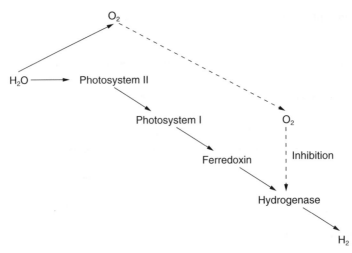

Fig. 6.17 The process of microalgal production of hydrogen and inhibition by oxygen.

will require an oxygen-stable reversible hydrogenase to function properly, which may be possible with advances in genetic engineering. The problem of inhibition of the hydrogenase by oxygen has been solved by some cyanobacteria such as *Anabena cylindrica* where the two reactions are compartmentalised (Fig. 6.16). The water splitting occurs in the vegetative cells and the carbon dioxide is fixed in the heterocysts. The heterocysts contain a nitrogenase enzyme, which in the absence of nitrogen will form hydrogen, and the thick heterocyst wall reduces oxygen diffusion into the cell thus delaying inhibition. An alternative in non-heterocyst species is the separation of the two stages in time, such as day–night cycles (Fig. 6.16). Another indirect process is to use organisms in which light is used to convert organic compounds into hydrogen and carbon dioxide or the formation of hydrogen by an anaerobic breakdown of organic compounds. Finally, one possible process is the production of hydrogen from carbon monoxide and water by photosynthesis bacteria in the dark.

Photovoltaic systems for the formation of hydrogen have steadily improved their efficiency up to 10% but the biological formation of hydrogen also needs improvement. Higher plants convert solar radiation at about 1% efficiency but microalgae can achieve efficiencies of up to 10%. Another restriction of photosynthesis is that both higher plants and microalgae can convert only 10–20% of normal daylight. Work is under progress using genetic engineering to improve photosynthetic efficiency. One process which may be possible is a two-stage process: the first stage is the photosynthetic fixation of carbon dioxide and then there is a switch to the dark anaerobic formation of hydrogen. The cultivation of microalgae in ponds and other bioreactors has been investigated for some time (Richmond, 1990). A disadvantage is that the conversion of the stored material is only 10–25% efficient, but this could be improved by incubation in the light by anaerobic conditions which will maximise the hydrogen formation (Benemann, 1997).

Table 6.17   Estimates of global renewable energy resources

Resources	Estimate
Solar radiation	1000
Wind	10
Tidal	0.1
Wave	0.5
Geothermal	30
Biomass	450 TW years*
Geothermal heat stored	>50 TW years*

* 1 TW year = 3.16×10^{19} joules.
Source: Johansson *et al.*, 1993.

6.9   Conclusions

Although the need for alternative fuels to replace fossil fuels as sources of energy for heating, transport and electricity generation may be delayed by increases in fuel efficiency and the discovery and extraction of new oil and gas fields, alternatives will eventually be required. What is needed are principally sources of energy for electricity generation and a liquid fuel for transport. Other, perhaps more urgent, requirements are fuels that will reduce or eliminate the emission of greenhouse gases and other atmospheric pollutants. There is a wide range of alternative energy sources, both biological and non-biological. The non-biological sources of nuclear, geothermal, hydroelectric and wind power are already being applied or under investigation. These are clean, renewable and long-lasting sources, but they do have an environmental impact and in the case of nuclear power a disposal and decommissioning problem. The potential for renewable energy sources is difficult to estimate but rough estimates have been made (Table 6.17). It is clear that biomass and thermal heat have the greatest potential, other than solar input, but which of these sources will be used will depend on a number of factors including capital cost and environmental impact.

   The biological sources of energy are also very diverse and can also provide liquid fuels. Biomass is already a source of fuel for electricity generation and heating and the use of specific crops is under investigation. Plants and microorganisms can also be used to produce liquid fuels such as oils, ethanol, butanediol and butanol. The cost of producing biomass-based energy is dependent upon many different factors such as agricultural and forestry costs, type of raw material, the location of plant and crop, labour costs, scale of production, and the type and operation of the process. All these factors need to be taken into consideration in developing fuels. Transesterified plant oils and ethanol have been successful in replacing diesel in Europe, the USA and Brazil. These fuels will be adopted only if they can compete on price (Table 6.18) or where specific conditions exist as in Brazil. Oil and gas are inexpensive at the present time when compared with renewable fuels (Table 6.18), apart from

Table 6.18   Relative electricity prices (pence per kWh) for fossil and renewable energy
sources

Energy source	Minimum price	Range
Fossil fuels		
Gas	2.2	2.8
Coal	1.8	3.8
Clean coal	4.4	5.6
Nuclear	2.2	5.5
Renewable		
Hydroenergy	1.8	2.8
Wind	2.5	6.2
Geothermal	3.0	5.2
Waste burning	2.5	4.2
Landfill gas	2.6	5.0
Modern biomass	5.5	5.8
Wave	10	—
Solar	10	—

Source: data from Milborrow, 1998.

hydroenergy, so that their adoption may take some time. Increases in process
efficiencies would bring the costs of renewable fuels within the range of fossil
fuels (Table 6.18). However, it may not be price that governs the future use of
non-fossil fuels, but legislation concerning greenhouse gases and other emissions
may force the adoption of these alternative fuels.

Thus at present the use of non-fossil fuels is only slowly being adopted, due
to the low prices of crude oil and gas, but the non-fossil fuels can deliver
energy sources which are

- diverse in source and form (solid, gas, liquid)
- clean, giving complete or considerable reductions in emissions
- carbon dioxide (greenhouse gas) zero or neutral, in order to slow global warming
- renewable and essentially inexhaustible
- advantageous in reducing or recycling waste products.

6.10   References

Anonymous (1997) World oil supply and demand. *Euro Energy Information Newsletter*,
    15.
Benemann, J. (1996) Hydrogen biotechnology: progress and prospects. *Nature
    Biotechnol.*, **14**, 1101–1103.
Benemann, J. (1997) Feasibility analysis of photobiological hydrogen production. *Int.
    J. Hydrogen Energy*, **22**, 979–987.

Boyle, G. (1996) *Renewable Energy: Power for a Sustainable Future*. Oxford University Press, Oxford.

Calvin, M. (1985) Fuel oils from plants, in K. W. Fuller and J. R. Gallon (eds), *Plant Products and the New Technology*. Clarendon Press, Oxford, pp. 147–160.

Coghlan, A. (1997) A perfect recipe for the North Sea. *New Scientist*, April, 23.

Energy Technology Support Unit (ETSU) (1994) *An Assessment of Renewable Energy for the UK*. ETSU, Harwell, Oxon, UK.

Fulkerson, W., Judkins, R. R. and Sanghvi, M. K. (1990) Energy from fossil fuels. *Scientific American*, September, 83–89.

Glazer, A. N. and Nikaido, H. (1994) *Microbial Biotechnology*. Freeman, New York.

Houghton, J. (1996) Climate change calls for action now. *Chemistry & Industry*, March, 232.

Houghton, J. T., Jenkins, G. J. and Ephraums, J. J. (1990) *Climate Change*. Cambridge University Press, Cambridge.

Johansson, T. B., Kelly, H., Reddy, A. K. N. and Williams, R. H. (1993) *Renewable Energy*. Island Press, Washington, DC.

Kendall, A., McDonald, A. and Williams, A. (1997) The power of biomass. *Chemistry & Industry*, May, 342–345.

Klass, D. L. (1981) *Biomass as a Non Fossil Fuel Source*. ACS Symposium Series 144, American Chem. Soc.

Kosaric, N. and Velikonja, J. (1995) Liquid and gaseous fuels from biotechnology: challenge and opportunities. *FEMS Microbiol. Rev.*, **16**, 111–142.

Kurano, N., Ikemoto, H., Miyashita, H., Hasegawa, T., Hata, H. and Miyachi, S. (1995) Fixation and utilization of carbon dioxide by microalgal photosynthesis. *Energy Convers. Mgmt*, **36**, 689–692.

Laws, E. A. and Berning, J. L. (1991) A study of the energetics and economics of microalgal mass culture with the marine chlorophyte *Tetraselmis suecica*: implications for use of power plant stack gases. *Biotechnol. Bioeng.*, **32**, 936–947.

Lewis, C. W. (1985) The energy content of crops, in K. W. Fuller and J. R. Gallon (eds), *Plant Products and the New Technology*. Clarendon Press, Oxford, pp. 11–28.

Martin, A. M. (1991) *Bioconversion of Waste Materials to Industrial Products*. Elsevier Applied Science, London.

Milborrow, D. (1998) Catching the breeze. *Chemistry & Industry*, March, 214–218.

Moreton, R. S. (1988) Physiology of lipid accumulating yeasts, in R. S. Moreton (ed.), *Single Cell Oil*. Longman Scientific and Technical, Harlow, UK.

Palz, W., Coombs, J. and Hall, D. O. (1985) *Energy from Biomass*. Elsevier Applied Science, London.

Primental *et al.* (1988) Food versus biomass fuel: socioeconomic and environmental impacts in the United States, Brazil, India and Kenya. *Advances in Food Research*, **32**, 185–238.

Ratledge, C. (1989) Biotechnology of oils and fats, in C. Ratledge and S. G. Wilkinson (eds), *Microbial Lipids*. Academic Press, London, vol. 2, pp. 567–668.

Richmond, A. (1990) Large scale microalgal culture and applications. *Prog. Phycol. Res.*, 7, 1–62.

Roberts, L. E. J., Liss, P. S. and Saunders, P. A. H. (1990) *Power Generation and the Environment*. Oxford University Press, Oxford.

Scragg, A. H. and Leathers, R. R. (1988) Production of fats and oils by plant and algal cell cultures, in R. S. Moreton (ed.), *Single Cell Oil*. Longman Scientific and Technical, Harlow, UK, pp. 71–98.

Scurlock, J. M. O., Hall, D. O., House, J. I. and Howes, R. (1993) Utilising biomass crops as an energy source: a European perspective. *Water, Air & Soil Pollution*, **70**, 499–518.

Shay, E. G. (1993) Diesel fuel from vegetable oils: status and opportunities. *Biomass and Bioenergy*, **4**, 227–242.

Staat, F. and Vallet, E. (1994) Vegetable oil methyl ester as a diesel substitute. *Chemistry & Industry*, November, 863–865.

Vilchez, C., Garbayo, I., Lobato, M. V. and Vega, J. M. (1997) Microalgae-mediated chemicals production and waste removal. *Enzyme Microb. Technol.*, **20**, 562–572.

World Energy Council (1994) *New Renewable Energy Resources*. Kogan Press, London.

Wright, P. M. (1998) Geothermal energy – harnessing heat from the centre of the earth. *Chemistry & Industry*, March, 208–212.

6.10.1   Recommended reading

Barry, R. G. and Charley, R. J. (1992) *Atmosphere, Weather and Climate*. 6th edition, Routledge, London.

Boyle, G. (1996) *Renewable Energy: Power for a Sustainable Future*. Oxford University Press, Oxford, UK.

Energy Technology Support Unit (ETSU). (1994) *An Assessment of Renewable Energy for the UK*. ETSU, Harwell, Oxon., UK.

Johansson, T. B., Kelly, H., Reddy, A. K. N. and Williams, R. H. (1997) *Renewable Energy*. Island Press, Washington, DC, USA.

Kohlmaier, G. H., Weber, M. and Houghton, R. A. (1998) *Carbon Dioxide Mitigation in Forestry and Wood Industry*. Springer Verlag, Hiedlberg, Germany.

Martin, A. M. (1991) *Bioconversion of Waste Materials to Industrial Products*. Elsevier Applied Science, London, UK.

Wellburn, A. (1994) *Air Pollution and Climate Change*. Addison Wesley Longman, Harlow, Essex, UK.

Chapter 7

Natural resource recovery

7.1 Introduction

Biological processes can not only be harnessed to reduce or eliminate pollution but also be used to extract oil and metals in the mineral and petrochemical industries. Metals and crude oil are both non-renewable resources which may have adequate supplies at present, but demand is unlikely to diminish so that new sources or improved extraction methods will eventually be needed. Microorganisms have the ability to extract metals from ores and have been used industrially since the 1950s for copper extraction (Agate, 1996). At present microbial mining is being used on an industrial scale for copper, uranium and gold.

This chapter first outlines the possible use of microorganisms and microbial products for the extraction of crude oil once the primary flow has ceased. The second half of the chapter covers the use of microorganisms for the recovery of metals from mining wastes, low grade ores and worked-out mines.

The primary recovery of crude oil can be from zero to 50% depending on the conditions of the source (Farouq Ali and Thomas, 1996). Some form of secondary recovery is normally applied to extract more of the oil and the techniques are collectively known as enhanced oil recovery (EOR). One method which can be included in EOR is based on the use of microorganisms to help to extract oil; this is known as microbially enhanced oil recovery (MEOR). MEOR is not used commercially at present because of its high costs in contrast to the present price of crude oil. However, crude oil stocks will diminish and the prices may rise, and under these conditions MEOR may be required.

7.2 Oil recovery

Crude oil accumulates in a diverse number of states from sand coated with viscous tars to light oils trapped in underground reservoirs. Crude oil originates from biological material which has been degraded anaerobically over a very long period of time at high temperatures and pressures. The majority of the compounds in crude oil are hydrocarbons, straight and branched chains, single, condensed and aromatic rings. These hydrocarbons can be aliphatics and aromatics such as benzene and toluene, and polycyclic hydrocarbons of

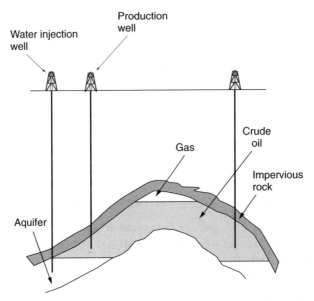

Fig. 7.1 The extraction of crude oil from an oil reservoir and the position of water injection wells.

higher molecular weight such as naphthalene. Higher molecular weight hydrocarbons are represented by the bitumens and tars. The proportion of the various components will affect the property of the oil which can range from light oils to heavy oils, bitumen and tars.

Crude oil is found in a number of sites and states and this will govern the extraction strategy. Tar sands are probably derived from oil reaching the surface, where the volatiles can be lost leaving the high molecular weight tars behind. These tar sands can be mined by opencast methods and the tar stripped from the sand by hot water and alkaline conditions. The oil needs to be dried before it can be shipped or treated. Treatment usually consists of upgrading the tar by cracking with heat and catalysis, to form lower molecular weight hydrocarbons. Underground accumulation of crude oil occurs at sites all over the world in porous sandstone, limestone and chalk. As oil is less dense than water and does not mix, oil is often forced upwards through the porous rock by rising water until the oil reaches a layer of impervious rock. If the impervious rock forms some type of dome an oil reservoir will form (Fig. 7.1). Reservoirs occur at all depths and often are under considerable pressure, mainly from dissolved gas and the pressure of the overlying rock; the presence of an aquifer can also increase the pressure. In many cases gas collects at the top of the reservoir. Oil is recovered from these reservoirs by first finding the dome by seismic investigation and then drilling into it. The pressure in the reservoir will force the lighter crude oils to the surface, as they are liquid at the well temperatures, which can be up to 90°C, but any bitumen and asphalt will

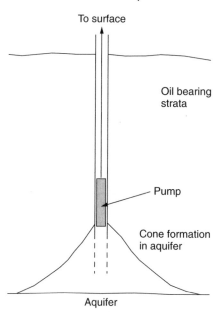

Fig. 7.2 The effect of 'coning' on the extraction of oil.

remain, as they are too viscous to flow, even at the elevated temperatures. If the pressure is very high in the reservoir the oil will be forced out of the well in what is known as a 'gusher'. The well is normally capped and the oil run off into storage and transport facilities. As the primary removal of the oil proceeds, the reservoir pressure drops, although pressure may be maintained by the aquifer. This primary extraction usually accounts for about 10–15% of the original oil in place (OOIP) (Millington *et al.*, 1994). Once the pressure has reduced to low levels the oil needs to be extracted by pumping. Mechanical (nodding donkey) or electrical pumps are placed at the base of the well and used to extract the oil. The suction applied at the base of the well may cause the water in the aquifer to rise if the rock is sufficiently permeable. If the water reaches the pump, water will be pumped out and this is a condition known as 'coning' (Fig. 7.2). This condition is a major problem in oil extraction and the pump may have to be stopped for some time to allow the cone to subside. Eventually the flow of oil is reduced to uneconomic levels which generally represent some 15–20% of the total oil (OOIP) in the reservoir.

Any further recovery of oil is known as secondary production and generally involves the injection of water or gas into the well to force out the oil. Water is used normally, as the gas from the reservoir is usually piped away and sold. Seawater can be used but the sulphate present will need to be removed, as any sulphur present will encourage the growth of sulphate-reducing bacteria which will degrade the oil. Water flooding involves the drilling of another well or wells (up to five) some distance from the production well, water normally

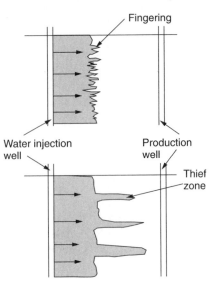

Fig. 7.3 Some of the problems associated with secondary oil extraction. Top, the process of 'fingering'; bottom, breakthrough or 'thief' zones.

being injected below the oil layers to force the oil out. This pattern can be arranged across an oil field (Fig. 7.1). Water can also be pumped into the oil-bearing rock itself to sweep out the oil. However, this technique is not without its problems. The rock, although porous, is unlikely to be homogeneous in structure; some channels will be considerably larger and allow the water to flow much more easily as it has a higher mobility than oil, causing a process called 'fingering' (Fig. 7.3). Another problem is that oil droplets can clog the small pores in low-porosity rocks, stopping any flow of liquid. In addition, fracture and channels will also allow the water to pass through without displacing the oil, forming what are known as thief zones (Fig. 7.3). The yield at the end of the secondary extraction is in the region of 35% (OOIP) which means that there is still a considerable amount of oil remaining.

7.2.1   Enhanced oil recovery (EOR)

Secondary recovery of oil can be enhanced and the methods involved can be divided into thermal or non-thermal (Fig. 7.4). The objective of any enhanced oil recovery is to influence the flow characteristics of the crude oil. The flow properties can be described by the mobility ratio and the capillary number (Farouq Ali and Thomas, 1996). The mobility ratio is the ratio of the mobility of the displacing fluid ($\ddot{Y}_{\text{displacing}}$) to the mobility of the oil ($\ddot{Y}_{\text{oil}}$):

$$M \text{ (mobility ratio)} = \frac{\ddot{Y}_{\text{displacing}}}{\ddot{Y}_{\text{oil}}}$$

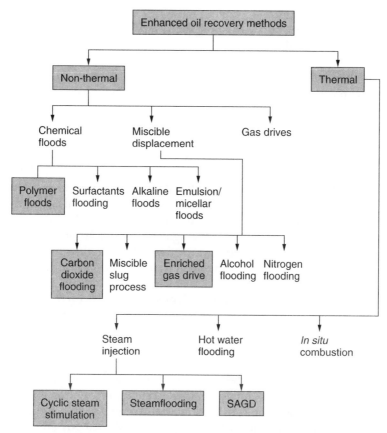

Fig. 7.4 Some of the methods used in enhanced oil recovery. Those in boxes are those which have been used commercially. SAGD is steam assisted gravity distillation (Farouq Ali and Thomas, 1996).

The mobility of the liquids $\ddot{Y}$ can be defined as k/μ where k is the effective permeability and μ the viscosity. If M is less than 1 the displacing liquid water moves more easily than the oil and therefore can move past the oil, leaving much of it in place. If M is very much larger than 1 the liquid will be very viscous and flow only in wide channels leaving oil droplets behind in the smaller pores in what is known as viscous fingering. The ideal situation is $M \geq 1$. The value of M can be reduced by increasing the viscosity of the waterflood by addition of high molecular weight polymers.

The other property which influences oil flow is the capillary number. The capillary number N_c is a measure of the permeability of the oil. It is defined as

$$N_c = \frac{\phi_p k}{Lq}$$

where

q = interfacial tension
k = effective permeability of the displaced fluid
ϕ_p/L = pressure gradient.

If the capillary number is increased this will decrease the residual oil saturation and release more oil. The capillary number can be increased by reducing the oil viscosity, increasing the pressure gradient, or decreasing the interfacial tension. It is these factors that EOR techniques attempt to influence, but in reality conditions in oil reservoirs are complex with the formation of emulsions, and the rock–fluid interactions are far from simple.

A number of non-thermal methods of EOR are shown in Fig. 7.4 but in practice consist of chemical and miscible floods. Chemical floods consist of the addition of high molecular weight polymers, surfactants, alkalis and emulsions or combinations of all four, but the only commercially used method is the polymer flood. A high molecular weight (2–5 million) polymer is added to the flood water at a concentration of 200–1000 mg/litre which has the effect of lowering the mobility of the flood water. A decrease in water mobility will bring the mobility factor close to 1 which will considerably reduce fingering and enhance oil recovery. The polymers that have been used are the chemically derived polyacrylamides or the biopolymers xanthan, curdulan and scleroglucan. The problems with polymer addition are the high cost of the polymers, the degradation of the polymers under the conditions found in the oil well and their adsorption to rock strata. Miscible oil recovery is the injection of a solvent, such as a hydrocarbon gas (propane), liquid carbon dioxide, liquid hydrocarbons, and alcohols. All these compounds are miscible with the oil and therefore reduce the interfacial tension to zero so that the oil can be swept from the pores in the rock. The commercial methods are the use of liquid carbon dioxide and enriched gas drive where solvent is added to a gas drive. Chemical flood and miscible displacement are mainly used for light oils, although they have been applied to some heavy oils.

Thermal extraction consists of steam injection, hot water flooding and *in situ* combustion. In all cases the heat applied reduces the viscosity of the oil and this can mobilise even heavy viscous oils (Fig. 7.4). Steam injection can take the form of cyclic steam stimulation where steam is applied for a period of time followed by removal of oil; when this declines another steam cycle is applied. This method is likely to be best with viscous heavy oils and is one of the most successful methods used to date. Steam flooding is the continuous application of steam. Steam assisted gravity drainage (SAGD) has been developed for tar sands. In this method steam is injected horizontally into the sands and the mobilised oil collected with another horizontal well at a lower level. *In situ* combustion is unusual in that the heat is generated by burning some 10% of the residual oil. Compressed air or oxygen is pumped into the well until the oil ignites spontaneously or is ignited. The combustion front is sustained by the pumping of air or oxygen and the heat generated lowers the viscosity of the oil and in some cases cracks the oil into lighter fractions. Successful application

Table 7.1   Typical conditions found in oil wells

Depth (m)	600–2200
Pressure (MPa)	6.5–21.0
Temperature (°C)	40–90
Oil density (g/ml)	0.84–0.90
pH	6.25
Salinity (g/l)	170–230
Oxygen (mg/l)	< 0.05

Source: Yakimov *et al.*, 1997.

of the technique has been carried out in Russia, Romania, California, Texas and Canada (Millington *et al.*, 1994). Although all these techniques have been shown to be effective, they are expensive due to the high cost of the chemicals and the energy required for steam generation.

7.2.2   Microbial enhanced oil recovery (MEOR)

Some EOR techniques involve the addition of biopolymers to increase the viscosity of the water flood or the use of gas to drive out the oil. Microbial enhanced oil recovery (MEOR) is the introduction or stimulation of existing microorganisms in the well so that the polymers and gas can be produced *in situ*. The *in situ* growth and production of microbial products such as polymers will clearly be more economic than the *ex situ* preparation. However, the conditions in the oil well are extreme and cannot be manipulated easily, and therefore any microorganism will have to function in anaerobic conditions at high temperatures, pressures and salinity (Table 7.1). Some species of *Clostridium* are capable of growth in anaerobic conditions at 45°C but are sensitive to high salt levels (< 5%). Some strains of *Bacillus* are capable of growth under oil well conditions, as are some strains of *B. licheniformis* (Yakimov *et al.*, 1997). Bacteria associated with oil wells may belong to the genera *Bacillus*, *Pseudomonas*, *Micrococcus* and *Acinetobacter* where partial aerobic conditions occur at the base of the well. In the remainder of the well there will be anaerobic species such as *Clostridium*, *Desulfovibrio* and *Methanobacterium*. Water injection will clearly decrease the temperature such that the full range of temperatures from 40–90°C may well be represented across the well. In general bacteria will grow at temperatures of up to 40°C, so that the bacteria will need to be thermophiles which can grow at temperatures up to 100°C.

Recently an increasing number of microorganisms have been isolated which are capable of growth under extreme conditions. These so-called extremophiles have been found in hot water springs, deep sea hydrothermal vents, alkaline lakes and Arctic environments and often belong to the kingdom Archaebacteria (Govardhan and Margolin, 1995; Newell, 1995). The pressure at the bottom of the wells will be high but most microorganisms appear to be pressure tolerant. Another possible problem may be the presence of toxins in the crude oil but data so far do not indicate this.

MEOR can participate in four processes for the enhanced recovery of oil (Moses, 1991):

- well stimulation (production of gas, surfactants, acids)
- matrix acidising
- profile improvement
- downhole polymer and surfactant flood.

One reason for the reduction in oil flow in the well is the particulate nature of some limestone and sandstone rocks which can block the pores in the rocks. Asphalt and bitumen may also constitute a high proportion of the crude oil and these will block the pores in the rocks. Metallic scale deposits may also be present and add to the problem of oil flow. Acid treatment will remove much of these particulates, particularly with limestones, but the application of acid is very expensive. Certain anaerobic microorganisms can produce acids, surfactants and gases. Acid production *in situ* could help to reduce this problem, and the production of gas and surfactant would also help to mobilise the oil. If microorganisms are injected into the well along with a carbon and nitrogen source and the well shut for some time, acid, gas and solvents will be produced *in situ*. The process of fermentation can be followed by monitoring well pressure. Although this type of injection may have an effect only for some 2–5 metres around the base of the well, there have been reports of a significant improvement in production, and the biological method is cheaper than the conventional application of acids.

Matrix acidising is a process where some of the rock structure is dissolved by the *in situ* generation of acid by microbial activity. One of the traditional methods of increasing oil flow is to fracture the rock strata in which the oil is held by applying high-pressure water. This procedure can be expensive and the fractures may close up after the pressure is released. Some of the rocks associated with oil are limestone or sandstone held together with carbonates, and acid generated by bacteria growth in the well will dissolve these, opening up the strata.

Profile improvement is the plugging of the large cracks (thief zones) in the rocks which allows the injected water to force the oil out of the small pores without passing through the large fissure only. The plugging of the fissures can be achieved by growing polymer-forming bacteria in the well. Although there are a number of anaerobic polymer-forming bacteria, the conditions at the bottom of the well are not easy to predict, particularly in terms of temperature. This will mean that the time scale of polymer formation, whether the polymers are produced at the correct site and how long the polymer will exist, are also unpredictable. Polymer formation can also be used to reduce 'coning' but in this case the bacteria will need to be injected into the production well.

Polymer and surfactant flood is the continuous microbial formation of both surfactant and polymers, which is different from the batch growth and

Table 7.2 Processes for the production of microbial polysaccharides

Polysaccharide	Microorganism	Substrate	Process
Curdulan (glucose)	*Agrobacterium* sp., *Alcaligenes faecalis*	glucose	batch
Scleroglucan (glucose)	*Sclerotium glucanicum*	glucose	batch
Xanthan	*Xanthomonas campestris*	glucose	batch

production of polymer used in profile improvement. A number of anaerobic bacteria have been isolated which can produce polymers or surfactants and many of the bacteria will become attached to the particles in the well. If nutrients are provided continuously as growth proceeds, the growing zone will expand outwards and the polymers will force the oil towards the production well.

Most of the practical work on MEOR has been carried out in Eastern Europe as oil prices are too low in the US and the West to justify the development of this form of recovery. Well stimulation has been carried out and anecdotal evidence suggests that this has been successful. None of the other techniques appear to have been used to date. The real application of MEOR will probably have to wait until crude oil prices reach values where enhanced extraction becomes economic.

7.2.3 Microbial polymers

Microbial polymers such as xanthan, curdulan and scleroglucan have been added to oil wells to increase the viscosity of the water flood. Microbial polymers have other uses in oil recovery as their pseudoplasticity has seen their addition to drilling muds. In addition, microbial polymers have found uses as thickeners and stabilisers in the food industries. The majority of the microbial polymers are polysaccharides which accumulate outside the cells or can remain attached to the cell surface. Research into microbial polysaccharides started in the 1940s with the development of dextran as a blood plasma extender. Several polysaccharides are now widely used in a number of industries, of which the best known is xanthan (Table 7.2). Xanthan is a polymer produced by *Xanthomonas campestris* and consists of an alternating glucose backbone carrying side-chains of D-mannose and D-glucuronic acid. Production at present exceeds 20,000 tonnes per year (Sutherland, 1998). Solutions of xanthan are pseudoplastic, being able to regain their viscosity after shearing. The pseudoplastic property is of particular value in drilling muds which act as a seal and lubricant during the drilling of oil wells. The mud needs to be viscous to form a good seal but flow when the drill bit is rotated. Curdulan is a neutral gel-forming 1,3-β-D-glucan (molecular weight 74,000) which can be formed by a number of bacteria such as *Agrobacterium* and *Rhizobium*. It forms a gel which is elastic and does not melt when heated. The property of forming a gel upon acidification has also suggested its use in oil wells.

Scleroglucan is a glucose homopolymer produced by a number of microorganisms including *Sclerotium glucanium*. Scleroglucan is produced commercially and has been developed as an alternative to xanthan for EOR by Elf Aquitaine (McNeil and Harvey, 1993). However, the yields are lower than for xanthan, and the process takes longer with a lower final concentration.

The processes for the production of microbial polymers are similar to those for the production of antibiotics apart from the viscosity of the culture, which means that the impeller design has to change. In large stirred-tank bioreactors the use of viscous pseudoplastic materials means that the culture thins when sheared, which means that the viscosity will be lowest near the impeller. This leads to the division of the bioreactor into well-mixed and aerated areas near the impeller with the remainder poorly aerated and mixed. Poor mixing and aeration will reduce growth and yield. A number of modifications to the impeller in the normal stirred-tank bioreactor have been proposed in a number of cases and one, the helical ribbon-screw design, did give a significant improvement (McNeil and Harvey, 1993). Microbial polysaccharides have not replaced plant or algal polysaccharides but have established a market of their own as they possess a number of advantages over conventional rivals.

7.3   Biorecovery of metals

The use of biological material in the recovery or extraction of metals can take a number of forms. The recovery and removal of metals from domestic and industrial wastes has been covered in Chapter 4. A variety of microorganisms have the ability to solubilise metals from insoluble metal deposits, usually sulphides. This ability, known as 'bioleaching', has been used to extract metals from lower-grade metal ores and in some cases this is carried out *in situ* (Curtin, 1983). Bioleaching is also an alternative method of extracting metals from difficult ores (recalcitrant) and has been used to rework mine waste and tailings (Rossi, 1990). Bioleaching has the advantage that it is a low-energy process compared with traditional ore crushing and extraction. It is not affected by the metal content of the ores which can have a significant effect on the costs of the traditional process. Mine waste dumps also suffer from uncontrolled natural bioleaching which can produce a strongly acid leachate that can pollute the environment. This can be eliminated by controlled bioleaching.

7.3.1   Recovery of metals from mining wastes

Research on iron- and sulphur-oxidising bacteria in 1920–1930 laid the foundation of bioleaching. Bryner *et al.* (1954) described how iron pyrites and copper sulphide could be oxidised by acid *Thiobacillus* bacteria from the Kennecott Bingham Canyon opencast mine. This work led to the first patent in 1958 (Zimmerley *et al.*, 1958).

Mining leaves behind very large quantities of tailings and low-grade ores which are too low in metal content to warrant conventional extraction. This is

Table 7.3 Some of the microorganisms involved in bioleaching

Organism	Optimum growth temperature (°C)	Substrates used
Mesophiles		
Thiobacillus ferrooxidans	30	Oxidises Fe, S, S_2O, metal sulphides CuS
Leptospirillum ferrooxidans	30	Oxidises Fe but not S
Thiobacillus thiooxidans	30	Oxidises S, S_2O_3 but not Fe or metal sulphides
Desulfovibrio spp.	30	Reduces S, SO_4, forms metal sulphides
Acidophilium cryptum	30	Grows on organic substrates
Thiobacillus neopolitanus	30	Oxidises S at pH 6.0
Thermophiles		
Sulfolobus brierleyi	70	Oxidises Fe, S, MoS_2, $CuFeS_2$
Thiobacillus TH-1	55	Oxidises Fe, metal sulphides, but needs an organic substrate
Sulfobacillus thermosulfidooxidans	50	Oxidises Fe, S

a considerable loss of metal and any process for the economic extraction of metal from this material will be of considerable value. It has been shown that microorganisms can extract cobalt, nickel, cadmium, antimony, zinc, lead, gallium, indium, manganese, copper and tin from sulphur-based ores. Recent developments have shown that gold can be extracted from pyritic ores.

Box 7.1

Chemolithotrophs obtain their energy needed for growth from the oxidation of ammonia, nitrate, hydrogen and sulphur. The carbon required for the synthesis of cellular components comes from the fixation of carbon dioxide. Examples are *Thiobacillus, Sulpholobus* and *Beggiatoa*.

Different bacteria have been isolated from natural and commercial bioleaching which are capable of degrading metal sulphides. An extensive list of organisms known to have bioleaching abilities is given in Krebs *et al.* (1997). They are classified according to their optimum temperature of growth (Table 7.3). The important mesophiles, growing at 25–35°C, are chemolithotrophic and highly acidophilic (pH 1.5–2.0) and include *Thiobacillus ferrooxidans, T. thiooxidans* and *Leptospirillum ferrooxidans* (Rawlings and Silver, 1995). *T. thiooxidans* can use only reduced sulphur compounds and *L. ferrooxidans* can use only ferrous ions. Thus while neither in isolation can reduce metal sulphides, together they rapidly degrade pyrites (FeS_2). Thermophilic bacteria, *Thiobacillus* TH-1 and

Sulfolobus brierleyi, have been found to grow on chalcopyrite ($CuFeS_2$). Most of these bacteria require some form of organic substrate for vigorous growth. *S. brierleyi* is an extreme thermophile which can grow at 70°C and can metabolise pyrite, chalcopyrite and pyrrhotite (FeS).

Many of the metals of commercial interest occur as sulphides and it is from these sulphur-based ores that microorganisms can remove the metals either by direct or indirect leaching. The bacteria involved with this form of bioleaching are mainly chemolithotrophs and direct and indirect leaching can operate at the same time.

7.3.2 Indirect leaching

This depends on the ability of the chemolithotrophs to generate ferric ion by the oxidation of the soluble ferrous ions. The ferric ions are oxidising agents which can oxidise the metal sulphite, releasing the metal as a soluble sulphate. The process follows the following equations as most metal ores contain pyrites (FeS_2):

$$2FeS_2 + 7O_2 + 2H_2O \rightarrow 2FeSO_4 + 2H_2SO_4$$

$$4FeSO_4 + O_2 + 2H_2SO_4 \rightarrow 2Fe_2(SO_4)_3 + 2H_2O$$

Both these reactions are catalysed by the bacterium *Thiobacillus ferrooxidans*. The ferric ion will oxidise the sulphite to ferrous sulphate and elemental sulphur which will be oxidised to form sulphuric acid, generating energy in the process.

$$FeS_2 + Fe_2(SO_4)_3 \rightarrow 3FeSO_4 + 2S$$

$$2S + 3O_2 + 2H_2O \rightarrow 2H_2SO_4$$

The ferric ion formed is an oxidising agent which can react with other sulphides, such as the copper sulphides $CuFeS_2$ (chalcopyrite), Cu_2S (chalcocite), $CuFeS_4$ (bornite) and CuS (covellite). The sulphuric acid formed keeps the pH of the medium down and will also leach other copper minerals. The full cycle is shown in Fig. 7.5.

$$CuFeS_2 + 2Fe_2(SO_4)_3 + 2H_2O + 3O_2 = CuSO_4 + 5FeSO_4 + 2H_2SO_4$$

7.3.3 Direct leaching

In this case the *T. ferrooxidans* bacteria become attached to the mineral particles and the overall reaction ensues by direct enzymatic reactions.

$$4FeS_2 + 15O_2 + 2H_2O \rightarrow 2Fe_2(SO_4)_3 + 2H_2SO_4$$

Some of the bacteria involved in metal leaching are given in Table 7.2 and as can be seen some are capable of growth at up to 70°C, which is of interest as temperatures of up to 60–80°C have been generated in some leaching systems due to biological activity.

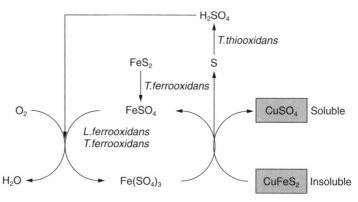

Fig. 7.5 The cycle of reactions involved with the leaching of copper from iron-containing ores.

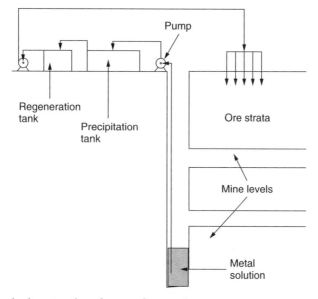

Fig. 7.6 The *in situ* extraction of copper from a mine.

7.3.4 Bioleaching processes

There are three main methods of applying bioleaching: *in situ* treatment, heaps or dumps, and bioreactors.

In situ bioleaching can be used in mines which have come to the end of their useful life but still contain metal ores. The leaching solution containing *T. ferrooxidans* is pumped into the mine where it is injected into the ore (Fig. 7.6). The leachate is recovered from lower down the mine, pumped to the surface where the metal is recovered, and the bacterial suspension aerated before pumping back to the mine.

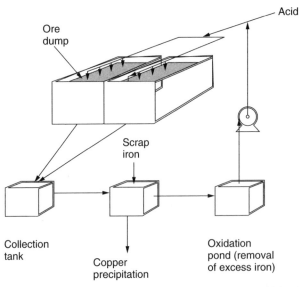

Fig. 7.7 The construction and operation of the dump system for the bioleaching of ores.

The treatment of low-grade ores or mine tailings using heaps or dumps is the most common method of bioleaching. An example of such a system is given in Fig. 7.7. The dump is often set on a slope with a depth of 7–20 metres of crushed ore or tailings. The dump is sprayed with water acidified with sulphuric acid to ensure that the pH is between 1.5 and 3, low enough to encourage the growth of *Thiobacillus* to increase the leaching rate, which gives bacterial populations of up to 10^6 cells/gram rock. The leaching solution is collected at the base and recirculated and in this way a population of *Thiobacillus* develops. *Thiobacillus* will leach the metal (such as copper) into solution and this can be collected by precipitation from the leachate. At this stage excess iron is removed in an oxidation pond and the liquid returned to the dump. The design of the dumps has improved over the years to give a more even particle size, to avoid anoxic zones. The construction of the dumps often overlooks the fact that the process requires oxygen, and the dumps should be as open as possible to allow for diffusion. Acid-consuming rock such as calcium chloride should be avoided and some may also contain compounds which are toxic to the bacteria, such as molybdate. Galena (PbS) also presents a problem as the lead sulphate formed during leaching is relatively insoluble and accumulates on the ore surface, preventing leaching. Anaerobes have also been detected in the anoxic zones of dumps, including the sulphate-reducing *Desulfovibrio* spp. These organisms form metal sulphides which coat the mineral and reduce leaching, which is why the process needs to be aerobic. In newly formed dumps which have not had acid added, a group of mesophilic sulphur-oxidising bacteria may occur. These are useful as they oxidise sulphides at pH values of 4–7 to give sulphuric acid which in turn reduces the pH and allows the other sulphur-oxidising organisms to flourish. Thus the dump is a very diverse and dynamic microbial community in which the microbial population can number up to 10^6 cells per gram of rock. The dynamics of such a population are difficult to follow, as sampling is difficult and special media are needed for the culture of many microorganisms. The use of DNA probes and PCR may allow a better understanding of population dynamics.

The use of bioreactors in bioleaching has been restricted to the ores of uranium, gold, silver and copper due to the extra costs involved. Conventional bioreactors such as the stirred tank and alternatives such as the airlift and immobilised bed bioreactors have been investigated up to pilot-plant scale. The use of bioreactors allows close control of the process parameters such as temperature, pH and aeration which are critical to the process. Initial results have indicated that the airlift design is more efficient than the conventional designs (Ferraiolo and Del Borghi, 1987).

7.3.5 Extraction of copper

The estimate in 1991 was that the biological recovery of copper exceeded $1000 million and accounted for 25% of copper production. Bioleaching has considerable advantages as it has no adverse side-effects apart from leaching into the groundwater and is a cheap method of utilising waste. The waste ore is generally that remaining after extraction of rock from a mine where the level is too low to be extracted economically (0.1–0.5%). In most mining operations the waste material is formed into terraced dumps 100 metres wide and 10 metres deep with an impermeable base. Dilute sulphuric acid is sprinkled or sprayed onto the dump so that as it percolates through the dump the pH is reduced to 2–3, which promotes the growth of *T. ferrooxidans* and other leaching microorganisms. On oxidation to copper sulphate, the copper is dissolved in the dilute acid and is collected at the bottom of the dumps (Fig. 7.7). The copper is removed from the solution by precipitation onto scrap iron, although newer methods of solvent extraction or electrowinning are being tried. Often, once the copper has been removed the dilute acid is recycled, but this has to be limited as it contains high levels of ferric salts which coat the ore, decreasing the availability of copper (Fig. 7.7). Some examples of copper leaching from dumps are given in Table 7.4.

7.3.6 Extraction of uranium

Uranium can be extracted by a bioleaching process from uranium oxides. Direct leaching by *T. ferrooxidans* has been proposed in the following equation:

$$2UO_2 + O_2 + 2H_2SO_4 \rightarrow 2UO_2SO_4 + 2H_2O$$

A second indirect bioleaching process uses pyrite which is often associated with uranium ores. In this case *T. ferrooxidans* produces the ferric ion which reacts with the uranium ore:

Table 7.4   An example of dump leaching operations

Company operation	Copper mineral	Amount of ore (10^6 t)	Solution method	pH	Copper extracted (kg/m³)
Asarco's Silver, AZ, USA	Chalcocite, chrysocolla	1300	Ponds, trenches	2.4	1.09
Anaconda Co, Butte, USA	Chalcocite	100	Perforated plastic pipes	2.2	0.8
Kennecott Copper Co., UT, USA	Chalcocite	40,000	Channels	2.5	1.8
Vlaikov-Vrah, Bulgaria	Chalcopyrite, pyrite	0.6	Sprays, trenches and channels	1.8	1.8
Compania Mineraria, Mexico	Chalcocite, pyrite, chalcopyrite	10	Spray nozzles	2.1	2.5
Phelps-Dodge, NM, USA	Chalcocite	41	60 × 30 m ponds	3.5	0.18

Source: Agate, 1996.

$$UO_2 + Fe_2(SO_4)_3 \rightarrow UO_2SO_4 + 2FeSO_4$$

$$UO_3 + H_2SO_4 \rightarrow UO_2SO_4 + H_2O$$

One example of uranium leaching is the Dennison mine in the Elliot Lake district of Canada which extracted 300 tons of uranium worth $25 million in 1988 (Rawlings and Silver, 1995).

7.3.7   Extraction of gold

In the case of extracting gold from various ores, bioleaching is used to remove arsenopyrites and pyrite so that the gold can be extracted in the normal manner. High levels of pyrite in the ore react with cyanide which is used for gold extraction, forming thiocyanate, and this uses large quantities of cyanide. *T. ferrooxidans* will degrade the arsenopyrite, exposing the gold for cyanide extraction:

$$2FeAsS + 7O_2 + 2H_2O \rightarrow 2FeAsO_4 + 2H_2SO_4$$

7.3.8   Recent developments

All bioleaching has been carried out with indigenous microbial strains whose proliferation has been encouraged by the acid conditions. However, there are methods whereby these microorganisms could be improved. The first is to isolate new bacterial strains from extreme environments such as mine drainage sites, hot springs and waste sites, and to use these to seed bioleaching processes. Secondly, the existing microorganisms could be improved by conventional mutation and selection or by genetic engineering. A number of genes have been isolated and characterised from *Thiobacillus* spp. (Rawlings and Silver, 1995). One possibility would be to introduce arsenic resistance into some bioleaching organisms, which could then be used in gold bioleaching. Also, more needs to be known about the population dynamics within the bioleaching dumps and the relative importance of various organisms and mechanisms. Various plating methods are available for the determination of the bacterial population, but these are not always accurate, as the conditions in the dump are difficult to reproduce. PCR techniques using small-subunit rRNA sequences can now be used to replace the plating techniques (De Wulf-Durand *et al.*, 1997).

7.4 Conclusions

In this chapter it can be seen that:

- Microorganisms are currently being used to produce polysaccharides used in drilling muds.
- Microorganisms could also be used to enhance oil recovery by growth *in situ* (MEOR) if the price of crude oil rose sufficiently to warrant further extraction. In addition the methods involved in MEOR require further research before the process can be fully understood.
- Microorganisms can leach a number of metals either directly or indirectly from low-grade ores, tailings and low-yielding mines in an *in situ* process.
- At present bioleaching is used extensively for copper and increasingly for uranium and gold extraction.

7.5 References

Agate, A. D. (1996) Recent advances in microbial mining. *World J. Micro. Biotechnol.*, **12**, 487–495.

Bryner, L. C., Beck, J. F., Davis, B. D. and Wilson, D. G. (1954) Microorganisms in leaching sulfide minerals. *Ind. Eng. Chem.*, **46**, 2587–2592.

Curtin, M. E. (1983) Microbial mining and metal recovery. *Biotechnology*, **1**, 228–235.

De Wulf-Durand, P., Bryant, L. J. and Sly, L. I. (1997) PCR-mediated detection of acidophilic, bioleaching-associated bacteria. *Appl. Environ. Microbiol.*, **63**, 2944–2948.

Farouq Ali, S. M. and Thomas, S. (1996) The promise and problems of enhanced oil recovery methods. *J. Canadian Petroleum Technol.*, **35**, 57–63.

Ferraiolo, G. and Del Borghi, M. (1987) Bioleaching, in J. M. Sidwick and R. S. Holdom (eds), *Biotechnology of Waste Treatment and Exploitation*. Ellis Horwood, Chichester, UK, pp. 236–255.

Govardhan, C. P. and Margolin, A. L. (1995) Extremozymes for industry – from nature and by design. *Chemistry & Industry*, September, 689–693.

Krebs, W., Brombacher, C., Bosshard, P. P., Bachofen, R. and Brandl, H. (1997) Microbial recovery of metals from solids. *FEMS Microbiol. Rev.*, **20**, 605–617.

McNeil, B. and Harvey, L. M. (1993) Viscous fermentation products. *Critical Reviews in Biotechnol.*, **13**, 275–303.

Millington, A., Price, D. and Hughes, R. (1994) *In situ* combustion for oil recovery. *Chemistry & Industry*, August, 632–635.

Moses, V. (1991) Oil production and processing, in V. Moses and R. A. Cape (eds), *Biotechnology, the Science and Business*. Harwood Academic, London, pp. 537–565.

Newell, J. (1995) Extremophiles. *Chemistry in Britain*, December, 925–927.

Rawlings, D. E. and Silver, S. (1995) Mining with microbes. *Biotechnology*, **13**, 773–778.

Rossi, G. (1990) *Biohydrometallurgy*. McGraw-Hill, Hamburg.

Sutherland, I. W. (1998) Novel and established applications of microbial polysaccharides. *Tibtech*, **16**, 41–46.

Yakimov, M. M., Amro, M. M., Bock, M., Boseker, K., Fredrickson, H. L., Kessel, D. G. and Timmis, K. N. (1997) The potential of *Bacillus licheniformis* strains for *in situ* enhanced oil recovery. *J. Petroleum Sci. and Eng.*, **18**, 147–160.

Zimmerley, S. R., Wilson, D. G. and Pratter, J. F. (1958) *Cyclic leaching process employing iron oxidising bacteria*. US Patent No. 2,829,964.

7.5.1 Recommended reading

Moses, V. and Capes, R. A. (1992) *Biotechnology, The Science and Business*. Harwood Academic Press, London.

Murck, B., Skinner, B. J. and Porter, S. C. (1996) *Environmental Geology*. Wiley and Sons, Chichester, UK.

Rawlings, D. E. (1997) *Biomining: Theory, Microbes and Industrial Processes*. Springer Verlag, Heidlberg, Germany.

Chapter 8

Agrobiotechnology

8.1 Introduction

Agriculture covers a very wide spectrum of activities, many of which may be affected by biotechnological advances which may in turn affect the environment. This chapter covers the main areas of biotechnological influence which may be in the following, where much of the input will be based on genetic engineering:

- Improved plants
- Improved animals
- Diagnostics for plant and animal diseases
- Animal vaccines
- Biological control rather than the use of chemicals
- Biodiversity
- Waste reduction and disposal.

8.2 Improved plants

Conventional plant breeding has proved very successful over a number of years in the development of new and improved plant varieties, but the application of biotechnology can offer considerable advantages. Genetic engineering can produce transgenic plants which have properties not possible with conventional breeding. The term transgenic plant can refer to 'plants with unique gene combinations that do not naturally occur and are produced by using either recombinant DNA technology or protoplast fusion technology' (Ratledge, 1993). In addition, genetic engineering and micropropagation can respond more rapidly than conventional breeding in the development of a new plant variety. However, there are some concerns over the release of genetic engineered plants into the environment, but the positive effects of the reduction in the use of pesticides and herbicides by use of these types of plants should not be ignored.

8.2.1 Plant genetic engineering

The techniques for genetic engineering of microorganisms (recombinant DNA technology) were developed in the 1970s and the rapid development of the techniques has enabled the genes from a wide range of organisms to be identified, isolated, and transferred to other species. Genetic engineering has been one of the fastest growing areas of biotechnology and has seen major advances over recent years. The techniques have allowed genes to be transferred between unrelated species, forming new combinations not possible by conventional techniques. The production of transgenic plants has advanced rapidly and has seen commercialisation in recent years with the Flavr Savr™ tomato and herbicide-resistant soya plant (Senior and Dale, 1996). At present the particular traits that have been transferred are genes which confer characteristics like herbicide resistance, and the traits have been mainly restricted to those that involve single genes. Complex characteristics such as drought tolerance are more difficult to transfer as more than one gene is involved and the exact biochemical basis of the trait is not fully understood.

In order to transfer a gene into a plant the following basic requirements need to be satisfied:

- The gene for a particular trait needs to be identified which requires information on the pathway and the controls involved.
- The gene needs to be isolated. The source of the gene for a particular trait can be a related plant species or a totally unrelated species such as a bacterium or animal, as in the case of the transfer of the flounder antifreeze gene to strawberries in order to reduce frost damage.
- The gene needs to be transferred to the target plant and be placed under the correct control so that the gene functions (expressed).
- The transformed plant material needs to be regenerated into a whole plant, tested for the gene activity, and if successful, the line multiplied and field tested.

8.2.2 Gene isolation

The isolation of the gene, from whatever source, can be carried out in a number of ways (Fig. 8.1):

- from total DNA, the cloning of restriction fragments
- by chemical synthesis, if the protein sequence is known
- from messenger RNA by the production of complementary DNA (cDNA)
- by PCR using primers derived from related genes.

The first step is to isolate the DNA from the donor cells or tissue. The method used will depend on the problem and knowledge of the system. There are a number of manuals covering the techniques involved in DNA extraction (Chung *et al.*, 1998; Sul and Korban, 1996; Chirikjian, 1995; Kobayashi *et al.*, 1998). In the method using total DNA the next step is to produce a collection or library of DNA fragments by cutting the DNA into a large number of fragments with restriction enzymes. Restriction enzymes cut DNA into specific fragments as the enzymes recognise specific sequences of four to eight bases in the DNA. The fragments produced by the restriction enzymes can be inserted into the appropriate vector by cutting the vector with the same restriction enzyme as the DNA, and the ends can be annealed and repaired with the enzyme DNA ligase.

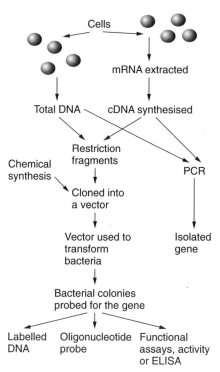

Fig. 8.1 The methods involved in the isolation of a specific gene. PCR, polymerase chain reaction; ELISA, enzyme linked immunoadsorbent assay.

If the whole gene is required, including the sequences removed during DNA processing, the gene will need to be isolated from the total DNA. However, if only the expressed protein is of interest complementary DNA (cDNA) can be used. Complementary DNA or cDNA is synthesised from the messenger RNA (mRNA) which can be extracted from the organism or tissue expressing the product in question. The isolated messenger RNA will contain the information for the protein in question and can be copied as DNA by using an enzyme, reverse transcriptase. More recently the polymerase chain reaction (PCR) technique has been used to select and amplify the gene required from either the isolated DNA or cDNA. The PCR reaction requires primers that can recognise the start of the gene and these can be prepared if the gene sequence or that of a related gene is known. This method is being used increasingly as it needs only a very small amount of DNA and, combined with a variety of either specific or more general primers, genes can be amplified, pathogens detected and the relationship between genomes assessed.

8.2.3 Vectors

There are, in general, two forms of vector available in bacterial systems for the transfer of DNA: plasmids or bacteriophages. Plasmids are extrachromosomal

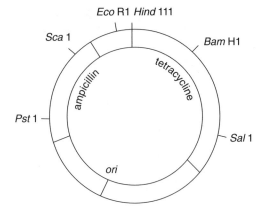

Fig. 8.2 A map of the bacterial vector pBR322 showing the two antibiotic resistance genes and a number of restriction sites.

DNA molecules found in many microbial species in the form of closed circles which can occur as multiple copies. The second vector is the bacteriophages which infect and are reproduced in bacteria. Plasmids have been extensively modified to give the following characteristics:

- as small as possible for ease of isolation and so that the maximum DNA can be added
- autonomous replication
- a number of single restriction sites
- the addition of a selectable marker such as antibiotic resistance.

An example of one of the best known plasmids, pBR322, is given in Fig. 8.2 which has two selectable markers – ampicillin and tetracycline resistance – and a number of restriction sites. If the vector and DNA are cut using the same restriction enzyme they can be annealed together and the join completed with the enzyme DNA ligase. The circular DNA formed can then be taken up by a bacterium, usually *E. coli*. Bacteria can be treated using a simple procedure so that they are capable of taking up DNA. If the vector taken up by the bacteria confers antibiotic resistance, those cells which have been transformed will be the only ones capable of growing on media containing antibiotics. If a large number of fragments of DNA are cloned into bacteria a large number of transformed colonies can be obtained. This collection is known as a library and, if sufficient colonies are collected statistically, the whole of the original DNA will be represented in these colonies. In the case of cDNA the number of colonies will be smaller as the mRNA does not represent the whole genome.

8.2.4 Selection of transformants

If a specific gene is to be detected in the library, some form of probe is needed to detect the colony or clone containing the gene of interest. A direct method

Table 8.1 Some marker genes used in plant transformation

Gene*	Selective agent	Action
npt11(NPT11)	Kanamycin	30S ribosome
npt11(NPT11)	Geneticin	30S ribosome
hpt(HPT)	Hygromycin	Peptide chain elongation
bar(PAT)	Phosphinothricin	Glutamine synthase
EPSPS + oxidoreductase	Glyphosate	EPSP synthase
dhfr	Methotrexate	Dihydrofolate reductase
csr-1(ALS)	Sulfonylurea	Acetolactate synthase
uid(GUS)	β-Glucuronidase	Blue colour formation
Gfp	Fluorescent protein	Light emission
luc	Luciferase	Light emission

* npt11, neomycin phosphotransferase; hpt, hygromycin phosphotransferase; pat, phosphinothricin acetyltransferase; EPSPS, 5-enolpyruvylshikimate-3-phosphate synthase.

is to use a nucleic acid probe to hybridise to the plasmid DNA extracted from each individual bacterial colony. Hybridisation can be carried out only if the gene has already been cloned, the base sequence of the gene is already known or a related gene has been sequenced. If the sequence of the whole protein, or the *n*-terminal sequence, is known then an oligonucleotide probe can be chemically synthesised. The conserved protein sequence from a related gene can also be used as the basis of a probe. The probe once prepared can be labelled with radioactivity, biotin or fluorescent protein and the labels can be used to indicate which bacterial clone contains the gene. The gene can also be detected if it is capable of producing a functional protein as an enzyme activity or by reaction with antibodies.

Once the bacterial clone containing the vector incorporating the gene has been identified, the gene can be isolated and manipulated in a number of ways depending on its final use. The gene can be placed under the control of a strong promoter which can function in a plant, such as the CaMV, the 35S RNA cauliflower mosaic virus promoter. The gene can also be transferred to a eukaryotic vector which should also have a marker gene in order to select transformed plants. A list of markers is given in Table 8.1, based on antibiotic or herbicide resistance such as kanamycin and glyphosate. Recent developments have been to use marker genes which produce products which are non-invasive and easy to use. Gus(uid) and Gfp are two examples; Gus codes for the enzyme β-glucuronidase which will convert the colourless 5-bromo-4-chloro-3-indolyl-glucuronide (X-Gluc) to a blue colour, and Gfp is a green fluorescent protein derived from the jellyfish *Aequorea victoria* (Chapter 2). The Gfp protein is very useful as it does not require cofactors to function and exhibits a green light upon exposure to long-wave ultraviolet light (Misteli and Spector, 1997).

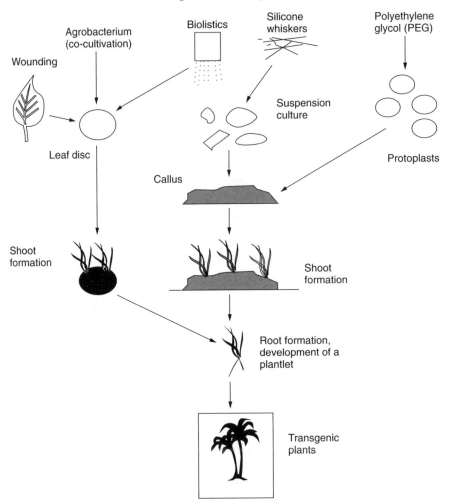

Fig. 8.3 Methods for the production of transgenic plants from protoplasts, cell suspensions and explants.

8.2.5   Transformation of plants

Once the gene has been isolated much of the manipulation can be carried out in bacteria, but once this has been achieved the gene needs to be used to transform the target plant. The process of transforming plant cells is not without its problems. Plants have strong cellulose-based cell walls which makes it difficult to transfer DNA into the cells, and whole plants have bark and waxy cuticles which compound the problem. Gene transfer to whole plants is therefore difficult and to avoid these difficulties various techniques have been adopted (Siemens and Schieder, 1996) (Fig. 8.3):

- Direct gene transfer into protoplasts using PEG (polyethylene glycol), liposomes or electroporation
- Direct gene transfer into intact plant tissue or cell cultures using electroporation, microinjection, silicone carbide whiskers, biolistics
- *Agrobacterium* infection by wounding or co-cultivation
- Vacuum infiltration of plant tissues.

8.2.6 Protoplasts

The first protoplasts were isolated from plant tissue in the 1960s when plant material was incubated with a mixture of fungal enzymes including cellulases. These enzymes removed the cell wall from a plant cell, resulting in the formation of a spherical cell bounded by only a cell membrane. The cell minus the wall will normally take up water and eventually burst, but it can be stabilised by the addition to the medium of an osmoticum such as mannitol. The removal of the cell wall makes the introduction of DNA into the cell much easier. However, once transformed the protoplast has to be regenerated into a whole plant. Protoplasts have been isolated by mechanical or more often enzymatic treatment from many plant species, but protoplasts capable of sustained division and regeneration are still restricted to a limited number of species. Leaf tissue is frequently used as a source of protoplasts except for monocotyledonous species where embryogenic cell suspension has proved to be the best technique. Regeneration of protoplasts is frequently difficult as protoplasts are sensitive to shear, cultural conditions and media components. In addition, as the protoplasts replace their cell walls and divide, forming minicolonies, their growth requirements change. The consequence of these difficulties is that the proportion of protoplast regenerating can be very low and optimum conditions can vary between species (Roest and Gilissen, 1993), although protocols for the production of protoplasts from plant tissues have been described (Blackhall *et al.*, 1994). Plants regenerated from protoplast are often sterile and phenotypically abnormal (Datta *et al.*, 1994).

DNA can then be transferred to protoplast by three methods: treatment with polyethylene glycol (PEG), with liposomes, and electroporation. The exposure of protoplasts to polyethylene glycol (molecular weight 4000 to 8000) (up to 28%) in a high magnesium chloride medium can result in DNA uptake. Liposomes containing DNA have been used to transfer DNA to protoplasts also using PEG. Electroporation is the application of high voltage DC pulses, which opens up the cell membrane and allows any DNA in the medium to enter the cell (Fig. 8.3). The voltage and pulse length for optimal DNA transference vary according to the source of protoplasts, the electroporation medium and the type of pulse. Electroporation reduces the viability of the protoplasts. Thus the PEG-mediated method is more widely used as it is easy to handle large numbers of protoplasts and the survival rate is higher. However, the method does introduce a high proportion of multiple or fragmented copies of the DNA into the plant genome. The introduction of DNA into

Box 8.1

A typical protoplast isolation protocol (from a plant such as tobacco):

- Select young, fully expanded leaves from a young plant.
- Cut the leaves into strips.
- Float the leaf strips on an enzyme mixture containing cellulase, hemicellulase, pectinase and 0.4M sorbitol (osmoticum).
- Incubate overnight at 25°C.
- Filter through a 50 μm nylon mesh to remove leaf fragments.
- Collect protoplasts by centrifugation at low speed (100 g for 5 min).
- Resuspend pellet in 2–3 ml 23% sucrose solution and centrifuge at 100 g for 5 min. This will allow those cells with cell walls to pellet through the sucrose while the protoplasts remain at the interface.
- Remove the floating layer.

A typical culture and regeneration of protoplasts:

- Disperse the protoplasts in the wells of multiwell plate or onto solid medium.
- Incubate in the dark at 25°C for 3–7 days.
- Examine and if division observed dilute with fresh medium.
- Repeat every 7 days for 3 weeks.
- Transfer to solid medium and incubate.
- When the colonies are 2–5 mm in diameter transfer to fresh agar plates.
- The colonies will now have to be exposed to different medium to induce organogenesis (roots and shoots) or embryogenesis and these will require maturation before they can be planted into soil.

the protoplasts can result in stable chromosomal integration which can be first assessed at the small colony or microcallus stage as antibiotic resistance. The transformation frequency of electroporation or PEG treatment is approximately 1400 per 3×10^5 (0.46%) treated protoplasts and for some species it is much lower. The key to successful transformation is the ability to regenerate plants directly from the microcalluses.

8.2.7   Direct DNA transfer

The direct transfer of DNA into intact plant tissue or cell cultures avoids the problem of the removal of the cell wall and its subsequent regeneration, and the technique is not limited by the ability to produce protoplasts. DNA can be transferred directly by microinjection, electroporation, silicone carbide whiskers and biolistics. Microinjection, the physical injection of DNA into a cell, is the most difficult and laborious, but it has the advantages that the number of DNA molecules transferred can be controlled, and that co-transfer of other DNA, RNA or even mitochondria is possible. Microinjection can be carried out with individual cells in large explants or whole plants. Despite these advantages the difficulties of the technique mean that the method has been used for only a limited number of plants.

Electroporation is carried out in a similar manner to that used with protoplasts and with this technique explants and embryos of maize, rice, sugarcane and cassava have been transformed (Siemens and Schieder, 1996). A recently developed technique for direct DNA transfer has been to mix silicone carbide whiskers with DNA and cell suspensions. When this mixture is agitated the needle-like whiskers penetrate the cells, which results in transfer of DNA (Fig. 8.3), but to date this method has been applied only to sunflower and maize cultures.

The most widely used method of direct transfer of DNA is carried out by particle bombardment (biolistics) using microscopic particles coated with DNA. The technique has several advantages over other methods:

- It is a mechanical process which is not limited by the host range of *Agrobacterium* and the restrictions of protoplasts.
- No plasmid manipulation is required.
- It is a simple process which can be used with large pieces of tissue.

The original design was described by Sanford (1988) where tungsten particles were propelled by a gunpowder charge. This design has been replaced by a number of methods for the acceleration of the particles, as the gunpowder system lacked control in the power applied and required a gun licence in some countries. In one design the explosive force of the gunpowder has been replaced by a burst of helium gas which accelerates the macrocarrier (Kikkert, 1993). The macrocarrier carries the particles and when this is stopped by a screen the particles continue onwards to the target (Fig. 8.4). In another design the gun has been replaced by an airgun which makes the apparatus cheaper and causes less trauma to the target tissues (Oard, 1993). A commercial design, ACCELL™, uses an electric discharge to accelerate the particles (Fig. 8.4) (McCabe and Christou, 1993). A development of the helium accelerator has been the low-pressure helium where the macrocarrier has been eliminated and the particle accelerated directly (Gray *et al.*, 1994). The small gold or tungsten particles 0.1–2 μm in diameter are coated with DNA and these are fired into plant tissue. The particles penetrate the tissue and transformation occurs. This method has been used for a wide range of plants, particularly those difficult to transform by *Agrobacterium.*

8.2.8 *Agrobacterium*

The Gram-negative soil bacterium *Agrobacterium* will form a crown gall if it infects dicotyledonous plants. The agent which is responsible for the gall formation is the presence in *Agrobacterium* of a large plasmid (Ti, tumour inducing), part of which integrates into the genome of the plant. The DNA transferred (T-DNA) is transported to the nucleus where it is integrated into the genome. The T-DNA codes for a number of genes: those responsible for

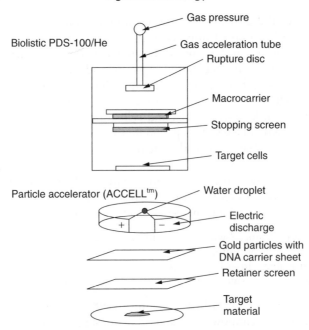

Fig. 8.4   The transformation of plant tissue with biolistics. Components of the Biolistic PDS-100/He device. The gas acceleration tube is filled with helium at high pressure until the rupture disc breaks. The gas shock is transferred to the macrocarrier. The progress of the macrocarrier is stopped by a stopping ring launching the particles towards the target (from Gray *et al.*, 1994). In the particle accelerator (ACCELL™) 15,000 volts DC is applied to the electrodes, creating an arc and evaporating the water droplet. The shock wave propels the carrier sheet towards the retainer screen which stops its progress but allows the gold particles to continue to the target (Kikkert, 1993).

the production of the plant growth regulators auxins and cytokinins (*onc*), and those which code for the enzymes involved in the synthesis of opines, amino acid and sugar derivatives (Fig. 8.5). The opines are secreted by the plant cells and consumed by the *Agrobacterium*. The Ti plasmid also contains genes for the overproduction of plant growth regulators, auxins, which cause rapid growth of the plant cells. There are a number of other components, including the *vir* (virulence) region which is required for infection. The Ti plasmid has been modified as a vector for the transfer of genes to the plant by removing most of the genes between the border sequences so that the plasmid does induce the overproduction of plant growth regulators and therefore does not form calluses. The reduction in size means that there is more room for the added DNA which includes an antibiotic resistance gene. The system has proved very successful, giving the integration of a number of copies of the gene into the plant genome. However, the *Agrobacterium* system is restricted by the size of the DNA that the T-DNA can contain and the host range of the bacterium. It was thought that

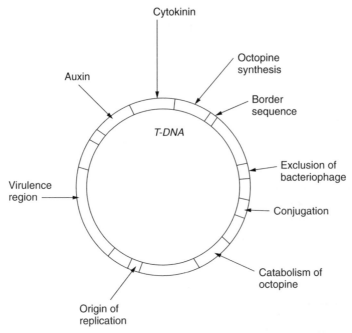

Fig. 8.5 The structure of the *Agrobacterium* plasmid including the T-DNA region.

Agrobacterium would infect only monocots in the Liliales and Arales orders, but important monocots such as wheat and maize have been transformed.

Agrobacterium-mediated DNA transfer is normally carried out by co-cultivation or by co-cultivation with wounding of the tissue, followed by cultivation on the appropriate medium containing an antibiotic to remove the bacteria and to initiate shoot regeneration. Another variation of the technique involves the sonnication of the cells or tissue prior to treatment with *Agrobacterium* (Trick *et al.*, 1997). In addition, *Agrobacterium* has been used to transform seeds and whole plants of *Arabidopsis thaliana* by vacuum infiltration.

Agrobacterium-mediated gene transfer is the method of choice as its host range continues to be extended and the technique is simple. The disadvantage is that the method depends on being able to regenerate the whole plant from the transformed tissue or cell. The size of the T-DNA was also thought to be a limiting factor for the amount of DNA which could be transferred (25 kb) but a new binary vector combined with *Agrobacterium* strains with enhanced *vir* genes can transfer up to 150 kb. The transfer of the genes between the two border sequences is far more precise than the random introduction of DNA used in the other techniques, which are suspected of introducing fragmented or multiple copies. Recent data suggest that DNA sequences outside the border sequences of the T-DNA can be transferred to the plant genome (Kononov *et al.*, 1997). The integration of these other sequences may affect the regulatory guideline for the release of *Agrobacterium*-transformed plants, as these may require a complete description of the transferred DNA sequences which may now include sequences outside the border regions.

8.2.9 Regeneration

In most of the methods described the plant cells or parts transformed need to be regenerated as whole plants. Whole plants can be regenerated from protoplasts, callus, suspension cells and parts of plants as the process of regeneration can be controlled by the use of growth regulators. Figure 8.6(a) shows the effect of growth regulators in the production of callus and suspension cultures. By using the correct balance of auxin to cytokinin, tissues and cells can be induced to go through a process known as organogenesis, forming either roots or shoots (Fig. 8.6(b)). A high auxin to cytokinin ratio (4:1) will encourage shoot formation, whereas a ratio of 100:1 will cause roots to form. Thus the shoots formed can be excised, and placed on rooting medium where the shoot can be encouraged to root, forming a plantlet which with careful handling will mature to a plant. This appears to be simple but in reality it is far from simple, since for each species the exact conditions have to be determined experimentally, although there is a body of information related to a large number of species. Under some conditions the plant tissue will undergo a process known as embryogenesis where somatic embryos are formed; these can be cultured to form whole plants. If part of a plant such as a stem section is placed on solid medium containing auxin and cytokinins with a ratio of 10:1, the cells will begin to proliferate in an unorganised manner, forming an amorphous mass known as a callus. Here again by altering the ratio of the auxin and cytokinin the callus can be induced to form either shoot or roots. Therefore, whatever plant tissue is used for transformation, a method is also needed to convert the tissue to a whole plant if the transgenic plant is to be used in the field. Thus transformed protoplasts are cultured so that they form calluses and these can be induced to form roots and shoots in order to regenerate a whole plant.

8.2.10 Plant improvement via plant cell culture

The techniques for plant cell culture, some of which have been described above, can facilitate the rapid production of plants. The techniques can also be used to select for variant plants. The procedures of plant cell culture introduce a high level of variation in the regenerated plants, known as somaclonal variation. Somaclonal variation strongly depends on the method used for regeneration, with the highest levels found in protoplasts. The genetic changes associated with somaclonal variation are point mutations, chromosome changes in number and structure, cryptic changes in chromosome rearrangements, altered sequence copy number, transposable elements, somatic crossing over, sister chromatid exchange, and DNA amplification and deletion (Karp, 1995). This variation is a problem in the production of a large number of identical

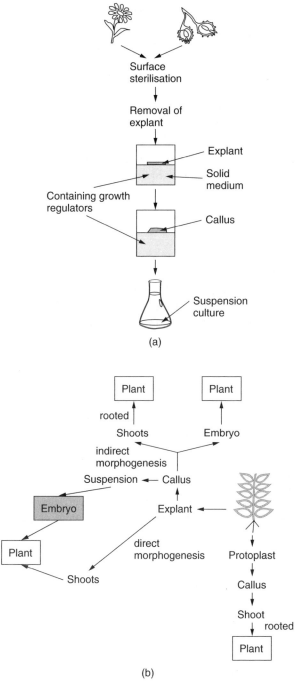

Fig. 8.6 (a) The procedure for the production of callus and cell suspensions from whole plants. The solid medium contains growth regulators which give rise to undifferentiated callus material. (b) The direct and indirect conversion of plant material via protoplasts, callus and suspension cultures to whole plants.

plants by micropropagation, but is of considerable advantage in plant breeding. The use of somaclonal variation involves the following steps:

- Induction and growth of callus or cell suspensions (Fig. 8.6(a))
- Regeneration of a large number of plants from these cultures
- Screening for desirable traits
- Testing the selected variants for the stability of the trait
- Multiplication of the selected variant.

The variation is unpredictable, which is a disadvantage, but variants have been produced in a number of plants including maize, tomato, spruce and ornamentals (Jain and DeKlerk, 1998). A particular tomato line has been isolated via somaclonal variation which has a higher solids content and has been used commercially for soup preparation.

8.2.11   Protoplast fusion

Protoplast fusion can be mediated by either chemical or electrical techniques. In the case of chemical fusion high concentrations of PEG, dextran or polyvinyl alcohol (PVA) are used in combination with high pH in calcium-containing buffers. When protoplasts are in contact and subjected to an electrical field, transient reversible pores form in the plasma membrane and the protoplasts fuse together. Two steps are usually involved; an alternating current (AC) needs to be applied to align the protoplasts and bring them into direct contact. Subsequently a short direct current (DC) pulse is employed to include membrane breakdown (Fig. 8.7). Although considerable research has been carried out, the commercial products have been limited.

8.2.12   Transgenic plants

The ability to transfer genes into plants or to alter the expression of those genes already present permits the production of a wide range of novel plants. The main traits of these novel plants are as follows:

- herbicide resistance
- insect resistance
- product quality
- viral resistance
- agronomic traits
- fungal resistance
- use as bioreactors

Genetically engineered plants and plant products have been approved for sale and consumption in Europe and the USA. Table 8.2 gives those products approved in the UK and Table 8.3 those approved in the USA. Table 8.4 gives an indication of the transgenic plants put forward for approval in the UK and EU. As can be seen in Fig. 8.8, the most frequently engineered trait

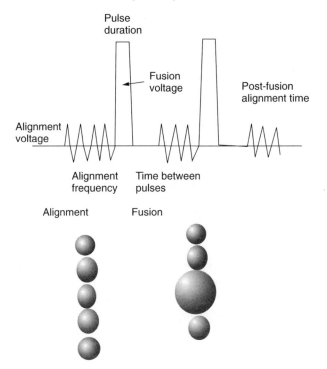

Fig. 8.7 The voltage pattern during the fusion of protoplasts.

Table 8.2 Genetically engineered crops approved in the UK

Crop	Product/properties	Company	Year
Maize*	Insect resistance, herbicide, glufosinate	Ciba-Geigy	1996
Maize*	Insect resistance	Monsanto	1997
Maize*	Insect resistance	Pioneer Hi-Bred	1997
Oilseed rape[†]	Herbicide resistance, glufosinate	Plant Genetics Systems	1995
Oilseed rape[†]	Herbicide resistance, glufosinate	AgrEvo	1995
Oilseed rape[†]	Herbicide resistance, glyphosphate	Monsanto	1996
Soybean*	Herbicide resistance, glyphosate	Monsanto	1995
Tomato*	Thicker paste	Zeneca Plant Science	1995
Tomato (Flavr Savr[tm])	Improved flavour	Calgene	1996

* Processed material.
† Extracted oil.

Table 8.3   Some of the genetically engineered crops approved in the USA

Crop	Properties	Year
Maize/corn	Insect resistance, herbicide resistance, male sterility	First approved in 1995
Cotton	Herbicide resistance, insect resistance	First approved 1994
Tomato	Insect resistance, altered ripening, altered ripening (Flavr Savr)	First approved 1992
Soybean	Herbicide resistance, altered oil content	First approved 1994
Squash	Virus resistance	First approved 1994
Potato	Insect resistance	First approved 1995
Rapeseed Canola	Herbicide tolerance, altered oil content	First approved 1994
Chicory	Male sterility	Approved 1997
Papaya	Virus resistance	Approved 1996

Table 8.4   Genetically engineered food products under consideration in the UK and EU

Product	Properties
UK	
Salad chicory (*Radicchio rosso*)	Male sterile chicory lines
Processed maize products	Insect/herbicide resistance
Rapeseed oil	Herbicide tolerance
Cottonseed oil	Herbicide/insect resistance
Processed potato products	Insect resistance
EU	
Oilseed rape	Herbicide tolerance
Maize	Insect resistance, herbicide resistance
Potato	Reduced amylose content
Chicory	Male sterile, herbicide tolerance
Oilseed rape	Male sterile, fertility restorer, herbicide tolerance
Fodder beet	Herbicide tolerance
Tomato	Delayed ripening
Cotton	Insect resistance, herbicide resistance

Source: compiled from the Public Register at the Department of the Environment (http://www.shef.ac.uk/-doe).

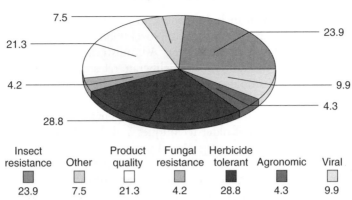

Insect resistance	Other	Product quality	Fungal resistance	Herbicide tolerant	Agronomic	Viral
■	■	□	■	■	■	□
23.9	7.5	21.3	4.2	28.8	4.3	9.9

Fig. 8.8 The most frequent traits put forward for field trials in the USA in 1997.

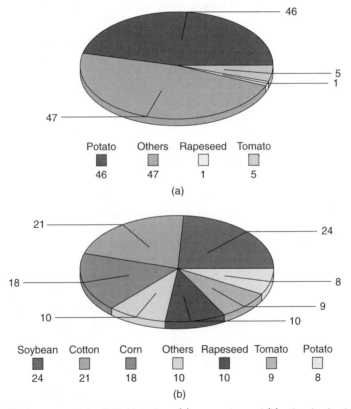

Potato	Others	Rapeseed	Tomato
■	■	□	■
46	47	1	5

(a)

Soybean	Cotton	Corn	Others	Rapeseed	Tomato	Potato
■	■	■	□	■	■	□
24	21	18	10	10	9	8

(b)

Fig. 8.9 Plants approved for field trials from (a) companies and (b) other institutions.

is herbicide resistance which is clearly of commercial value. The traits put forward for approval in the USA (Fig. 8.9) are divided by crop from both commercial and academic institutions. Six crops dominate: soybean, cotton, corn (maize), rapeseed, tomato and potato.

Any novel food, which includes genetic engineered plants, has had to be approved by the Advisory Committee on Novel Foods and Processes (ACNFP) in the UK and by the Food and Drugs Administration (FDA) in the USA before it can be sold. In addition, the deliberate release of genetic engineered plants and microorganisms also needs approval by the relevant bodies, such as the Deliberate Release Directive (90/220/EEC).

The consensus holds that the technique of genetic engineering involves refinements or extensions of older techniques and that the risks are from the genes transferred. The release of genetically manipulated organisms (GMOs) into the environment is a very different situation from the production of vaccines and hormone in genetically engineered organisms, which is carried out under controlled conditions in production plants. In conventional breeding crop plants have been hybridised to wild lines and other breeding techniques have produced a number of different plant lines, all of which have been released with no problems. However, profound ecological changes have been produced when certain plants have been introduced to different ecological conditions, such as the weed water hyacinth. Thus, it is the introduction of genetic information from distant organisms such as fish which causes some concern as these combinations would not be possible by traditional methods. The possible problems which may apply to the release of transgenic plants are as follows.

Effects on humans may come from not only the introduced gene product but more likely from the marker or selectable genes for antibiotic resistance which are introduced along with the target gene. One of the most commonly used markers is the gene from *E. coli* coding for aminoglycoside 3-phosphotransferase, commonly known as neomycin phosphotransferase 11 (ntp11) which gives resistance to kanamycin. The concern is that the ntp11 gene product will be toxic or, more worryingly, that the antibiotic resistance may be transferred to other microorganisms in the environment. The transfer of the resistance gene to bacteria in the human gut is not a problem, since kanamycin-resistant bacteria are widespread in humans and in the soil due to the widespread use of antibiotics. Despite this, other forms of selectable marker have been suggested to replace antibiotic resistance. One example is the bar gene which confers resistance to the herbicide glufosinate. One other problem which could affect humans would be the production of allergenic pollen from transgenic plants, which could cause a problem on a large scale.

The transfer of the genes from GMOs to microorganisms in the environment could also occur. Bacteria can transfer DNA by transformation, conjugation and transduction, and plants by cross-pollination. Transference of the gene to bacteria will survive in the bacterial population only if this constitutes an advantage and in this case antibiotic resistance genes should be avoided. The extent of gene transfer from crop plants to wild populations depends on a number of factors, as the crop plants and wild species must be compatible, growing at the same location, flower at the same time, and have a means of pollen transference. The genetic strategies to avoid the transference include the introduction of male sterility so that the transgenic plant produces no

Table 8.5   Information requirements for the release of genetically engineered organisms

Characteristics of the modified organism

1. Methods used for the modification.
2. Methods used to construct and introduce the insert(s) into the organism or to delete a sequence.
3. Description of the insert and/or vector construction.
4. Purity of the insert from any unknown sequence and information on the degree to which the inserted sequence is limited to the DNA required to perform the intended function.
5. Sequence, functional identity and location of the altered, inserted or deleted DNA with particular reference to any known harmful sequences.

Potential environmental impacts

1. Potential for excessive population increase in the environment.
2. Competitive advantage of the genetically modified organism over the unmodified organism.
3. Identification and description of the target organisms.
4. Anticipated mechanisms and results of interactions between the released modified organism and the target organisms.
5. Identification and description of non-target organisms that may be affected by accident.
6. Probability of shifts in biological interactions or host range after release.
7. Known or predicted effects on non-target organisms in the environment, impact on population levels of competitors – preys, hosts, symbionts, predators, parasites and pathogens.
8. Known or predicted involvement in biogeochemical processes.
9. Other potentially significant interactions with the environment.

Source: Kappeli and Auberson, 1997.

pollen, linking the gene with a gene that is lethal in pollen, the removal of flowers from the transgenic plant, the removal of compatible species and the planting of buffer plants. A recent solution was to direct the introduced gene to the chloroplast which is not transferred to the pollen and therefore cannot be transferred in cross-breeding. This also has the advantage that the chloroplast has a high copy number or a large number of gene copies (Daniell *et al.*, 1998). Other methods of gene transfer reduction include treating the plants with growth regulators so that they flower before any compatible plants.

Another problem of transgenic plants may be that the new gene will give the plant a selective advantage, causing it to become a new pest or weed. A similar problem may be the transfer of the gene from the transgenic plant to a weed that gives the weed advantages, making it more of a problem. The transgenic plant may also compete with local beneficial plants and upset the plant communities. Therefore, when considering the release of transgenic plants the risks are considered on a case-by-case basis (Table 8.5) and the following should not be forgotten:

● Of the antibiotic resistance genes only kanamycin has been tested for its effect on humans and this type of marker should be replaced by non-antibiotic markers if possible.

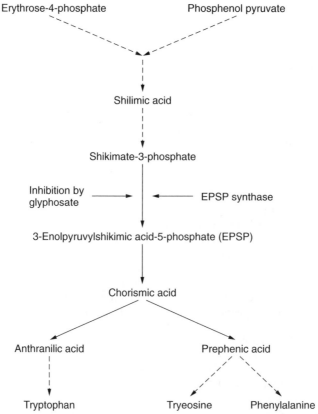

Fig. 8.10 An outline of the shikimate pathway indicating the enzyme inhibited by the herbicide glyphosate.

- Field trials are needed to determine the best strategies to avoid the transference of genes on a case-by-case basis.
- Field evaluation is needed to determine the level of expression which can vary greatly.

8.2.13 Tolerance to pesticides and herbicides

It is normal practice for farmers to spray for weed control using a variety of herbicides which are not very selective and in some cases are persistent in the environment. One approach to reducing herbicide use is the transformation of crops to herbicide resistance. The mechanisms of action of many herbicides are not well understood but the strategy of resistance can take three forms: the increase in the affected enzyme, the expression of a mutant enzyme, and the expression of an enzyme which detoxifies the herbicide. One of the best examples is the herbicide glyphosate which inhibits the enzyme 5-enolpyruvylshikimate-3-phosphate synthase (Fig. 8.10). This enzyme is found in the chloroplast and is part of the pathway leading to the formation of aromatic amino acids. The gene has been isolated from plants (petunia) and bacteria. Overexpression of this gene in a plant gives tolerance to glyphosate. In another case the enzyme was cloned from a bacterium in which some of the amino acids have been substituted to make the enzyme less susceptible to glyphosate. A number of plants have been transformed to glyphosate resistance (Table 8.3), including cotton. In 1997 glyphosate-resistant cotton plants were grown commercially for the first time. Some of the growers have found that the cotton bolls drop prematurely or are deformed (Fox, 1997) which indicates some of the problems that may occur with transgenic plants.

Another example of glyphosate resistance is the development of transgenic soya bean. Soya (*Glycine max*) is an important food crop and the beans and processed products are used in a number of food products. Monsanto had developed this bean by transforming a commercial soya bean with an *Agrobacterium* gene (CP4) for EPSPS which is insensitive to glyphosate. The beans also contain part of the EPSPS gene from *Petunia hybrida* which encodes for a chloroplast transit peptide (CTP). The peptide delivers the bacterial EPSPS to the chloroplast, its site of action. The bean was transformed by particle gun bombardment with a plasmid containing two EPSPS genes and the CTP sequences under the control of three plant promoters. The plasmid also included a gene coding for the enzyme β-glucuronidase (GUS) from *E. coli* and the nptII gene which confers resistance to kanamycin. On transformation the plasmid DNA breaks at one or more positions and integrates into the genome. During the propagation of the transformed lines normal segregation of the inserts occurred. PCR and Southern blot analysis confirmed that the transformed soya contained only the EPSPS and CTP genes and not the GUS and ntpII genes. If the antibiotic genes were still present there may be concern that the genes may be transferred to the organisms in the environment. The Advisory Committee on Novel Foods and Processes concluded that due to the extensive processing of soya beans these genes presented no problems.

8.2.14   Resistance to pests

Plants are often attacked by insects, nematodes and molluscs which can severely affect the crop yield. An alternative to the use of chemical pesticides is to use genetic engineering to produce plants resistant to these pests by introducing certain genes. The best known example of a biological form of pest control is the production by *Bacillus thuringiensis* of a protein, endotoxin, which is toxic to a number of caterpillars but does not harm animals or other insects (see section 4.2.3). The protein is produced as the bacillus forms spores in the form of an inactive protein of 1200 amino acids. If the protein is ingested by a caterpillar the protease activity in the gut of the caterpillar cleaves the protein to form the active 68,000 dalton protein. The protein binds to the surface of the midgut cells, killing the caterpillar. Plants transformed by inclusion of the gene responsible for the BT toxin include poplar, elm, spruce, maize and cotton. Maize showed resistance to caterpillar attack, in particular to the important pest the European corn borer. Cotton plants have had their resistance increased by modifying the toxin by using a truncated toxin gene, and substitution of the plant-preferred codons in the gene gave a 100-fold increase in toxin levels. Transformed trees showed resistance to the gypsy moth (Podila and Karnosky, 1996). Other possibilities of introducing pest resistance may be the inclusion of the protein chloresterol oxidase (Vip3A), amylase inhibitor and systemic wound-response proteins (Dempsey et al., 1998).

8.2.15   Resistance to pathogens

Pathogens which can affect plants can be viruses, bacteria or fungi. Viral infections are normally treated by killing the virus vectors with pesticides to stop further transmission. If plant cells are transformed with genes or sequences from the viral genomes the plants become resistant to those viruses (Dempsey et al., 1998). This resistance is known as pathogen-derived resistance (PDR) and provides protection against a variety of viruses. One of the first examples of this type of resistance was the expression of the coat protein of tobacco mosaic virus (TMV) in tobacco plants which made them resistant to TMV. Transgenic lines of squash and papaya exhibiting PDR have been approved for commercial cultivation. Plants have been engineered to express a mutant form of the viral movement protein which has produced resistance. Another form of viral resistance is the presence of the ribosome-inactivation protein (RIP) such as the pokeweed antiviral protein which exhibits antiviral activity. Transgenic plants have been produced containing the pokeweed antiviral protein, but unfortunately they were stunted and difficult to grow due to the toxic effect of the protein. Transgenic potato lines have been produced which express a double-stranded RNA-specific ribonuclease pac1 from a yeast. These lines were resistant to potato spindle viroid, as the ribonuclease digested the double-stranded RNA regions of the viroid when these formed during replication (Sano et al., 1997).

Bacterial diseases are of considerable importance to crop plants, causing losses in valuable crops such as cereals, vegetables and fruits. There have been two major approaches to the development of resistance: firstly to introduce antibacterial proteins and secondly to enhance the plants' natural defences (Table 8.6). There are a number of proteins which can be introduced to give bacterial resistance, including lytic peptides, lysozymes, lactoferrin and toxins. Insect lytic peptides which form pores in bacterial membranes have been expressed in potato and tobacco; these were derived from the cecropins from the giant silk moth (Mourgues et al., 1998). The enzyme lysozyme is found widely and will degrade peptidoglycan which forms part of the bacterial cell wall. In many cases this degradation will cause lysis and death of the bacteria. Lysozyme genes have been inserted into tobacco plants and the plants have shown partial resistance to Erwinia carotovora atroseptica, a plant pathogen.

Table 8.6 Examples of transgenic plants with improved resistance to bacterial diseases

Protein	Origin	Plant	Resistance
Antibacterial proteins from non-plant origin			
Shiva-1	Giant silk moth	Tobacco	*Ralstonia solanacearum*
MB 39	Giant silk moth	Tobacco	*Pseudomonas syringae* pv. *tabaci*
Attacin E	Giant silk moth	Apple	*Erwinia amylovora*
Lysozyme	T4 bacteriophage	Potato	*Erwinia carotovora* pv. *tabaci*
Lysozyme	Human	Tobacco	*Pseudomonas syringae*
Lactoferrin	Human	Tobacco	*Ralstonia solanacearum*
Tachyplesin	Horseshoe crab	Potato	*Erwinia carotovora*
Inhibition of bacterial pathogenicity or virulence factors			
Tabtoxin-resistance	*Pseudomonas syringae*	Tobacco	*Pseudomonas syringae*
Phaseolotoxin-insensitive OCTase*	*Pseudomonas syringae* pv. *phaseolicola*	Bean	*Pseudomonas syringae* pv. *phaseolicola*
Enhancement of natural plant defences			
Pectate lyase	*Erwinia carotovora*	Potato	*Erwinia carotovora*
Resistance protein Xa21	Resistant rice strains	Rice	*Xanthomonas orzyae*
Glucose oxidase	*Aspergillus niger*	Potato	*Erwinia carotovora*
Thionin	Barley	Tobacco	*Pseudomonas syringae* pv. *tabaci*
Artifically induced cell death			
Bacterio-opsin	*Halobacterium halobium*	Tobacco	*Pseudomonas syringae* pv. *tabaci*

* OCTase, ornithine carbamoyltransferase.
Source: Mourgues *et al.*, 1998.

Inhibition of bacterial pathogenicity has also been attempted by the insertion of monoclonal antibodies or enzymes to inactivate bacterial toxins.

Plants have a number of natural defences to bacterial infection and these can be enhanced to give increased resistance to bacterial infections. One example is the cloning of a pathogen recognition gene (R) from a resistant line into a susceptible plant. In this way rice has been transformed with an R gene from a resistant line and this led to resistance to *Xanthomonas orzyae*, which causes bacterial leaf blight in rice. An early response in plants to bacterial infection is the production of reactive oxygen species such as hydrogen peroxide. The production of large amounts of hydrogen peroxide has been induced by the expression of a glucose oxidase gene from *Aspergillus niger* in tobacco plants which gave increased resistance to *E. carotovora*. Bacterial infection can also induce rapid and localised cell death at the site of infection which limits the

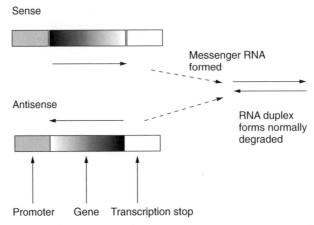

Sense

Messenger RNA
formed

Antisense

RNA duplex
forms normally
degraded

Promoter   Gene   Transcription stop

Fig. 8.11 The use of antisense technology for the suppression of the activity of a normal gene. The gene for polygalacturonase has been inserted in the reverse phase so that when transcribed into mRNA it forms a duplex with the normal mRNA. This double-stranded RNA is then degraded.

spread of the infection. The genes responsible for this response are under investigation as a possible source of resistance to infection.

Phytoalexins are small antimicrobial compounds which are produced in response to the infection of a plant and have been the target for genetic engineering (Dempsey *et al.*, 1998). Attempts have been made to increase phytoalexin levels in order to confer resistance to both bacterial and fungal pathogens. The problems associated with this approach are that phytoalexins are synthesised via long complex pathways and the final product is toxic to the plant itself, so that the effect of overproduction on the plant may be deleterious.

8.2.16 Fruit quality

One example of a transgenic plant which has become a commercial product in Europe and the USA is the Flavr Savr™ tomato developed by Calgene. The Calgene tomato has an increased shelf-life, as an antisense silencing of the polygalacturonase slows ripening. The polygalacturonase enzyme is involved in cell wall degradation as part of fruit ripening. The antisense technology involves the reversal of the coding region of the gene which results in the transcription of the antisense DNA rather than the normal sense strand (Fig. 8.11). The antisense mRNA appears to interfere with the normal mRNA, reducing or eliminating enzyme formation. The Zeneca tomato uses a truncated sense polygalacturonase gene to reduce the activity in order to produce the longer shelf-life and a higher solids content. The Calgene product is sold as a fresh product, whereas Zeneca is sold processed as a tinned paste. Considerable efforts have been put into the testing of these transgenic tomatoes so that they could be sold to the public as a food. The questions asked by the FDA and

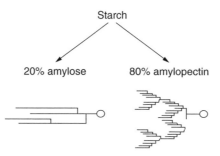

Fig. 8.12 The structure of the components of starch, amylose and amylopectin.

ACNFP were as follows: do the genes introduced into the tomato affect the tomato as a food? Has this altered the naturally occurring toxins? Are there too many copies of the introduced gene present? A series of field tests were set up in 1988 and the conclusions were that the Flavr Savr™ tomato is a food and no unintentional changes were detected.

8.2.17 Agronomic traits

Genetic engineering can offer considerable potential in the change of the traits of crops, such as colour, nitrogen fixation, starch synthesis, resistance to all forms of stress, and modification of oils accumulated.

Starch occurs in almost all plants and comes in two forms as transitory and storage starch. Starch is stored in granules or amyloplasts and is the main storage product in seeds of cereals such as wheat and maize and tubers such as potato. The storage granules are made up of two forms of starch amylose and amylopectin. All starch molecules are polymers of glucose, but amylose is a linear polymer whereas amylopectin is a branched polymer (Fig. 8.12). Natural starches are mainly amylopectin. Starch is synthesised in the amyloplasts using sucrose as the main substrate; the pathway is shown in Fig. 8.13. The key enzymes are the ADP-glucose pyrophosphorylase, starch synthase (elongase) and the branching starch synthase. Genetic engineering has been used to increase the level of starch in potatoes by transforming them with a mutated bacterial gene (*glg*C16) encoding for ADP-glucose pyrophorylase and targeting the enzyme to the amyloplast. In this case low-starch-producing potatoes have had their starch content increased by 60%. The type of starch stored had considerable importance in the industry (Bruinenberg *et al.*, 1995). The straight-chained amylose gives it a tendency to recrystallise after dispersion in water, and this stable and defined viscosity for a long period is required in many starch products. If pure amylose or amylopectin were to be produced they would have a large number of applications. At present the only waxy maize contains 100% amylopectin. The amount of amylose in potato starch has been reduced by expressing a cDNA coding for the granule-bound starch synthase in the antisense orientation, which reduces amylose synthesis.

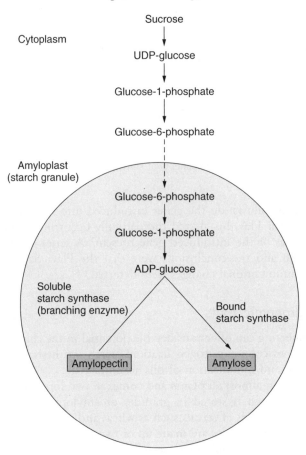

Fig. 8.13   The pathway for the synthesis of amylopectin and amylose.

Soybean, oil palm, rapeseed and sunflower oils account for 72% of the world's vegetable oil, with a volume of 100 Mt at a value of $70 billion (Murphy, 1996). Rapeseed was one of the first targets for genetic manipulation, as there has been a good transformation system in place for some time. Herbicide-resistant lines of rapeseed have been approved for commercial cultivation since 1993. Current interest in rapeseed is in the alteration of the oil composition in the main oil-producing plants (Table 8.7). Rapeseed has seen most of the advances, as it is related to *Arabidopsis* where genetic manipulation has been used to elucidate many of the steps and to isolate the genes for the enzymes of lipid synthesis. The knowledge acquired with *Arabidopsis* can be easily applied to rapeseed and a number of transgenic plants have been produced. One transgenic rapeseed plant forms 40% of the total lipid as lauric acid (C12), because the ACP thioesterase from the California Bay plant has been introduced, which causes premature chain termination at C12. Another line of rapeseed accumulates 40% stearic acid which is formed due to the

Table 8.7   Some of the transgenic rapeseed strains currently under development

Oil	Industrial products
40% stearic acid (18:0)	Margarine, cocoa butter
40% lauric acid (12:0)	Detergents
60% lauric acid (12:0)	Detergents
80% oleic acid (18:1^9)	Food, lubricants, inks
Petroselinic acid (18:1^6)	Polymers, detergents
Jojoba wax (C20, C22)	Cosmetics, lubricants
40% myristate (14:0)	Detergents, soaps, personal care
90% erucic acid (22:1)	Polymers, cosmetics, inks, pharmaceuticals
Ricinoleic acid (18:1–OH)	Lubricants, plasticisers, cosmetics, pharmaceuticals
Polyhydroxybutyrate	Biodegradable plastics
Phytase	Animal feed
Industrial enzymes	Fermentation, paper manufacture, food processing
Novel peptides	Pharmaceuticals

Source: Murphy, 1996.

engineered presence of an antisense copy of *Brassica* stearate desaturase which under normal conditions would desaturate stearate to oleate. Table 8.7 indicates the varieties of rapeseed under development.

Genetic engineering can be used to change flower colour by the inactivation of the endogenous enzymes or by introducing new genes. Both approaches have been successfully applied, the first by reducing the activity of CHS chalcone synthase which reduces the formation of red and blue pigments (Holton and Tanaka, 1994). Although considerable research has been carried out on nitrogen fixation, much more is needed before nitrogen fixation, which is a bacterial process, can be transformed into plants. One of the problems is that nitrogen fixation is very sensitive to oxygen and therefore a low oxygen environment will be required for the process to function. The engineering of plants to tolerate various stresses such as chilling, heat, drought, salinity, freezing and flooding has clear advantages, but the tolerance is likely to be a multifaceted characteristic involving a number of genes and therefore not easy to manipulate. However, a number of methods have been attempted to improve stress tolerance (Holmberg and Bulow, 1998). These are outlined in Table 8.8 and the most successful have been the formation of osmoregulatory products, membrane-modifying enzymes, radical-scavenging enzymes and stress-induced proteins.

8.2.18   Plants as bioreactors

Apart from changing or improving the properties of plants, genetic engineering can also modify plants to produce foreign compounds which could have a

Table 8.8   Transgenic plants expressing genes for stress tolerance

Origin	Gene	Host	Stress
Escherichia coli	BetA	Tobacco	Salinity
E. coli	BetA	Potato	Freezing
Arthrobacter globiformis	codA	*Arabidopsis*	Salinity, drought
Vigna aconitifolia	p5cs	Tobacco	Drought
E. coli	Mltd	*Arabidopsis*	Salinity
E. coli	Mltd	Tobacco	Salinity
Saccharomyces cerevisiae	TPS1	Tobacco	Drought
Bacillus subtilis	SacB	Tobacco	Drought
Arabidopsis	fad7	Tobacco	Chilling
Anacystis nidulans	Des9	Tobacco	Chilling
Barley	HVA 1	Rice	Salinity, drought
Winter flounder	Afp	Tobacco	Freezing
Winter flounder	afa3	Tomato	Freezing
Nicotiana plumbaginifolia	Mn-Sod	Alfalfa	Drought, freezing
N. plumbaginifolia	Mn-Sod	Tobacco	Oxidative
Arabidopsis	Fe-Sod	Tobacco	Oxidative
E. coli; rice	Gr/Cu, Zn-Sod	Tobacco	Oxidative
Vitreoscilla stercoraria	vhb	Tobacco	Hypoxia, anoxia

Source: Holmberg and Bulow, 1998.

commercial value. Plants represent a versatile, renewable and low-cost source of products such as carbohydrates, fatty acids, proteins, enzymes, pharmaceuticals and biodegradable plastics. Some examples of possible products are given in Table 8.9. Plants are particularly attractive systems for the production of heterologous proteins and biodegradable plastics. Poly-3-hydroxybutyrate (PHB), a polyester with thermoplastic properties (see Chapter 3), was synthesised in *Arabidopsis* by introducing the genes for acetoacetyl-CoA reductase and poly-(3-hydroxybutyrate) synthase (Fig. 8.14). However, these genes were expressed in the cytoplasm, where the supply of acetyl-CoA was thought to be limiting. There is a much higher level of acetyl-CoA in the plastids as these are the site of fatty acid synthesis, so that redirecting the enzymes to the plastids resulted in a 100-fold increase in PHB accumulation (10 mg/g wet weight) (Goddijn and Pen, 1995).

8.3   Diagnostics

The detection of disease in both animals and plants is important in terms of both health and commerce. The production of pure antigens by genetic

Diagnostics

Table 8.9 The production of foreign compounds in plants as a result of genetic
manipulation

Compound	Origin of gene	Plant	Application
α-Trichosantin	Chinese plant	*Nicotiana benthamiana*	Inhibition of HIV replication
Angiotensin-1-converting enzyme inhibitor	Milk	Tobacco, tomato	Anti-hypersensitive
Antibodies	Mouse	Mainly tobacco	Various
Antigens	Bacteria/virus	Tobacco, tomato, potato, lettuce	Oral vaccines
Antigens	Pathogens	Tobacco	Subunit vaccines
Enkephalin	Human	Oilseed rape, *Arabidopsis*	Opiate activity
Epidermal growth factor	Human	Tobacco	Proliferation of specific cells
Erythropoietin	Human	Tobacco	Regulation of erythrocytes
Growth hormone	Trout	Tobacco, *Arabidopsis*	Growth stimulation
Hirudin	Synthetic	Oilseed rape	Thrombin inhibitor
Human serum albumin	Human	Tobacco, potato	Plasma extender
Interferon	Human	Turnip	Anti-viral
α-Amylase	*Bacillus licheniformis*	Tobacco, alfalfa	Starch liquefaction
β-Glucanase	*Trichoderma reesei*	Barley	Brewing
Phytase	*Aspergillus niger*	Tobacco	Animal feed
Xylanase	*Clostridium thermocellum*	Tobacco	Animal feed, paper pulp

Source: Goddijn and Pen, 1995.

manipulation will allow the formation of monoclonal antibodies which are more specific than the normal polyclonal antibodies. This will allow a very accurate and specific detection of infections in both plants and animals since the monoclonal antibodies can distinguish between closely related species. The techniques involved are radioimmune assay (RIA), fluorescence immunoassay (FIA), enzyme-linked immunoassay (EIA) and enzyme-linked immunoadsorbent assay (ELISA). Recombinant DNA technology can also provide pure antigens for the development of antibodies and PCR can be used to detect very low levels of organisms (see Chapter 2).

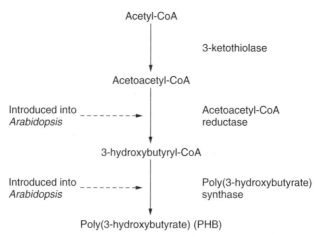

Fig. 8.14   The pathway for the production of poly(3-hydroxybutyrate), indicating the two genes that have been introduced into the plant *Arabidopsis*.

8.4   Improved animals

The improvement of animal stocks by selective breeding has been carried out for centuries using conventional techniques, but it is a slow process. Just as genetic engineering can be applied to plants for their improvement, so can it be applied to animals. The production of transgenic animals falls into two main areas: the use of animals to produce foreign protein of medical use, and as part of a breeding scheme. The use of animals to produce foreign products is sometimes known as biopharming, as most of the products are high-value pharmaceuticals. For example, the blood factors VIII and IX have been made in sheep and lactoferrin in cattle. Extraction of the product without sacrificing the animal is the best option; this can be achieved by linking the gene for the protein to one being produced in milk, so as to ensure that the protein can be extracted from the milk. The use of genetic engineering in the breeding of animals has focused on improvements in growth. Both animals and fish have been engineered to contain more growth hormone to ensure faster growth.

The improvement of animals does not always involve genetic manipulation. An example is embryo cloning, which has had considerable publicity recently. In this technique a 16-cell embryo from the artificial insemination of a favoured breeding line is used as a source of nuclei. These nuclei are transplanted into enucleated eggs from other cows and cultured until they can be used for implantation into a number of other cows. In this way the 16 nuclei will give rise to 16 identical calves. More recently it has been shown that nuclei from an embryo-derived mouse cell-line can be transplanted into unfertilised eggs (Willmut *et al.*, 1997) to yield viable offspring. This has been repeated with the transfer of nuclei from cell populations from sheep mammary, fetus and embryo to unfertilised sheep eggs to produce lambs, one of which was named Dolly. These types of advances are perceived as cloning by the public and regarded with some suspicion. Whether these types of techniques will be widely adopted will depend on public perception as well as the results.

Another example is bovine somatotrophin (BST) which is a hormone involved with growth promotion and increased lactation. If administered to lactating cows it will increase the milk produced by 10–25%. Under normal conditions BST is too expensive to use in the dairy industry, but the gene has been cloned and expressed in *E. coli* and produced in large quantities. The genetically engineered BST when given to cows also increased milk production by 10–25%. Recombinant BST has been approved for use in milk production but its use has been resisted. Although BST has been approved for injection, the additional milk production will require an increase in feed, and other adverse effects have been reported including increased mastitis, reduced pregnancy rates and lesions of the knee. Perhaps the best argument against the use of BST is its economic impact on the dairy industry. It has been argued that extra milk is not required at a time when milk production is in surplus, particularly in Europe where milk quotas have been introduced. In addition, at a time when food is marketed as natural, there are considerable doubts as to whether the public would accept milk produced with the help of an injected hormone (Potter, 1994).

8.5 Animal vaccines

Traditional vaccines can be either live vaccines containing attenuated viral and bacterial cultures or killed vaccines containing dead whole cells, viruses or inactivated toxins. Genetic engineering will be applied to the development of vaccines against animal diseases such as rabies, Newcastle disease, foot and mouth, swine pseudorabies, fowl plague, and bacterial infections such as colibacillosis (scours) and pasteurellosis (respiratory infection). Developments in recombinant DNA technology have enabled antigenic molecules to be identified, cloned and expressed in bacteria. These antigens are difficult to purify by conventional methods so that their expression in bacteria means that there is a source of large quantities of antigen. This has enabled new forms of vaccine to be developed as these vaccines use a single molecule rather than the whole organism. These forms of vaccines are known as subunit vaccines and their production has the advantages that they are easy and inexpensive to produce, and the antigen is devoid of other material and has no chance of containing live organisms. However, subunit vaccines do have certain problems of low expression of the cloned gene, and the protein formed does not fold properly and is therefore not antigenic. Incorrect folding is often caused by producing an animal protein in a bacterium, where the post-translational processing is different or absent. For example, a protein for fowl plague has been expressed in *E. coli* but the product was not antigenic. To eliminate the problem of folding the protein could be expressed in animal cell cultures where the processing would be compatible. However, animal cell culture is expensive and the extraction process has to ensure that all animal DNA was removed from the antigen. The problems of protein folding and the short life of these vaccines are the reason that subunit vaccines have seen only restricted use, although a subunit vaccine against human hepatitis B has been produced.

The weak response of the subunit vaccines can be improved by using a concentrated antigen and combining this with some bacterial cell wall material. The addition of bacterial cell wall material has been successful, as traditional antigens are presented on the surface of the bacterium or virus and this clearly influences the antigenic response. Another method of presenting the antigen in a natural manner was to incorporate the subunit vaccine gene into live, attenuated virus or bacteria. Presented in this manner, smaller doses of antigen would be needed, giving a stronger response with no need to inject to elicit a response. One method has been to incorporate the subunit vaccine into the vaccina virus. The large vaccina virus has proved difficult to manipulate but, by cloning the subunit gene between two vaccina sequences in an *E. coli* plasmid, the subunit gene can be recombined on infection of an animal cell (Brochier, 1991). Using this approach, a vaccine has been produced against rabies using a glycoprotein from the virus as the antigen. The viral vaccine has been shown to eradicate rabies in field trials and a product, RaboraR, is now on sale in France to control rabies in the wild animal population. Other live recombinant vaccines are available for Newcastle disease and fowl pox in poultry.

As subunit vaccines use only part of the antigen molecule (epitopes), it is possible to use just this region to give an antigenic response, which has the advantage that the region can be chemically synthesised, eliminating the need for purification. This method has been used to develop a vaccine against the foot and mouth virus. The traditional vaccine against this virus uses killed virus particles but it loses activity rapidly. The foot and mouth virus contains four capsid proteins and one of these (VP1) has been produced in *E. coli* in large amounts, but does not fold properly. The 140–160 VP1 peptide was linked to a large carrier protein, expressed in *E. coli*, and the vaccine was successful in guinea pigs but was ineffective in cattle. Further development continues.

8.6 Biodiversity

The world is losing plant and animal species at an increasing rate and the loss of genetic material cannot be replaced. In the main this loss is being caused by agricultural practices of land clearance and cultivation.

The convention on Biological Diversity (UNEP, 1995) during the Rio conference defined biodiversity as 'the variability among living organisms from all sources including terrestrial, marine and other aquatic ecosystems and the ecological complexes of which they are part; this includes diversity within species, between species and of ecosystems'. It is essential that biodiversity be maintained for the following reasons:

- All species have genuine intrinsic value regardless of any value they may have to human welfare.
- Many species have a value to human society and only a limited number of species have been tested for their potential value. An example is the screening of plants for new drugs which has led to the production of medicines such as the antileukemic vinchristine from the plant *Catharanthus roseus*. The availability of plant and animal species is required for breeders to maintain a high degree of variation.
- Species make up ecological communities which are involved with processes such as nutrient recycling, provision of oxygen and carbon dioxide removal. In only a few cases are there sufficient data to evaluate the ecological importance of particular species, but this does not diminish their importance.

Plant and animal cell culture biotechnology can rescue endangered species where multiplication is not possible by conventional means, and cryopreservation technology can also store germplasm indefinitely.

8.7 Conclusions

Biotechnology through the application of genetic engineering has had and will continue to have a considerable effect on agriculture. Perhaps the advances will appear less spectacular than those in medicine, but transgenic plants may affect more people and have a longer-lasting effect. Overall, these changes may affect the environment in the following ways:

- The production of new subunit vaccines should reduce the use of antibiotics in animals. The overuse of antibiotics is one of the major causes of the development of antibiotic resistance in microorganisms.
- There will be increased use of genetic engineered products and monoclonal antibodies for diagnosis in both plants and animals.
- The continued introduction of transgenic plants should reduce the use of both herbicides and pesticides. However, there is public concern and resistance at the possible danger of the widespread release of transgenic plants, particularly those containing antibiotic resistance genes. Labelling of all transgenic products may go some way to reduce these fears, and market forces may limit the introduction of transgenic plants and products. For example, transgenic brewers' yeast has been available for some time and has been approved for use, but genetic engineered beer is not on sale to date.
- Continued introduction of transgenic animals and fish will occur but many concerns over their production may be a limiting factor.
- Other biotechnological products such as microbial inoculants, biopesticides and anaerobic digestion of wastes will be introduced.

8.8 References

Blackhall, N. W., Davey, M. R. and Power, J. B. (1994) Applications of protoplast technology, in R. A. Dixon and R. A. Gonzales (eds), *Plant Cell Culture: A Practical Approach*. IRL Press, Oxford, pp. 41–55.

Brochier, B. (1991) Large-scale eradication of rabies using recombinant vaccina-rabies vaccine. *Nature*, **354**, 520–522.

Bruinenberg, P. M., Jacobsen, E. and Visser, R. G. F. (1995) Starch from genetically engineered crops. *Chemistry & Industry*, November, 881–884.

Chirikjian, C. (1995) *Biotechnology*, Vol 11. Jones and Barlett, Boston, MA.

Chung, C.-H., Kwon, O.-C., Yi, Y.-B. and Lee, S.-Y. (1998) Isolation of quality genomic DNA from tenacious seeds of sesame. *Plant Tissue Cult. & Biotechnol.*, 4, 42–48.

Daniell, H., Datta, R., Varma, S., Gray, S. and Lee, S.-B. (1998) Containment of herbicide through genetic engineering of the chloroplast genome. *Nature Biotechnol.*, 16, 345–348.

Datta, S. K., Datta, K., Soltanifar, N., Donn, G. and Potrykus, I. (1994) Herbicide-resistant indica rice plants from IRRI breeding line IR72 after PEG-mediated transformation of protoplasts. *Plant Mol. Biol.*, 20, 619–629.

Dempsey, D. A., Silva, H. and Klessig, D. F. (1998) Engineering disease and pest resistance in plants. *Trends Microbiol.*, 6, 54–60.

Fox, J. L. (1997) Farmers say Monsanto's engineered cotton drops bolls. *Nature Biotechnol.*, 15, 1233.

Glazer, A. N. and Nikaido, H. (1994) *Microbial Biotechnology*. Freeman, New York.

Goddijn, O. J. M. and Pen, J. (1995) Plants as bioreactors. *Tibtech*, 13, 379–387.

Gray, D. J., Hiebert, E., Lin, C. M., Compton, M. E., McColley, D. W., Harrison, M. and Gaba, V. P. (1994) Simplified construction and performance of a device for particle bombardment. *Plant Cell Tissue Org. Cult.*, 37, 179–184.

Holmberg, N. and Bulow, L. (1998) Improved stress tolerance in plants by gene transfer. *Trends in Plant Science*, 3, 61–66.

Holton, T. A. and Tanaka, Y. (1994) Blue roses – a pigment of our imagination. *Tibtech*, 12, 40–42.

Jain, S. M. and DeKlerk, G.-J. (1998) Somaclonal variation in breeding and propagation of ornamental crops. *Plant Tissue & Biotechnol.*, 4, 63–75.

Kappeli, O. and Auberson, L. (1997). The science and intricacy of environmental safety evaluations. *Tibtech*, 15, 342–349.

Karp, A. (1995) Somaclonal variation as a tool for crop improvement. *Euphytica*, 85, 295–302.

Kikkert, J. R. (1993) The biolistic PDS-1000/He device. *Plant Cell Tissue Org. Cult.*, 33, 221–226.

Kobayashi, N., Horikoshi, T., Katsuyama, H., Handa, T. and Takayanagi, K. (1998) A simple and efficient DNA extraction method for plants, especially woody plants. *Plant Tissue Cult. & Biotechnol.*, 4, 76–80.

Kononov, M. E., Bassuner, B. and Gelvin, S. B. (1997) Integration of T-DNA binary vector 'backbone' sequences into the tobacco genome: evidence for multiple complex patterns of integration. *Plant Journal*, 11, 945–957.

McCabe, D. and Christou, P. (1993) Direct DNA transfer using electric discharge particle acceleration (ACCELL™ technology). *Plant Cell Tissue Org. Cult.*, 33, 227–236.

Misteli, T. and Spector, D. L. (1997) Applications of green fluorescent protein in cell biology and biotechnology. *Nature Biotechnol.*, 15, 961–964.

Mourgues, F., Brisset, M. N. and Cheveau, E. (1998) Strategies to improve plant resistance to bacterial diseases through genetic engineering. *Tibtech*, 16, 203–209.

Murphy, D. J. (1996) Engineering oil production in rapeseed and other oil crops. *Tibtech*, 14, 206–213.

Oard, J. (1993) Development of an airgun device for particle bombardment. *Plant Cell Tissue Org. Cult.*, **33**, 247–250.

Podila, G. K. and Karnosky, D. F. (1996) Fibre farms of the future: genetically engineered trees. *Chemistry & Industry*, December, 976–981.

Potter, M. (1994) BST: science's own goal. *Chemistry & Industry*, October, 836.

Ratledge,C. (1993) Containing genetically modified organisms. *Biologist*, **40**, 78–79.

Roest, S. and Gilissen, L. J. W. (1993) Regeneration from protoplasts: a supplementary literature review. *Acta Botanica Neerlandica*, **42**, 1–23.

Sanford, J. C. (1988) The biolistic process. *Trends Biotechnol.*, **6**, 299–302.

Sano, T., Nagayama, A., Ogawa, T., Ishida, I. and Okada, Y. (1997) Transgenic potato expressing a double-stranded RNA-specific ribonuclease is resistant to potato spindle tuber viroid. *Nature Biotechnol.*, **15**, 1290–1294.

Senior, I. J. and Dale, P. J. (1996) Plant transgene silencing – gremlin or gift? *Chemistry & Industry*, August, 604–608.

Siemens, J. and Schieder, O. (1996) Transgenic plants: genetic transformation – recent developments and state of the art. *Plant Tissue Cult. & Biotechnol.*, **2**, 66–75.

Sul, I.-W. and Korban, S. S. (1996) A highly efficient method for isolating genomic DNA from plant tissues. *Plant Tissue Cult. & Biotechnol.*, **2**, 114–117.

Trick, H. N., Dinkins, R. D., Santarem, E. R., Di, R., Samoyolov, V., Meurer, C. A., Walker, D. R., Parrott, W. A., Finer, J. J. and Collins, G. B. (1997) Recent advances in soybean transformation. *Plant Tissue Cult. & Biotechnol.*, **3**, 9–26.

UNEP (1995) *Global Biodiversity Assessment.* Cambridge University Press, Cambridge, UK.

Willmut, I., Schnieke, A. E., McWhir, J., Kind, A. J. and Campbell, K. H. S. (1997) Viable offspring derived from fetal and adult mammalian cells. *Nature*, **385**, 810–813.

8.8.1 Recommended reading

Alberts, B., Bray, D., Lewis, J., Raff, M., Roberts, K. and Watson, J. D. (1996) *Molecular Biology of the Cell.* Garland Publishing, New York.

Altman, A. (1998) *Agricultural Biotechnology.* Marcel Dekker, New York.

Pierpoint, W. S. and Shrewry, P. R. (1996) *Genetic Engineering of Crop Plants for Resistance to Pests and Diseases.* British Crop Protection Council, Farnham, Surrey, UK.

Redenbaugh, K., Hiatt, W., Martineau, B., Kramer, M., Sheehy, R., Sanders, R., Houck, C. and Emlay, D. (1992) *Safety Assessment of Genetically Engineered Fruits and Vegetables.* CRC Press, Boca Raton, FL.

Chapter 9

Future prospects

The book *The Silent Spring* by Rachel Carson was written in 1962 over 30 years ago, and although some of the problems laid out in the book were over emphasised, it did signal the start of the gradual change in the public's view of the use of pesticides and chemicals in agriculture. It also changed how the environment was viewed, and initiated the development of anti-pollution legislation which is being enacted today. An example is the banning of the use of the pesticide DDT, which was shown to accumulate in the food chain and was responsible for the reduction in the population of some birds. Two other books published later, *Since Silent Spring* (Graham, 1970) and *Beyond Silent Spring* (Van Emden and Peakall, 1996), have revisiting the issues covered by the first book. *Silent Spring* dealt mainly with the problem of organophosphate pesticides and since that time their use has been reduced in most countries and eliminated in some countries. At the same time, other environmental dangers have become apparent such as climate change due to the build up of greenhouse gases, ozone depletion due to CFC release, acid rain caused by the release of hydrogen sulphide from power stations and industry, and finally, discussions on the release of genetically engineered organisms.

   In the book, the application of biotechnology to many aspects of the environment have been explored. Biotechnology is best defined as 'the controlled use of biological information' and is a multidisciplinary approach to the solution of problems. While the traditional technologies such as waste treatment or those newer ones like biofuels are regarded as benign by the public, genetic engineering or the production of transgenic plants and animals is regarded with suspicion. It is seen as going against nature and is compared with other problems such as the use of the drug thalidomide, which causes deformities. This is particularly true when dealing with transgenic humans and animals where the treatment of disease is accepted but any mention of cloning invokes the idea of 'playing God'. In the case of the introduction of transgenic plants it is clear that this is being carried out by large agrochemical companies whose motives may well be profit alone and little to do the improvement of the environment – the technology has hidden risks, which have not been either considered or evaluated. This is a compelling argument in view of the case of bovine somotropin (BST); the growth hormone which can increase the milk yield in cows by some 15–20%. Supplies of BST can be obtained easily now that the gene for the hormone has been cloned in the bacterium *E.coli*, making it available in bulk. The argument against its use is that it imposes further stress on cows at a time when there is a surplus of milk in developed countries, especially in Europe. There is also an argument that milk produced in this way should be labelled.

It is clear that any technology does involve some form of risk and if the technology is to be adopted both the risks and the advantages of the technology need to be fully explained. In this way biotechnology is partly responsible for the suspicion that transgenic organisms engender, as the ability to transfer genes at will has been widely publicised but the advantages to the general public has not been emphasised (except for the obvious medical applications of vaccines and other cures). The average person knows little about biotechnology and has views of fish genes being transferred to strawberries to give some sort of monster! It seems that the lack of knowledge about biotechnology is to be blamed and that the remedy for this fear is education. Some regard this type of education as close to indoctrination and to show confidence in the products of biotechnology the risk assessment should be discussed. If this is not achieved the public must rely on the authority of the scientists to indicate the value of the biotechnology products. Many of the scientists are employed either by the companies seeking to introduce the products or by government institutions, which have lack credibility since the BSE outbreak. The problem of public confidence may also be influenced by the move away from factory farming to more natural organic products in the developed nations. Genetically engineered plants and foods may be seen in the same light as those products which are available throughout the year irrespective of season as a result of factory farming. In contrast there can be no argument against the use of transgenic crops in underdeveloped counties if their application relieves famine. This is perhaps the reason for the resistance to transgenic plants, which bring with them some risk, at a time when good quality food is freely available.

The Human Genome Project included ethical, legal, and social implications from the start in order to reduce public resistance. In the pharmaceutical industry a number of genetically engineered products have been approved and put on sale, such as the human growth hormone. In the pharmaceutical industry there is a clear need for the product, and its production is closely regulated with the organism restricted to growth in a production plant.

The release of transgenic plants or microorganisms into the environment is a very different situation and concern has been expressed by the scientific community. The problems which may occur are:

- gene transfer from a released organism with those in the environment. Transfer of the gene in the case of microorganisms is brought about by conjugation, transformation, or tranduction. Transfer in plants is by cross pollination
- the transfer of a marker or selectable gene to organisms in the environment. This may be more of a problem as many of the markers code for antibiotic resistance. If the plant is to be used as a food will the gene product of the marker gene be safe?

This would appear to be true for one of the most frequently used markers, gene NTP 11, which gives resistance to kanamycin (Sawahel, 1994)

- a new transgenic plant may have a selective advantage and become a dominant species
- enhancement of existing pests
- harm to non-target species
- disruptive effect on the balance within a population.

The risk of the new biotechnologies is by consensus the nature of the recombinant organism or product, the environment into which it is released and not the techniques involved in its production. Thus the risk is a function of the characteristics of the product rather than the techniques used. Any release of transgenic organism will need to have the following factors considered on a case by case basis:

- risks to humans such as highly allergenic pollen
- origin of the plant can affect potential risk depending on site of release
- colonization potential, how much the plant may spread
- ecological relationships, which includes the disruption of pollination systems, the enhancement of pests and the competition with local beneficial organisms.

It has been concluded that organisms engineered with the new techniques, despite the greater range of genes transferred, are generally better characterised than those produced by conventional breeding. However, the National Academy of Sciences (USA) concluded that there was no evidence of unique hazards associated with the transfer of genes between unrelated species (Miller, 1994). The risks associated with transgenic plants are the same as those for unmodified organisms (Sawahel, 1994). Nevertheless, the selectable markers need to be tested for their effects on human health as only the npt11 gene has been tested to date and more field trials are needed to determine whether there is any gene transference. Risk assessment is a qualitative measure of the probability of harm occurring from a known hazard. However, this is perhaps not appropriate for GMOs and at present the information is perhaps insufficient to make an estimate. The rational for the regulation on GMOs is to have a scientific based judgement to replace the vague fears of transgenic plant release. Nevertheless, many genetically engineered crops have been field tested including maize, squash, canola, cotton, soybean, tomato, and rapeseed. These plants have been engineered for herbicide resistance, resistance to insects and for improvement of fruit quality. Considerable effort has been made in the case of tomatoes by Calgene and Zeneca where antisense technology has reduced the onset of fruit softening. Both products have been passed for public consumption; the Calgene product Flavr Savr™ as a fruit and Zeneca as a canned paste. It remains to be seen as to whether the public will purchase these products – if so then there are a number of genetically engineered plants under development. Whatever happens, genetic manipulation will have a major influence on agriculture and the environment, more than any of the other biotechnologies.

The application of biotechnology to existing and new environmental problems will come under three sections:

- the reduction or recycling of waste in end-of-pipe treatments where waste formation cannot be eliminated
- the elimination of waste production in what is known as 'green technology'
- the clean-up of contaminated sites in the process known as 'bioremediation'.

The application of biotechnology to environmental issues ranges from the traditional processes such as aerobic and anaerobic waste treatment to the application of recombinant technology to all areas of biotechnology but particularly agriculture. Environmental biotechnology within the areas stated above will develop in the following topics:

- diagnosis/bioindicators/biosensors; to be able to estimate the levels of pollution, the microbial populations and the real time analysis of conditions biosensors are being developed, and biomarkers are being engineered to be able to indicate pollution *in situ*
- bioremediation; the area of bioremediation will probable see continued expansion as polluted sites require cleaning of metals, organic compounds and xenobiotics. This will involve the *in situ* and *ex situ* enhancement of natural microbial populations for the process of degradation
- bioleaching; this will continue to be used to extract metals form low grade ores and may be more important as the higher grade ores become depleted. Metal removal from mine leachate etc. will also be necessary
- biopharming; we may see the development of crop plants for pharmaceutical production but this will greatly depend on the outcome of the present release of transgenic plants. The release of plants with human genes in them on a large scale may be resisted
- preservation of biodiversity; an area that the public know little about but one of considerable concern to the scientific community. Techniques like PCR will see the analysis of microbial populations *in situ* which should give some interesting results as only 1% have been identified to date
- biofuels; alternative fuels will be needed eventually, the only consideration will be as to when. Biotechnology can provide oils and alcohol at present as fuels and may be able to provide hydrogen in the future
- biocontrol; this again will depend on the public debate on the release of transgenic plants but plants with their own insect/pathogen control will mean a reduction in biocide use
- transgenic plants with a large number of alterations to their characteristics such as flavour, colour and resistances; the potential and problems have been discussed in Chapter 8, it is certain that this will be an area of considerable debate in the future
- cloning of animals; the public may have some concerns but it may develop as a more frequently used technique for high grade animals
- vaccines/growth hormones/transgenic animals; the production of animal vaccines or semi-vaccines will continue due to the commercial potential and need for these, but whether the public needs or will accept BST produced milk or transgenic salmon and animal remains to be seen
- clean technology; the philosophy behind clean technology is to reduce or eliminate pollution by applying biotechnology. The possibilities are discussed in Chapter 4,

which the Integrated Pest Management biocontrol are part of the process with the reduction in pesticide use. Other possibilities will see the expansion of the use of enzymes from extremophiles in order to reduce pollution for a number of industrial processes.

All of the areas of technology given above are really aimed at the development of a sustainable future, 'the development that meets the needs of the present without compromising the ability of future generations to meet their own needs'.

References

Bialy, H. (1997) Biotechnology, bioremediation and blue genes. *Nature Biotechnology*, **15**, 110.

Carson, R. (1962) *Silent Spring.* Penguin Books, London.

Kappeli, O. and Auberson, L. (1997) The science and intricacy of environmental safety evaluations, *Tibtech*, **15**, 342–349.

Sawahel, W.A. (1994) Transgenic plants: performance, release and containment, *World Journal of Microbiology & Biotechnology*, **10**, 139–144.

Van Emden, H.F and Peakall, D.B. (1996) B*eyond silent spring*, Chapman and Hall, London.

Glossary

Acetone/butanol/ethanol fermentation: The fermentation of sugars usually molasses by *Clostridium* species forming a mixture of acetone, butanol and ethanol.

Acid rain: The deposition of acidifying substances from rain, snow or mist having a pH of less than 5.65.

Activated sludge: A mixture of aerobic microorganisms produced in the aerobic treatment of sewage or other wastewater.

Aerobic microorganism: An organism which requires oxygen for growth and metabolism.

Agarose: A polysaccharide extracted from seaweed and used as a gel medium for chromatography and for the electrophoretic separation of RNA and DNA.

Agrobacterium: A genus of soil bacteria which is responsible for the production of crown gall tumours due to the presence of the Ti (tumour-inducing) plasmid. The plasmid is inserted into the plant cell's genome inducing tumour formation; this property has been used to insert genes into plants.

Airlift bioreactor: A bioreactor where mixing and aeration are achieved by the introduction of air at the base of the vessel and the aerated section is separated from the rest of the vessel by a draft tube.

Ames test: A test for potential mutagens and carcinogens. The compounds are screened for their ability to revert a series of frameshift mutants of *Salmonella typhimurium*.

Anaerobic microorganism: A microorganism which can grow in the absence of oxygen.

Antibody: A protein produced by blood plasma cells that binds specifically to a foreign substance.

Antigen: A substance (usually a protein) or organism that induces the formation of antibodies.

Aquifer: A stratum of water filled rock.

Autoradiography: A process in which an image of a radioactive sample is obtained using photographic or X-ray-sensitive film.

Auxin: A plant growth regulator, which can be both natural such as indoleacetic acid or synthetic such as 2,4-dichlorophenoxyacetic acid (2,4-D).

Bacteriophage: A virus which infects bacteria by inserting its nucleic acid into the host.

Baculovirus: A group of viruses which only infect arthropods.

Bagasse: The solid residue remaining after the sugar has been extracted from sugar cane.

BATNEEC: The best available techniques not entailing excessive cost.

Bioaccumulation: The biological accumulation or sequestering of a substance to a higher concentration than that found in the environment (*see* bioconcentration).

Bioaugmentation: The addition of extra microorganisms to an activated sludge system when under stress.

Bioconcentration factor: (BCF) The factor by which a substance has been accumulated compared with that found in the environment.

Biocontrol: The use of living organisms as pest control agents (*see* biological control).

Biodiversity: This is a measure of the variation in biological organisms from populations to species in the environment.

Biofiltration: The process of wastewater purification using active microorganisms growing on solid supports.

Biofuel: A solid, liquid or gaseous fuel obtained from biological materials.

Biogas: A gas produced during anaerobic digestion which is a mixture of methane, carbon dioxide with traces of hydrogen, and hydrogen sulphide.

Bioleaching: The use of microorganisms for the recovery of metals from ores.

Biolistics: The insertion of DNA into plant cells by firing small spheres of gold or tungsten coated with DNA into the target tissue.

Biomagnification: The increase in a pollutant in the tissues of successive organisms in the food chain.

Biomarker: An natural or genetic engineered organism which has a specific property which enables it to be followed in the environment. A method of assessing environmental contamination.

Biomass: In microbiology this is the cell mass or total weight of living material, and in environmental studies the quantity of living and/or dead material in an ecosystem.

Biopesticides: Pesticides in which the active ingredient is a virus, fungus, or bacterium, or a natural product from a plant.

Biopharming: The production of proteins in transgenic plants.

Biopile: A system of bioremediation where the contaminated soil or waste is placed in a pile.

Bioreactor: A vessel used to carry out a biological reaction which includes the growth of microorganisms or the use of enzymes.

Bioremediation: The use of microorganisms or plants for the clean up of environmental pollution.

Biosensors: The combination of biological material and a physico-chemical device for the detection or measurement of a compound.

Biosorption: The removal of metals from liquids by microorganisms.

Biosparging: The sparging of air into a contaminated site in order to increase biodegradation.

Biotechnology: The application of organisms, biological systems or processes to manufacturing and service industries.

Bioventing: The application of a vacuum to a contaminated site to remove volatile contaminants and to encourage biodegradation.

BOD: Biological (biochemical) oxygen demand is a measure of the degree of organic pollution of waterways. It is the amount of oxygen (mg/l) used in the metabolism of organic materials in water by a mixture of microorganisms.

Callus: An undifferentiated growing mass of plant cells.

Capillary number: This is a measure of the permeability of oil within the rock that it is found.

Carcinogen: A substance, virus or ionizing radiation that causes cancer.

cDNA: Complementary DNA is a single stranded DNA that is formed from a messenger RNA (mRNA) by the enzyme reverse transcriptase.

CFC: Chloroflurocarbons are a family of chemicals which can deplete ozone in the stratosphere.

Chelation: The formation of a chelate where a polyvalent metal ion combines with an organic compound (chelating agent).

Chemolithotroph: An organism that obtains energy by oxidizing inorganic compounds such as nitrate and hydrogen.

Clean technology: The development of technology which produces low levels of waste and uses the minimum of energy.

Clone: A group of organisms that are genetically the same since they are produced by an asexual process or sexually by inbreeding of pure lines.

Co-metabolism: This is the metabolism of a compound not required for growth which gives no apparent benefit to the organism.

COD: Chemical oxygen demand is the measure of the amount of oxygen required to oxidize the organic material using a chemical method.

Composting: The aerobic decomposition of organic wastes to form a humus rich material.

Confocal laser scanning microscope: CLSM is a laser scanning microscope that focuses on a single plane of light which gives high-resolution three-dimensional images.

Continuous culture: The continuous supply of medium to a bioreactor containing growing organisms while removing culture at the same rate. This keeps the volume constant and the culture at a stable rate of multiplication.

Convention: An international treaty in law.

Curdulan: A microbial polysaccharide formed from glucose produced by *Alicaligenes faecalis*.

Denitrification: The microbial reduction of nitrates to nitrites, nitrous oxide or nitrogen by facultative aerobic soil bacteria under anaerobic conditions.

EIA: Enzyme immunoassay is an assay where the antibodies are labelled with an enzyme, the presence of which can be detected by a change of substrate from colourless to coloured. EIA in the context of the environment can also mean environmental impact assessment, which is an interdisciplinary approach to the determination of the environmental consequences of certain actions.

ELISA: Enzyme-linked immunosorbent assay is a sensitive technique where an enzyme is complexed with an antigen or antibody. The enzyme can be detected by the change of substrate from colourless to coloured.

EOR: Enhanced oil recovery involves the application of steam and viscous material to extract crude oil from an oil well after the primary flow has ceased. At this stage there are still large quantities of oil remaining.

Epitope: The part of the antigen to which the variable part of an antibody binds. The area which determines antigenic response.

Eutrophication: The biological effects when the inorganic nutrient concentration in a waterway increases. Often associated with algal blooms.

Explant: A tissue sample used to initiate tissue cultures.

Facultative anaerobe: An organism which can grow in both the presence and absence of oxygen.

Fermentation: The metabolism of organic materials by organisms in the absence of oxygen.

FIA: An immunoassay in which a fluorescent agent is used as a label.

Flow cytometry: An automatic machine which can separate and analyze individual cells in mixed populations.

Gasohol: A mixture of petrol (gasoline) and alcohol (10–20%) used for motor vehicles.

Gas chromatography: A sensitive analytical technique which depends on the relative speeds at which various compounds pass through a long narrow tube packed with inert material through which a gas is flowing.

Gene: A unit of hereditary material that forms a discrete part of the chromosome of most organisms carrying information as a DNA sequence.

Genetic manipulated organisms: (GMO) Organisms which have been genetically engineered in some way.

Glyphosate: N-(Phosphonomethyl) glycine, a broad spectrum herbicide.

Gratuitous metabolism: This is the ability of some enzymes to act on compounds other than their normal substrate, probably due to the broad enzyme specificity.

Greenhouse gases: These are water vapour, carbon dioxide, ozone, nitrous oxide, methane, and, CFCs. These gases absorb longer wavelength radiation emitted by the earth's surface thus retaining heat which would be lost by radiation.

HPLC: High performance liquid chromatography is a liquid chromatography system which is run at high pressure so that the separations take only a short time.

HRT: Hydraulic retention time is a measure of the average time that liquid remains in an activated sludge system.

Hybridization: A process in which a strand of nucleic acid joins with a complementary strand through base pairing.

Hybridoma: A hybrid cell produced by the fusion of a myeloma (antibody producing tumour cell) with a plasma cell. A clone of these cells will produce one specific antibody.

Hyperthermophile: An organism which has a growth optimum above 90°C.

ICM: Integrated crop (pest) management. A complex system which combines a number of crop or pest control techniques in and integrated manner.

Immobilisation: The physical or chemical process of restricting the movement of enzymes or cells.

Landfarming: A process where contaminated soils, sludges or sediments are spread onto land, and the land cultivated by ploughing and fertilizing in order to increase the degradation rate.

Leachate: An aqueous solution containing organic and inorganic compounds derived from water running through landfill sites or other waste dumps.

Lysozyme: An enzyme that hydrolyses the β-(1–4)-glycosidic bond between the n-acetylmuramic acid and n-acetylglucosamine residues making up the cell wall of many bacteria. This will weaken the cell wall causing the cell to rupture.

mRNA: messenger RNA is an RNA type which carries the coding information from the DNA template to the site of protein synthesis (the ribosomes).

MEOR: Microbially enhanced oil recovery is the use of microbially produced material or the application of microorganisms *in situ* to extract oil after the primary and secondary flow has ceased.

Mesophile: A microorganism with a temperature optimum between 20 and 50°C, although typically between 30 and 37°C.

Metallothioneins: Proteins which are capable of binding metals.

Methanogenesis: The final step in the formation of methane where acetate, carbon dioxide and hydrogen are converted to methane.

Mineralization: The conversion of an organic substance to carbon dioxide and water.

MLVSS: Mixed liquor volatile suspended solids is a measure of the biomass in an activated sludge system.

Monoclonal antibody: An antibody produced by culturing a single type of cell produced by fusing an antibody producing cell with a myeloma cell.

Nick-translation: A method of obtaining a labelled DNA probe. Nicks are introduced in the DNA by treatment with DNAase I. If this DNA is incubated with labelled nucleotides and DNA polymerase 1 the nicks are repaired with radioactive material.

Nitrification: The conversion of ammonia to nitrate by two genera of bacteria. *Nitrosomonas* converts ammonia to nitrite and *Nitrobacter* converts nitrite to nitrate.

Obligate aerobe: An organism which will only grow in the presence of oxygen.

Obligate anaerobe: An organism which will only grow in the absence of oxygen. The presence of oxygen will inhibit growth or kill the organism.

Oleophilic: A substance which will dissolve better in lipids than in water.

Operon: A genetic element that regulates the expression of inducible enzymes in prokaryotes.

Opine: A guanidoamino acid formed by plant cells following infection by the Ti plasmid from *Agrobacterium*.

Osmotolerance: The ability to tolerate high osmotic conditions such as high sugar or salt media.

PCR: Polymerase chain reaction. A technique for the synthesis of specific DNA sequences. Two nucleotide primers that hybridize to opposite DNA strands are annealed at one temperature, the primers are extended by a thermostable DNA polymerase, the double-stranded DNA is separated by raising the temperature and the two single strands can then act as templates. The reactions are carried out in a thermal cycler so that the DNA formed doubles every cycle.

PHB: Poly-β-hydroxybutyrate, a thermoplastic polymer produced by the bacteria *Alcaligenes, Azotobacter, Bacillus, Nocardia, Pseudomonas and Rhizobium.*

Phytoremediation: The removal of pollution using plants to either sequester the pollution or to degrade the contaminants.

Plasmid: A circular molecule of DNA that is found widely in prokaryotes and in eukaryotes and can code for important genetic traits not normally found in the organism such as metal resistance, and antibiotic resistance.

Pollution: The release of natural or manufactured compounds or energy into the environment in sufficient quantity as to cause harm.

Post-translational processing: The alterations in protein structure or composition after synthesis.

Primary oil production: The first stage of extracting oil from an oil well in which the oil reaches the surface under the pressure of the reservoir or by pumping.

Primer: A substance which is required for a polymerase reaction and is similar to the product of the reaction.

Protocol: A subsidiary agreement on an international treaty or convention.

Protoplast: A cell where the cell wall has been completely removed. The integrity of the membrane bound structure is maintained by including an osmotic material such as mannitol in the medium.

Pseudoplastic: This describes the flow characteristics of a liquid. Pseudoplastic liquids become thinner when a force is applied in a process known as shear thinning.

Recalcitrant: These are compounds which do not degrade under any circumstances.

Restriction enzyme: The enzyme is an endonuclease capable of cleaving DNA at a specific site depending on the sequence of bases. There are two types of restriction enzymes; those recognising a sequence and cutting the DNA strands somewhere nearby, and the type II where the enzyme recognises a site and cleaves at a specific place within this sequence.

RFLP: Restriction fragment length polymorphism. This is an analytical technique where the DNAs from various sources can be compared by fragments produced by a restriction enzyme. The fragments are normally separated by gel electrophoresis and the fragments probed with a specific probe.

Rhizofiltration: This is the removal of contaminants from flowing water by the plant itself or the associated microorganisms.

Rhizosphere: The rhizosphere is the microbial population associated with the roots of plants.

RIA: Radioimmunoassay is an assay technique based on a radioactively labelled proteins used to follow the reaction between the antigen and antibody.

SAGD: This is steam assisted gravity distillation where steam is injected into tar sands which mobilises the oil which flow out of the base.

Schleroglucan: A microbial polysaccharide composed of glucose found in *Scherotium glucanicum*. It is highly viscous and stable to pH and temperature changes.

Semiochemicals: Natural chemical messengers used as pesticides.

Short rotation coppice: The regular cutting of plants such as willow.

Single cell protein: SCP is the cell mass of yeasts, bacteria, fungi or algae which have been grown for human or animal food, especially for their protein content.

Somaclonal variation: Variation that occurs in plants propagated from cell or tissue cultures.

Southern blot: A technique used in genetic manipulation where DNA fragments separated on agarose gels are transferred to a cellulose nitrate filter. The filter can then be probed with a labelled probe to reveal areas of hybridization.

Stabilization: The inactivation of the microbial content of sewage or other wastes.

Surfactant: A chemical acting as a wetting agent which helps fats and oils to mix with water. Acts like a detergent.

Thermophile: A microorganism with a temperature optimum between 40 and 70°C.

Transformation: A permanent genetic change induced in a cell following the incorporation of DNA.

Transgenic organism: An organism that has had novel DNA introduced into its genome (*see* GMO).

TOC: Total organic carbon which is a measure of the carbon content of a sample. The value can be obtained by electrical pyrolysis followed by infrared analysis of the carbon dioxide released. It is used as an indication of the organic content of a sample.

TOD: Total oxygen demand is a measure of the oxygen required in the combustion of all organic carbon in a sample.

Totipotent: The ability of a cell to grow and differentiate to form a whole plant or animal.

Vacuole: An intracellular body containing fluid contained within a membrane.

Vector: A small plasmid, virus or bacteriophage used for the transformation of cells in gene manipulation.

Xanthan: A microbial polysaccharide composed of glucose, mannose, glucuronic acid, acetyl groups and pyruvate formed by *Xanthomonas campestris*. It is highly viscous and is used in the preparation of salad dressings, tomato ketchup and drilling muds.

Xenobiotic: A chemical compound that does not normally occur in nature but is chemically synthesised.

Index